Stories from the Heartland

Nebraska Writers Guild

Literary Anthology

NWG Publications
Scottsbluff, NE

Nebraska Writers Guild
PO Box 493
Scottsbluff, NE 69363

Publisher's Note: This is primarily a work of fiction. Except in certain cases, names, characters, places, and incidents are products of each author's imagination. Locales and public names are sometimes used for atmospheric purposes.

Ordering Information:
Quantity sales. Special discounts are available on quantity purchases by corporations, associations, and others. For details, contact the "Special Sales Department" at the address above.

Cover Photo: *Sunset Fires the Platte* by Kim Sosin

Stories from the Heartland

ISBN: 978-1-7357016-6-0 (paperback)
ISBN: 978-1-7357016-7-7 (ebook)

Library of Congress Control Number: 2021924374

Contents

2021 NWG Poetry Contest Winners

Poetry

Essays

Short Stories

Nonfiction

Excerpts from a Novel

Memoirs

Flash Fiction

Foreword

What does it take to write a great story? Ask twenty different people, and you'll get twenty different answers—all perfectly valid. But ask those same twenty people what it takes to send those stories out into the world, and there's really only one good answer.

Guts.

Even seasoned authors who've submitted their work to a myriad of publications and contests have to be pretty ballsy to put a piece of their soul into the hands of strangers to be judged and criticized and possibly rejected.

That's what makes the authors in this collection—and, in fact, all the authors who submitted for a *chance* to be in the collection—so amazing. It's not just the hours and hours they've spent crafting their stories but the sheer force of will it took to hand those stories over to us.

And let's talk about craft for a moment. Each style of writing requires a slightly (or even not-so-slightly) difference in craft, and I'm always amazed by those authors who excel in more than one. Look at Janet McMillan Rives, for example, who writes wonderful poetry, and then takes those poems and infuses them into memoirs and essays. As if poetry, memoirs, and essays aren't difficult enough to write separately! And what about Julie Paschold, whom you'll find in the poetry and essay sections, and Johnnye Gerhardt who captures our attention with both short stories and novels.

Of course, one doesn't have to write in multiple categories to show off. Between their contest-winning poems and anthology entries, Ellie Luebbe Janda and Steve Rose both have a whopping seven poems in this volume. William Smutko graces us with three short stories, and both Sammi Hoard and Bill Roberts have three novel excerpts! And those are just a few of the authors with multiple works in the collection.

Then there are those of us with just a solitary contribution, myself included (I promise I got in fair and square!), appearing within these pages. Regardless of how many page numbers follow our names in the Index by Author, we're all here because we put our hearts on the page and fretted over every word.

And at the end of the day, each of the authors featured within these pages, along with any of our fellow NWG members who submitted but did not get in, have a great deal to be proud of, from our creativity to our discipline, patience, and hard work to our bravery in the face of possible criticism and rejection.

For the third year in a row, I'm so proud to bring this collection of Nebraska Writers Guild members into being. To be able to amass some of the finest writing Nebraska authors have to offer and gift that collection to the world is an honor I do not take lightly.

If you're a featured author, congratulations! If you're a reader, buckle up, cuz this collection will take you on quite a ride!

Julie Haase
NWG Publications Chair

2021 NWG
Poetry Contest Winners

First Place

Steve Rose

"The Bedroom"

"Safe Harbor"

Second Place

Ellie Luebbe Janda

"After Life"

Third Place

Charlene Neely

"The Farmer's Wife and Her Knife"

Steve Rose • Indianola, IA

Bedroom

Ellie moved first, taking Sarah's old room.
At last her nights were free of my snoring,
safe from my cold feet sliding glacially
until they found the islands of her calves,

away from my dreams where I still fought
the purchasing department—dimesucking
bastards that they were—although
I've been retired near thirteen years.

Our master bedroom felt like a storage locker
without her; I didn't want to be a cardboard box.
So I took Sam's room, empty this century.
It smelled of ball gloves, motor oil and bong hits

Then Ellie's nights ended. A flu settled into her heart,
chewed it to silence. The children visited
then left, their cars packed with grief and trinkets
I moved back to our room; the chasm matched my mood.

From our bed I look at her mirror. I used to watch her,
my eyes over the cover of a book, a thief scaling a height;
she'd let a necklace fall on her neck to sparkle while
her hands moved behind her in a ballet, locking the clasp.

Tonight, the chandelier dances across the mirror,
uninterrupted by her presence, mimicking jewels:
emerald, ruby, sapphire, topaz;
green, red, blue, gold. So many choices
she never had.

Steve Rose • Indianola, IA

Safe Harbor

Hannah and I discard the basement refugees
unneeded in the new place. It will be smaller.
So are we; we've aged. Our cupboards have grown.
The shelves now demand we stretch tiptoed to reach
the wine glasses. Our hallways: long enough
to host kingpins, the upstairs steps, Olympics.

Behind coon traps and such catacombed in cobwebs
lurk crockery purloined from my last marriage,
beige as that union, the pattern as forgettable.
My ex and I once traded for them with Green Stamps
redeemed inside the Safeway where we shopped.

My children's bumpy tongues labored over the stamps.
They smudged them in place with the heels
of their hands, creases mapped with ink. Those scamps,
my lieges, used to press at my side, each begging
to be the knight errant: the right to bear home
a paper sack with the piece-of-the-month wrapped twice.

Our flotilla grew: six dinner plate cruisers,
as many soup bowl destroyers, coffee cups floating
at their sides, even a gravy boat submarine.

Now the fleet has changed alliances, as if boats were
ever loyal. Our street curb is a beach, and someone
will find them, hoist the box into his trunk, sail home
victorious to his kin, a pirate safe from penalty.

Hannah and I will find safe harbor, all of one level,
shelving at the proper height for elves, or the elderly,
plumbing pristine, hallways short, to the point.

We'll drydocked without the hope or worry of repair.

Ellie Luebbe Janda • Beaver Crossing, NE

After Life

It’s true you can’t take it with you
but consider accumulating a few collections
So if your possessions are divided up
or when the estate sale comes
people will enjoy knowing
how much you loved ceramic unicorns
or felt cactus magnets with googley eyes
and music boxes shaped like food
Perhaps they can wonder
about a confusing number of yard sticks
or pickle jars filled with left handed scissors
and well preserved bottles of old soda
Because what you can’t take with you
can become a treasured memory
for all of the people you leave behind
to smile and giggle at for years to come

Charlene Neely • Lincoln, NE

The Farmer's Wife and Her Knife

It's still here, in the drawer to the right of the sink.
It's been there in every apartment or house
I have lived in since I left my parents' home.
A ten-inch blade, tapering from the handle
to a sharp point. I use it daily to cut onions,
carrots, peppers, slice cheese. I have other knives.
Knives made just for slicing cheese or bread
but this one fits my hand, feels good
when I bring it out of the drawer.
I was chopping onions at our café
when I told him I needed an operation.
It was in my hand when he replied,
but who will take care of the kids,
who will scrub the floors at close,
who will cover all your hours?
And before I could form a response,
I found myself circling the butcher-block table,
round and round much like the 'farmer's wife'
in the song the children sing, wielding my knife
as that blind-mouse-of-a-husband
ran in circles ahead of me, yelping,
until he fled out the back door.
And I put the knife down, went out front
to refill the coffee cups of the old guys

at the big table who did not say a word.
Years later, husband gone (natural causes
they said), the knife still waits
in a drawer to the right of the sink.

Poetry

Ellie Luebbe Janda • Beaver Crossing, NE

Julie

In reality, change wasn't the tidal wave
but rather a ripple spreading slowly
touching everything in its own time.
News floating in on emails and phone calls
but also announcing itself in silence,
a Schrodinger's Cat of possibilities—
both alive and dead.
And one more survivor found
amid gossip of other families receiving phone calls
or supposed muffled voices from under the rubble.
Fact of fiction, the silence took over
until the debris was cleared
with no final trace found.
Held breaths were exhaled
as the tidal wave of grief arrived
and everyone held on
riding it out in their own way.

Amy Haddad • Omaha, NE

We Have Two Children

I lied in halting French.
The woman from Sarlat
at the two-top to our right chatted
through dessert. She spoke no English.
We spoke about food, the Musée d'Orsay
when she turned that conversational corner
women do and asked about children.
I knew how to reply, "*Nous n'avon*
malheureusement pas d'enfant."
Even in another language I added "unfortunately."
I was fed up with the "why?" in the eyes of strangers
when they learned we were childless.
This time, I decided we did. We have two children.
I stumbled a bit when in precise French she posed the obvious
next questions she should not have to ask. Any real mother
would have provided gender and names without prompts.
I quickly created one of each, named them after a niece
and neighbor's son. Of course, she queried, "*Quel âge ont*
vos enfants?" Calculating their ages confounded me, I am as bad
at math as I am at lying. How old would I have been
when I bore these fictitious infants? What ages would they be
now? I think of a friend, steal the ages of her son
and daughter. "*Notre fils a dix-huit ans,*" a high school senior,
the girl is twenty now in college. My husband spoke

almost no French. He played with his coffee until
he heard our niece's name, then watched the exchange
with keen interest.
What were you two talking about? he asked later
as we walked in the Paris night to our hotel.
There was no need to translate. I lied to him too.

Steve Rose • Indianola, IA

Fishing in August

Grasshoppers' wings waved promises to a ten-year-old boy
on the North Platte River bottoms. Fishing had been thin.
Worms were locked in the loam baked to brick by August.
Grade school was wagging its ruler at him two weeks away.

Dad's trout net was reserved for the headwaters in Wyoming,
a dream to the boy, so he lashed castoff panty hose to a hayfork,
tied off the legs to streamers and swung this net
through bluestem, milkweed and Scotch thistle.

The fork's tines stunned a locust or two at each scoop. He scraped
them into the jam jar first fashioned as a firefly lamp in July.
The holes in the tin lid leaked hopper juice into his overalls,
staining his right pant pocket the color of Copenhagen chew.

After jarring a baker's dozen or so, he grabbed his Zebco,
hook and bobber hanging like a crane's ball, lashed it
to his three-speed, and spun off to Jenkin's pond, a tootsie roll
keeping company with the dripping jar of oversized crickets.

His Keds ankle deep in tepid water, filled with sand ground
from the Rockies, he cast, the bobber's weight as ballast,
a hopper's thorax impaled on his hook, its wings dragging
against the breeze, puny as wind socks in a tornado.

The bass were indifferent in the doldrums of August, rolling
on the surface for a moment to catch some sun, but bluegill
celebrated, carnivorous and comic as the bugs kicked and
    flickered.
The boy used up his bait; the sunfish so eager that fishing became

a replay, like the cartoons he watched Sundays before church.
He hooked and released, not wanting the weight of a stringer
on his ride home, the angling grown akin to throwing logs
to a fire that burns too easy, no luster to it. After supper,

Bonanza and bedtime, he dreams, not of borrowing fish
from the water, but of gathering bait, the greed of filling the jar,
the mad clatter on the hoppers slapping against the glass,
the fluttering of their wings, brave and small, against his palms.

In the corner of the garage the rod and reel lean next to
the pitch fork still sporting its plumage like a war bonnet:

a pen knife next to a scepter.

Janet McMillan Rives • Oro Valley, AZ

Notes on Lost Splendor

Cities and towns where I have lived, worked,
glimpsed in passing or in books—
they are in shambles, yet still I picture them
as the vibrant places they once were.

Handsome ships, newly christened,
are launched on the Delaware River
as Walt Whitman wanders Linden Street,
sniffs lilacs in backyards. Ladies, hatted
and gloved, frequent shops along Broadway.
These days Camden rots in Philly's shadow.

Kites made of yellow, red, purple tissue
float high, strings pulled by boys
with wrapped fingers. Snow-capped mountains
protect palaces, gardens, bazaars—elements
of lost opulence now gone from Kabul,
replaced with decades of war rubble.

A fancy supper club in out-state Nebraska—
patterned carpet, paneled walls, chandeliers—
welcomes families dressed in their best.
They share stories, pass scalloped relish trays.

Today this lapsed luxury stands abandoned
on the edge of a town no longer alive.

Tomorrow I will visit an upscale mall,
wander from one chic boutique to the next,
memorize images of finery, not knowing
when these places too might crumble.

James Luebbe • Beaver Crossing, NE

Annabelle

Last dog of many,
better friend to me
than my neglect showed.
Bright eyes, keen ears, intelligence,
tennis ball speed, a nose attuned
to the radar of rabbits.
Last name in a line
naming my decades,
Happy, Sonny, Boomer,
Summer, Goldy, Rowlf.
Buried six feet down
under cover of night,
for shame and anger
at mistaking her cough
for a chicken bone,
Belle wrapped in my work coat
beside her throw stick
forever chasing
a neon green ball.

Joslyn Rojewski • Carrollton, TX

Us

maybe every storm of doubt
and cunning shard of chaos,

maybe every thread of conversation
in my head and out of it

maybe every anxious sleep
and endless night
and hapless try
has led to

you and me,

sitting on the porch,

watching the rain.

Kim Sosin • Omaha, NE

Of the Girls I've Been

Reminiscing about
the girls I've been,
one ten-year-old girl
stands out, the
fearless tomboy
on her horse
during those warm

summer days.
In that halcyon time,
an embracing small town
  my front yard,
a rolling ocean of grass
  my backyard,
endless possibility

  my universe.
Going riding with Janis
I slammed the back door,
off to saddle sweet Peggy.
Or not, maybe just a bridle,
no restrictions on
this luminous

summer morning.
Mother through a window
Be home by supper.
Nothing more.
Not *Where are you going?*
Not *Don't go too far.*
Through my seventy years

since that summer,
no freedom is as joyous
as that of a
young girl, riding
her bareback pony
on a day as wide as
the prairie sky.

Charlene Neely • Lincoln, NE

His Shadow

He left his shadow
in the foxhole of a far off
country, left it buried
under a cloud of mustard gas,
came home a shadow
of himself standing off
to the side of all the noise
and hubbub that seemed
even more daunting than
the bullets and mortars
he left behind, came back
an empty shell of a man,
not enough for the shadow
to bother following around.

Steve Rose • Indianola, IA

Tiny Knives

Mother's fingernails unsheathed from the calluses
of her palms where they'd rested within her fists.
Her hands open, blades so fine fairies would not land
on their edges, so quick, angels balked at singing nearby.

I was not careful in my play. Boisterous, a boy
who built forts erected from household debris:
brooms and sheets, kitchen chairs, couch cushions.
Tabby's kittens enlisted, then AWOL in an instant.

Her right hand came at me: a breeze against my ear
until it landed, her palm forcing blood to my cheeks
where the fingers struck, projectiles held back
by sinew, claiming purple divots from a boy's thin skin.

I'm seventy now and pass them off as pock marks.
Maybe they are, left by a hidden virus, one
only she and I shared.

Tammy Marshall • Neligh, NE

A Maxim Lesser-Known

A maxim known by all: *no parent should outlive his child*

A maxim lesser-known: *no teacher should outlive her students*

For more than a quarter of a century, I've taught many kids—
Watched them grow, graduate, and go off to great things.
I've lost track of most of them as they leave this tiny town,
But that's a loss easy to accept—normal, expected.

A few, though, have been lost forever, taken far too soon,
Cruelly wrenched from their promised futures,
Caught unawares by disease, fate, happenstance, and evil.
Empty desks serve as their markers in my classroom.

The first, gone nigh on thirty years I'd say, could easily
Have been a grandfather by now, but he died a teenager,
A victim of his friend's sleepiness behind the wheel,
An unpaved shoulder and a flip that pinned him under a car.

The next, another teenage boy, sucked dry by cancer's
Gaping maw of greed, stayed in school as long as he could
And his funeral was held in the gymnasium where the rickety
Wooden bleachers groaned from the weight of our grief.

Another young man, battling depression with drugs, succumbed
To the demons that haunted his mind—left their remnants
All over the living room wall behind his head and an ever-
Expanding hole of emptiness in his mother's heart.

A fourth boy rounded a curve too fast and rolled his car,
Injuring his passenger but killing himself. I got the phone call
The next morning, my reaction of disbelief compounded
Because I'd seen and spoken to him only hours before he died.

Somewhere in there—my timeline is fuzzy—a young female grad
Working on highway construction got yanked into an asphalt
Grinder or pavement miller or some other death machine.
Frankly, I don't know the details, nor do I want to.

The sixth, another boy, crossed the yellow line, only a fraction
But enough to kill him instantly, while reading a text. The two old
People in the vehicle in front of him bore witness to his death—
His own grandparents, unable to save him from himself.

The most recent, a young woman, and the hardest yet to believe—
Her death was no accident nor was it from illness of any kind.
A devil killed her—murdered her, strangled her, dismembered her,
Tossed her into a Nebraska field in fourteen garbage bags.

Know them: Shawn, Troy, Jason, Jordan, Raven, Scotty, Sydney.
They were my students. They were my kids, if only for one
Hour a day, one quarter or semester of the year. I loved them
As all teachers love their students. They were mine, and I weep.

No teacher should outlive her students, yet I've outlived these
Seven, and there could be more. I've lost touch with many, and
My memory isn't so great nowadays, but these I'll never forget.
Their deaths, each awful in its own way, are indelibly seared.

I often wonder why I teach eternal content to ephemeral beings,
Knowing that the knowledge that's in them will disappear when
They die, as will my own. I trick myself into believing my students
All have years and years ahead of them to use my skills, but do they?

Day by day, when my classroom is full of young people and the life
They exude, it's easy to forget their mortality, but when one dies,
It's hard to keep fooling myself, to believe that what I do matters.
After all, it did nothing to save them, nor will it rescue others from death.

Shawn—a goofy boy with a perpetual twinkle in his eye; Troy—ornery
Until the end and beloved by all; Jason and Jordan—laid-back slackers with
Good hearts; Raven—the epitome of her name in looks and attitude; Scotty—
A class clown unlike any other; Sydney—a gentle friend to anyone in need.

None of them survived beyond a quarter of a century, yet I'm into
My second half. Not only do their deaths sadden me, but the ways
In which they died anger me greatly. Perhaps life isn't
    fair—another
Famous well-known maxim—but wouldn't it be wonderful if
    death was?

Ricardo Moran • San Diego, CA

Saint Cecilia

I wait in the vestibule,
the ruby red light
fills the chamber.

You pull open wounds
in quiet footsteps.

And your scowl grows
as tears etch the lines
on your face.

While your grip
on the trigger
grows tighter.

Kneeling here,
so many miles from home,
I know that you have given up,
that your rage consumes you,
that your faults taunt you,
living like bullets lodged in your mind.

While your despot-loving parents are too crazy
even for me to handle, at times.

Now grab a hold of my hand
and let the sadness roar
out of your chest,
so that my love
casts its magic into you.

Let my eyes take your sins,
so that I may eat them,
taste them, chew on them
for a little while and spin
them into magic
to spoon-feed you.

To remind you
that your divinity can be broken,
it can be flawed,
but it is still magical.

Steve Rose • Indianola, IA

Double Clutch

We need to double clutch after all these miles.
We're both over warranty, even
our drivetrains, but paid for at last. True,
I take some fuel additives.

I remember when I first saw you
with nothing but the radio on.

Your skin still feels satin, soothing
the nobs of my age-spotted fingers,
and your wrinkles undulate
as I follow the vein up your arm,
a blue highway I know down to its ditches.

We're copping a ride on this century:
two hitchhikers with a long-haul driver
heading south as we croon along,
our voices crackling, like gravel, with age.

Remember top-forty radio pulsing
through speakers tinny as soup cans,
as we cruised in separate Chevies down Jeffers
and back up Main, our radio signals
crackling with thunderstorms as

the Bee Gees and Beatles beamed from Tulsa,
before the church folk locked the station down.

Yah, the road home takes longer tonight,
in each other's arms, but that can be nice, turning
down a lane for the hell of it, revving the engine
with the clutch pushed in.

Leopold J. Kovar • Brainard, NE

The Gray Pickup

Under the box elders
past the phalanx of fireweed
and elephant-eared burdock
the boys' vehicle stands
picked up for a few bucks
stick-shift, no trade-in value
branches, bales, and buckets
carried in its box
bumping around pasture gullies
and gopher holes
careening over stubble
charging through dry weeds
during hunting season
the passenger door, the imprint of a tree
the front bumper loosened by a post
cigarette burns on the upholstery
beer spilled on the floor
bits of chips in crevices
an engine run to ruin in midnight races

To mask their shame, cover their tracks
the boys now a few years older
pull the battered hulk out of sight
rust beginning its slow conquest

I stare at it seeing all the history it bears
Some dignity owed for long hard service
titling it now a contemporary sculpture
a true reflection of its time and place

Ellie Luebbe Janda • Beaver Crossing, NE

Visit

On a night otherwise dotted with nonsensical dreams
he showed up at my family's table at some sort of potluck
to smile at my middle child and ask her about the cookie
crumble cake
she was trying
My dream self-stared with eyes unblinking
aware it was a dream
but wanting to see just five more minutes of friendship with him
Real or not, knowingly unconscious
content to enjoy his smile again

James Luebbe • Beaver Crossing, NE

Morning Sprayer

December 2, 1984, Bhopal, India—
Leaking gas storage tanks expose
half a million people to methyl
isocyanate, an intermediate
product in the manufacture of
certain insecticides.

I am still cocooned in the single-seat
Piper Pawnee Brave, stick in one hand, throttle
in the other, concentration focused forward,
in the power and grace and glory of flight,
thin finger tracing mile and a half long
meanders in the great sky near the Blue River.
Descending from heaven on unsuspecting
earth, trusting the hallowed roar of my engine,
I plummet toward power lines on a field's end,
then rise above startled Interstate drivers
on the other, shadow swiftly passing
like a thunderclap so close
I see their lips curse my name
and if I wanted I could count coup
on their rooftops with the rubber tomahawk
of my landing gear.

Of all the pretty poisons
this is my favorite, cut from the bag's throat
with a carbide blade, hopper filling
as I turn my face aside
from the sweet smell of death.
Days of dusting these beetles, their will undone
upon my neighbors' crops, preventing
Malthusian famines in a soft pink sleet,
in a snowfall of heroin insects won't resist,
sliding into leaf whorls or catching on cornsilks,
the light rustle of granules still as first stirrings
of a Bhopal morning years later.

Even my engine's bedlam would not wake
those taken from last restless thoughts
of reverent mantras to the destroyer of sorrows.
Those recitations broken instead by the periodic
genealogy of synthetic man, aniline dyes,
organic compounds, I.G. Farben nerve gas
and unfortunate orphan-making molecules
on the opposite side of our reality.
And that is our temptation, never to trespass
their reality, but delivering there the full
unknown fruits of our science, the bread
of our exceptional dreams, our 2,4,5-trichloro clouds
over the Ho Bo Woods of Southeast Asia,
our math confusing the count of hands and feet
for generations. In our defense we plead not guilty
of wanting to know in advance the human faults

of good business, the progress of our unchecked walk
from Babylonian superstition to Greek-like logic,
proclaiming our Western progress good for anyone
who gets in its way, for us, for all men.

Julie S. Paschold • Norfolk, NE

Antelope, Tiger

It's so hot the gravel makes snapping noises
as my feet press each piece into the melted asphalt
on the edge of the county road as I walk.

The wind stirs the heavy air
heated oven hot, expanding with the breeze
creating no relief as it enters my lungs.

Usually the sight of the bright green grass
stretching long towards the sky,
waving, rattling back and forth gently
cools my sight with its color.

But not today.

Today I am an antelope
looking wildly at each blade
seeking stripes of orange and black
hidden in the green stretching upwards
towards the sun.

Today I am the tiger
unaware that I am orange with black
color deficient in my view on life

seeing green and black
where orange and olive and lime and black span the expanse.

Today the heat holds me captive
and only one foot in front of the other
down this blacktop road coated in gravel and asphalt
is how I'm progressing forward,
making it anywhere,
holding on from suffocating in the oven hot air
as sweat drips down my back and
I reach for that door that will lead me away
from all of this, lead me back
into the cool jade and blue vista,
back into the cyan waters
bubbling hope and relief and
telling me surely there must be

one more tomorrow
left
for this antelope,
this tiger,
one more tomorrow
to trudge down the road again
in a world of color
not heat
where the green grass waves
in stretches of upward currents
ever reaching
for that radiant, iridescent sun.

Charlene Neely • Lincoln, NE

The Turpentine Sestina

My Dad used turpentine
to clean car parts, those corners,
nooks, and crannies. No amount of blow
could dislodge the crud that clung
like a child's wild night dreams.
He prayed his children would be wiser.

If only they could be a little wiser,
they wouldn't have to work with turpentine
and perhaps they could follow their dreams,
which if nourished would take them to all corners
of the earth. Never having hands to which dirt clung.
Following wherever their fate would blow.

He'd pause in his daydreams to blow
away the cobwebs forming the shop. A wiser
man would not have clung
to a trade that involved turpentine.
He'd have a workplace where all the corners
were as tidy as an old maid's dreams.

But who is he to know what dreams
an old maid dreams when winds blow
last night's paper around corners.

They make neither of them any wiser.
She still dreams, he dips his hands into turpentine,
whose fumes got in his lungs and there they clung.

And though he'd quit, the odors clung
as firmly in the shop as in his dreams.
He carried with him scents of turpentine
which has caused his better sense to blow
away for good. It leaves him wiser,
telling me to avoid dark corners

where dreams are wedged. For corners
are where the demons have clung,
waiting to pop out when least expected. Wiser
men than we have found their dreams
caught in the muck that refuses to blow
away the odor of ancient turpentine.

So clean those corners, give your dreams
that have clung for years a good blow,
clean any muck that clung there, emerge a man much wiser.

Ricardo Moran • San Diego, CA

Poplar Street

Poplar Street cuts
at an angle, like a midrib
on a leaf.

Baptized as the Boulevard
of Hollywood, its stars lie
unconscious on concrete reels.

On Poplar, the holy spirit rises at 420
and spills like rancid baby formula on
a chalk outline, blessing silhouettes
where high heels pivot.

On Poplar, where emerald crowns will never reign,
ramshackle cars drag race, shopping carts rattle,
despondent polka music thumps.

Voices call out, "Who is the father
of this baby?" Throats scream
that the air has eyes.

But no rustling, no gentle dances of leaves,
no caresses of sliding bodies of chlorophyll
sunbathing in a gentle canopy.

That is not Poplar Street.

Ellie Luebbe Janda • Beaver Crossing, NE

Fireworks

The night before I had sat alone
crisscross applesauce on cool tile
rifling silently, quickly
through a stranger's storage space
three drawers, a closet, medicine cabinet
From the window pearls of color shot across
a transparent sky
bursting into clouds of sparkle
for the enthusiastic lawn chairs spread about
While I searched for something secure
to entomb the scraps of my heart,
these blobs of flesh flushed out far too early
And I stand now, exposed, under the sun
as I realize that my secret holder had
sprung a leak
because my impending loss was more reality
than she could handle
Listening repeatedly to well wishers
thoughts and prayers
that my pregnancy will work out fine
No idea it sits in a toilet paper tube
waiting in the freezer
already over and out
and certainly anything but fine
which is also how I feel

Steve Rose • Indianola, IA

Labors

A vulture labors off the ground,
straining, scrawny neck girded,
wings as clumsy and slow as the
farmhand's legs scrambling below,
spindly and slopping through
snow melt and April rain
to the milking barn. For both
bird and man these tasks
are regular but never easy.

By day's end the vulture spies
a dead doe, cured by the sun
and flavored by worms. The raptor
winds down in a surprise of grace
to dance a wake and then twist
his beak in the corpse, his flame
red head bald, antiseptic.

Meanwhile

the farmhand sets the machines,
cold and firm as November,
on the piebald udders, then
pulls a hungry silver vacuum

off a teat, aims it, and savors
pearled milk squirting down
his throat, his mouth round
and greedy as a cat's.

My head bows down to a planet
that allows us to reap milk
from mothers not our own,
to fill ourselves on flesh
that is not our kill.

Kim Sosin • Omaha, NE

Not Enough Pages

Stamps for each country,
slapped down with apathy
on the smeared pages
          of my passport
behind the appalling selfie
and the given first name
I never use.

Retirement tabulated by
swirls of designs
          in indelible ink.
Country stamps
squeezed everywhere,
overlapping at the edges,
just as they do in my memories.

I struggle to read
the oldest faded stamp:
          China and Tibet.
The train ride into heights,
low on oxygen.
Passport checked, stamped,
characters pressed in, Hanzi
as red as monks' robes.

Monks praying, arguing,
texting with smartphones.

Passport stamps refocus
fading memories.
African photo safari,
hot nights in the Sahara,
the tunnels of Saigon.
A lifetime of trips
          of a lifetime.
On it goes, I go, until
no pages remain.

Then, 2020,
remembered
by a glaring absence
of country stamps
          in my passport.
The year that wasn't.
The year of home.

James Luebbe • Beaver Crossing, NE

Birthday Goldfinch

The flame flickers afresh one day
a month after the easing of winter
and so long since we've seen it,
we've nearly forgotten
why we wished it back.
It flies with a rising and falling
as though searching,
waiting and searching,
like an anxious heartbeat
that calls and coasts,
calls and coasts,
never quite content
but still reliable, faithful, saying
another year, another year,
another year.

Amy Haddad • Omaha, NE

The Ravished Rose

He wears a yellow mask
that fades to grey at the nape
of his sleek neck. Hanging
upside down, the finch hooks
his claws in the heart
of a fragrant bloom and digs
deep with vicious pecks
unveiling cloistered aphids.
He flings vermillion
over his supple shoulders
where it falls
in tatters on the emerald
grass. When he releases
the rose and flies off,
the flower rebounds up and down
trembling back into place
its ravaged face raw among
the untouched buds.

Tammy Marshall • Neligh, NE

Amavida

A village unchanged with time,
guarded by the great Gredos,
a place of infinite peace.

Belled bovines bed beside
their keepers' stone homes.
A burro breakfasts in a garden,
munches amidst the family's fodder.

There are no stores here
where trucks pass through
selling their wares: cured hams,
natural gas for stoves, shoes.
Toothless grins mark the need
for a traveling dentist as well.

The June air is thin, pure, crisp;
my lungs suck it in and rejoice—
I am intoxicated.

Gates made from whatever is available—
a metal box spring, branches fashioned together,
an old door—are framed with vibrant
clutches of wildflowers and climbing roses.

Dogs are caretakers of cattle and territorial sentinels—
no pets, these scrawny, work-hardened animals.

Stone houses are small, and ancient door frames
come barely past my shoulder.
Cobbled streets are crooked and meander
the way a great walk should wend its way to a discovery.

Who knew I'd find this village and lose my heart?
Such a simple slice of civilization.
A place that **loves life** as it was meant to be lived—
        Ama vida.

Amavida, España

Julie Paschold • Norfollk, NE

The Supervisor's False Predator

We were attempting to put in stepping stones
and it was taking twice the effort than we thought it would.

This robin would come within arm's reach
of us, feathers ruffled in a distinctive wind-swept style.

He would wait for us to upend the soil
and then his lunch would swim to the surface
in the wheelbarrow where he perched, tilting his head.

We called him our supervisor; we were the axis
about which his world was turning, for the moment,
until, exhausted, we put the brakes on the whole project.

I encountered this same robin the next weekend
when I brought out my domesticated cat, a false predator,
to sit on the patio with me after doing yard work.

The robin with ruffled feathers went straight to alarm mode
although my cat paid no interest in the bird,
lying down on the edge of the pavement as I sipped my coffee.

Ever the supervisor, the robin took earnest in his plight,
perched on a metal post, in the midst of a verbal anxiety attack.

What I didn't see until later was his flightless youngling
sitting on the ground below, a child for which this parent volunteered to bleed.

Ellie Luebbe Janda • Beaver Crossing, NE

Haikus of Motherhood in the Country

My bath water is much too hot
Baby must eat soon
Steaming myself back awake

Vacuum floor all clean
Crackers, cheese, and pickle chips
Did not think that through

Sticky residue
Covers all the clean clothing
Empty pockets well

I hear a cricket
Trying to get in my door
Please hand me a shoe

So happy to leave
Cold and flu season behind
And then the ticks come

Saw a leaf fall off a tree today.
Hey, autumn. Too soon.
Pull it together, summer.

Joslyn Rojewski • Carrollton, TX

in the living room

The room felt bright with cinnamon paint
and flowered curtains.
Alive with clicks and giggles that rang out long into the night,
drifting lazily
through drafty windows like a perfume,
sweet and soft.
Sometimes I catch the scent of it
and there I am again.

Steve Rose • Indianola, IA

Annie and Sam

roost expectant in their Oldsmobile
under the streetlights, her hair bobbed and thin,
her face like a grackle's, pinched and pointed.
His head, a hand taller, the contour of a fist.
They wait. The café opens six a.m. sharp,
its lights blinking on in a slow yawn.

Sam exits the bronze sedan first. His stroke-numbed
steps slap the street, like a tin can tossed
from a window. Annie creaks out the passenger side,
the door's hinges squeaking in harmony.

The waitress opens the cafe with a click.
It could be the lock. It could be her tongue.
They back into their booth as if it were a stall.
They share toast buttered both sides, eggs
hard fried with side of hash browns; all served
without a menu, without a word.

Their creased faces hover over coffees,
occasional forks interrupting the steam. They talk
of vegetables, not that any but catsup grace
this repast celebrating a garden to be planted.

Annie leads the confab, announcing each crop,
seeds slipping from her tongue. She sketches
rows of tomatoes on a napkin, weaving
melon and squash around their stalks;
plants a few sunflowers on the west end
to guard against the ending of the day
when the sun turns dull orange and mean.

Nodding, a lackey to her dreams, Sam agrees—
his hand plow already hovering over the ground.

James Luebbe • Beaver Crossing, NE

The Borrow Pit

I grew up baling hay in the borrow pit,
watched my uncle throwing bales
below the freeway where the state took out
ten feet of soil to build an overpass.
All day long the strangers' cars
shimmered through that heat and dust,
wavering weak as signals from a foreign land.
I wondered were their lives like ours,
or if they laughed at us? Cattle, deer and
farmers in their fields, baling down inside
that god-damned dusty pit. I thought
they meant to borrow more than they could buy.

But besides the payment for the ground,
there was the crop. Where the hill
turned into hollow, it turned the logic
of production upside down. The clay,
though much less fertile, holds more rain,
to leave an average crop each year, as if
in secret it has stored its yield in years
of wealth, to spend it in a drought.

We have been up that road and back
with cars the same as theirs, and traveling

those thoroughfares we nearly
think alike. But the borrow pit
is full of dust, and the work, though not
so bad, is hard. We wonder what the state
will borrow next. And we eye that overpass
with envy and joke some night we'll tear it down,
put back our ground where it belongs,
to leave the cars backed up at the hacked out
highway's end. "Sorry," we will say,
"We make no loans to strangers."

Charlene Neely • Lincoln, NE

Harold's Hardware Sold Pocketknives for Two Bits

He'd been barefoot back then,
hugging a fifty-pound burlap bag
of sugar around the middle.
A penny for each sack he'd haul
from the old man's Ford pickup truck
through the back door of the bakery.
Once a week, twenty-five bags.
It was hard work, but he stood tall
each Saturday when he gave his Ma
the two bits to put in the sugar bowl.
Until the day Bobby Van Fleet
ran by with his new knife
and six weeks wages fell
in a small mountain at his feet.

Ellie Luebbe Janda • Beaver Crossing, NE

First Aid Kit

Holder of horrid anecdotes
Box of memories not entirely wanted
But still treasured

Bandages unable to stick
Adhesive like lined paper or damp chalk
Completely worthless

Athletic tape, not for an athlete
But for a baby with an eye patch
Learning lessons about rough play with straws

Dye free acetaminophen
For the child who can tolerate so much
But not blue food coloring

Little cuts, big scrapes
Leaky wound or gaping gash
All part of growing up

Janet McMillan Rives • Oro Valley, AZ

Survivors

Up north it was easier, a matter of pulling plants
before the first frost, knocking the dirt off roots,
cutting back tops, tucking them into cardboard boxes.
On Mother's Day I would plant withered remains
in fresh potting soil, then watch their magic,
each year's blooms better than the last.

Everything is backwards here in the desert.
I plant in early November then glimpse pink, red,
orange blossoms open to warm winter sun.
I protect them on a dozen freezing nights, old towels
covering memories of gardens I've abandoned
in half forgotten yards. Each May I drag pots
to the covered patio or under lacy mesquite leaves
profiting from the scant shade of summer.

Over time geranium leaves yellow, stems shrink,
buds drop. By August I surrender, toss dying plants.
Now just two remain, so long since they've bloomed
I've forgotten their colors—tangerine, perhaps,
lipstick pink. Into shortened days, temperate nights,
I will shepherd us beyond the brink of our exhaustion.

Brandy L. Prettyman • Papillion, NE

Nature's Art

I stumbled upon
a natural made painting
done in sand
by the Wind and the Sea

I studied its gentle curves,
watched as rivets of water
formed chevrons
and guided the sea home
Unable or unwilling to disturb such art
I stepped around the picturesque creation,
letting the tide do what it may
without unnatural interference
from something, or someone,
as insignificant in this world as I

Amy Haddad • Omaha, NE

When Sleepy and Louche and Amenable Were Beautiful

~from *The Weekend* by Charlotte Wood[1]

Sitting at the end of a bar, dressed for a date
with my husband who is late, I feign interest in the lanterns of gin

illuminating the bar back. A man a few seats away,
handsome in profile, turns and meets my gaze.

I look down and twirl the olives in my martini,
a drink I never have unless I am in a bar alone.

He signals the bartender, pushes a few bills across the bar.
Oh no, I think, *he wants to pay for my drink.*

That hasn't happened in ages. My girlfriends and I used to high heel
into a room, drunk with our potency. We played at teasing,

practiced looking bored, turned down drinks or dances
and always radiated heat. Pleasure rouges my cheeks.

---

1 Charlotte Wood, *The Weekend* (New York: Riverhead Books, 2020), 50.

I decide to be kind and arrange my face in a gentle rebuke
    just as he rises and leaves. He was merely paying his tab.

I could see he wanted no part of me. I concentrate on the winking circle
    of ice floating in my drink and the constant small shocks of aging.

Ricardo Moran • San Diego, CA

Time to Move On

Outside of Alliance,
in the fields of Nebraska
I found a Buick
perched on a pedestal.

And I figured that this
was the right time to run away.

He creaked and peeled,
tearing his prison sentence
into flakes of floating paint.

He waved to me.
"Hey, buddy. Can you give me a hand?"

I held out my arms
ready to catch him
as he clambered down.

I cleaned his headlights
covered in grey paint
so he could see more
clearly, so I could see.

And he coughed when I turned the ignition key.

"Where to?" he asked.
"Let's just go." I replied.
" 'Til we run out of time."

Kim Sosin • Omaha, NE

The White Prairie

White crosses
standing at attention
rows
angles
diagonals

in wave upon wave
each cross protecting
a seedling
entombed
never to bloom.

No teachers
No artists
No scientists
No gardeners
No babies

Death
This is thy sting.

Ellie Luebbe Janda • Beaver Crossing, NE

Fairy Treasures

Church meetings were long,
the babysitter was busy.
Mom was sick with the flu
(sitting up made her dizzy).
Dad said he was sorry,
there was no other way,
Betsy had to come along
and wait quietly today.

"But don't worry," said Dad.
"If you look under your seat
I think you'll find something
to play with that's neat."
Betsy looked under her seat
and found a small doll
with a tiny pet puppy
and a miniature ball.

"Where did this come from?"
Betsy asked in surprise.
"The Car Fairy," said Dad
with a twinkle in his eyes.
"The Car Fairy? Who is that?"
Betsy asked with a smile.

"She tries to help out," said Dad
"When you'll be stuck for a while."

Betsy played with the doll
and the ball and the dog.
She had them play fetch
and bounce around like a frog.
The meeting was over
before Betsy knew it.
She got a tiny bit bored,
but playing got her through it.

Dad said the Car Fairy
wanted to say:
"I can't fix your problem,
I can't take it away.
But I can give you a gift
to brighten your day."

There was snow on the ground,
and snow in the trees.
Snow piled up on the yard
as it blew down in the breeze.
There would be no school today,
for the roads were too bad.
Show and Tell Day was canceled.
It made Betsy feel sad.

Dad saw that sad Betsy
and gave her a hug.

He pointed to the kitchen, saying,
"Hey, check under the rug."
Betsy looked under the rug
and found a square box.
It was a puzzle with a picture
of bright, colorful socks.

Betsy smiled, even though
her eyes had been teary.
"What is this?" she asked,
feeling more cheery.
Dad said, "The Snow Day Fairy
must have left you a gift.
Why don't we put it together?
It'll give you a lift."

Dad, Mom, and Betsy worked hard
the whole day long.
They got that puzzle together
while they listened to songs.
It was exactly the thing
to brighten Betsy's mood.
Show and Tell Day was cancelled,
but what can you do?

Dad said the Snow Day Fairy
wanted to say:
"I can't fix your problem,
I can't take it away.

But I can give you a gift
to brighten your day."

The new baby was coming
a couple weeks early.
The family needed to get
to the hospital in a hurry.
Grandpa would come when he could
to take Betsy out
to the lobby or a park
to wander about.

In the hospital room,
Dad threw Betsy Mom's purse.
"Take a look inside," Dad said
as Mom talked to a nurse.
She found some small figures
next to the wallet and keys.
Betsy asked, "Who do you think
left me all these?"

Dad was very distracted
with the baby coming soon,
but said, "The Hospital Fairy,
of course, has been in this room."
Betsy was worried
(and for the early baby, even scared).
But she felt better as she played with
a plastic giraffe, chimp, and bear.

Grandpa came to get Betsy
after twenty minutes or so.
He said the lounge would be
the best place to go.
Betsy showed Grandpa her animals,
making them dance and twirl,
until Dad came out to say,
"Guess what! It's a girl!"

Dad said the Hospital Fairy
wanted to say:
"I can't fix your problem,
I can't take it away.
But I can give you a gift
to brighten your day."

Meetings can be long,
missing Show and Tell is no fun.
It can even be scary
when Mom has a new little one.
A visit from the fairies
helped Betsy feel better.
She decided to write
all of the fairies a letter.

"Thank you, sweet fairies,
for bringing me toys
when I was bored or worried
or needed some joy.

Thank you so much
for being prepared
with little gifts that always
remind me you care."

Betsy took the letter and a treat
and right before bed
left them on Dad's desk
with an extra note that said,
"By the way, here's a treat
that is just for you.
The Candy Bar Fairy
says thank you too."

Getting stuff can be fun,
new toys are nice to get.
But it's important to remember
the love behind it.
Sometimes those small, little gifts
have a big message to tell.
They say, "Hey, you're special.
I care how you feel."

Betsy said the Candy Bar Fairy
wanted to say:
"Daddy, I love you,
and I know you love me.
I won't ever forget
how you take care of me."

Essays

Julie S. Paschold • Norfolk, NE

What We Give in Gardening

There is a certain amount of forgiving that goes into a garden.

Gardening isn't just sticking things into the ground and then, weeks later, something comes out of it. You put certain amounts of qualities of yourself into that garden—into that small plot of earth that develops into what you hope will be a fruitful bounty edible enough for your kitchen table.

There is a certain amount of forgiving that goes into a garden. The day after a good rain or if you've just watered the soil, it is the best time to pull weeds. Forgive them. Forgive those weeds for growing where you didn't want them, for taking up space and soil and nutrients you intended for other plants. There is forgiving in the weeds you miss, or when you accidentally pull off a couple of marigold blooms or tomato branches instead of the weeds you were reaching for. You forgive the tomatoes for growing outside of their cage or the cucumber for taking over the row of radishes because you weren't out here one week to train them into the right places. You forgive the borers for taking your row of neatly placed sunflowers in the rear of your garden, and you forgive them again for taking the second row when you replant them and the insects strike again, leaving only one sunflower standing.

And in that forgiving you learn to forgive in other places too. You forgive yourself for not being so far along in your career—for leaving to change jobs and start over in your 40s for better benefits and healthier working conditions. You forgive your son for not calling and not coming to see you for the weekend because you and he were both exhausted. You forgive yourself for leaving things undone on the to-do list this weekend because you went to the lake with your sister instead and the last time you did that was several weeks ago. You forgive your friend for not stopping by because sometimes we get depressed or anxious and life gets to be too much for us introverts and there will be a next time. And you forgive yourself for not having a forever mate because last time you tried that you had to avoid abuse, and although you are out of that situation and healing, you are learning to trust again, reaching out, and maybe agreeing to feel something for the first time in a long time again.

There is a certain amount of waiting that goes into a garden. In the winter, when you are scraping ice off your windshield and scooping snow off your sidewalk, it seems like the growing season will never come. But spring does arrive. And once you've planted those seeds in rows and put the small plants far enough apart to allow for growth, there seems to be too much earth. They seem too far away from each other. Your garden seems too big for what you've planted. Summer seems too far away. But then the summer comes and with it the storms—and with each one a little wind damage or hail takes out some of your plants and it seems like they will never outgrow the damage. But they do. And the last waiting is for the plants to change from their vegetative state to their reproductive state, to give their fruits to you. You wait for tomatoes to ripen, for cucumbers to grow, for radishes to develop, for squash to bulk out on the vines. You wait for the fruit of your labors.

In the waiting for your garden you learn patience in other areas of your life. You learn that the pain of loss takes time to heal. You learn you must stay in a house that's too big for you and has no garage where you were abused, so you redecorate, move some things around, and wait until the time is right to move. You make improvements on yourself but learn that in order to see those improvements you will have to wait. It takes time for new habits to take form. Time takes time. And for that you have to wait.

There is a certain amount of growing that goes into a garden. Those seeds you plant do sprout and push up out of the soil. The plants you put carefully in the ground develop leaves. Your garden gets bigger and greener and as you care for it, as you water and fertilize and weed and guide each stem, it grows up and out, covering the area you've left out for it, rewarding you for your care.

In the same regard, there is growth in your life. As time goes on, the pain does lessen from the loss. The improvements you are attempting in your life: each time you try at them, you grow and learn from it. You are seeing those improvements. Healing happens. Growth happens. You accept people into your life. You go to those meetings. You have your son and your daughter and your friends over. You visit your parents. You grow.

There is a certain amount of love that goes into a garden. Each weed you pull, you do out of love. Each time you water, you do out of love. Each time you scatter fertilizer, you do so out of love. You love the crooked tomato plant that managed to branch out prolifically and escape its cage. You love the wayward cucumber that you have to keep training back from the edge of the garden. And you love your plants for producing for you, for giving you the fruits of their labors, for laboring with you during this season of waiting, forgiving, and growth.

In your life, each time you make improvements on yourself, you are showing self-love. All the time you spend waiting for growth and trying to become a truer version of you was spent in self-love. All the grief you went through to get to the other side was done in love. Visiting your parents, calling your mom and dad regularly, are done in love. Seeing your son and daughter together and listening to your daughter's big plans beyond college and meeting your son's new girlfriend, all done in love. And finally, finally opening yourself up to new friends and new adventures. Finally opening the door you had guarded so long because you were so damaged, but now the world doesn't seem safer but you seem more prepared to go out and meet it, and to accept new friends to join you in meeting that world—that, indeed, is love.

So the next time someone asks you if you want something from their garden—if they have their own bounty to share—please remember that this is not simply free food. What they offer you is, indeed, nourishment. But what they offer you is so much more. It is a piece of their process of forgiving, waiting, growing, and loving. It is a piece of themselves. Accept it with gratitude.

There is a certain amount of forgiving, waiting, growing, and loving that go into a garden.

Originally published on August 2, 2021, on medium.com.

Colleen Gallion • Grand Island, NE

Precarious and Precious

At the foot of my bed is an oak-colored cedar chest for my daughter. We found it at a very large furniture store in a very small town, and it was perfect. It featured a sunrise carved in the front, which looked more like a pineapple. Smaller than normal, it stored all my daughter's mostly pink things so nicely—her baptismal gown, her birth certificate and imprint of her feet, her baby blankets and several of her baby outfits as well as her baby book—an empty baby book.

Not that I couldn't have filled out some of it. I just couldn't stand the thought of not filling out the whole thing and having all those blank pages stare back at me, a painful reminder of what we didn't have and what she never got to do.

It wasn't supposed to be this way. As we sped through Lincoln like we were racing in Daytona, I couldn't stop my mind from racing. The OB/GYN appointment in Grand Island had us running late and that was just the beginning of the horrible turn of events.

Just a month earlier, my husband bought a dark blue minivan for our expanding family, a minivan, a blinking neon billboard that might as well read "family hauler." At the time, though, we had no idea that instead of two children, we would be hauling my husband, sister, and me, with my uncomfortably bulging belly. Uncomfortable was an understatement. Under my blue maternity top, the skin stretched across my pale beach ball-sized abdomen so tightly that you could bounce a quarter off it. All that pressure wreaked havoc on my spinal column and every nerve in it felt pinched. I hadn't been able to sleep much in the last two months, not only because of the pain, but my imagination running wild kept me awake as well. Midday in the June heat and humidity of Nebraska did not help either.

Desperate to speak with my former doctor, I spent most of the drive trying to figure out how to send him an email from my cellphone. He had taken care of me with my first pregnancy and delivered a healthy baby boy just two years earlier. I had stayed in contact with him when I found out we were expecting again, another miracle pregnancy despite all my fertility issues. Shortly after my son's birth though, my doctor moved to Oregon, and I was forced to choose a new doctor.

Negative thoughts kept running through my mind, playing repeatedly like a broken record, complements of that new doctor, a young blonde with not much experience I would soon learn.

"Oh, that's way too much fluid," she said just the day before, looking at the monitor while running the ultrasound probe over my belly glistening with a cold blue gel.

What does that mean, too much fluid? I wondered.

She called me at home later that day to tell me I was having a baby with a chromosome abnormality, something along the lines of Down syndrome. My husband was furious she gave me that news, not only over the phone but when I was home by myself. I had suspected something was wrong through most of the pregnancy. No one believed me. It's a maddening feeling, like when you are dreaming and trying to scream, but nothing comes out.

So now we were on our way to an ultrasound specialist in Omaha, twisting and turning along the interstate at eighty miles an hour, all the while keeping an eye open for our exit. I'm not going to lie. I grabbed the 'oh crap' handle more than once. I would have given anything to trade places with some of these people that were passing us like we were standing still. I'm sure they were all going somewhere that was better than where I was going, maybe the zoo or even shopping at the mall. Neither me nor my husband knew how to get where we were going. Fortunately, my sister had been to the University of Nebraska Medical Center several times for infertility treatments and knew the way.

The closer we got, the more I felt like throwing up and it wasn't just because of the pregnancy. I've always been a nervous person with OCD—and not in a productive "I have a super clean house" kind of way—but the useless kind that just makes me neurotic.

Once there, like a weeble-wobble, I waddled toward a help desk, explaining who I was and why I was late. I didn't even know if we would still have the appointment or if it had to be rescheduled. Specialists are funny like that, but they got us in and lead us through a maze of winding corridors, and even though they were pleasantly decorated with artwork, I couldn't have found my way out even if I had wanted to. Apparently, we had come to the wrong building, and they took us through a back way labyrinth. My legs felt like Jell-O and between that and the extra pressure on my back from the excess fluid around my tiny baby, I really could have used a wheelchair, though no one offered.

They took us to a tiny room, more like an oversized closet, dimly lit with canned lights in the ceiling. I lay on the exam table while the technician turned off the lights above me for the procedure. It didn't take long as she rolled the wand over my belly, and I heard clicking as she saved multiple images. The technician said nothing, only that the doctor would be in shortly.

I stared at the doorknob, waiting for it to turn. The lights above me were still dimmed, but my husband and sister were each illuminated with small lights in their chairs next to each other. I was glad because they couldn't see me sniffling or wiping tears with the back of my hand, or at least that's what I told myself.

It was so quiet. I sat on the edge of the thin-padded table, swinging my feet back and forth like a pendulum. My sister bounced her knee nervously over her leg. My husband, who would normally be chewing his fingernails down to nubs, stared blankly in a daze. We kept waiting.

"Does anyone else have a sense of impending doom?" I said, just to break the silence.

Finally, the doorknob turned, and my heart skipped a beat. The doctor came in and introduced himself, then told us the news as he brought up the ultrasounds on a bright white display, big enough for all of us to see. He didn't mince words and, in fact, appeared to stiffen himself in his white doctor's coat with his perfectly trimmed dark hair, not an emotion on his face. I started to cry in a sort of a whimper, and my husband started to cry in a way I had never seen a man cry before. His eyes swelled with tears and turned red; his bottom lip began to quiver. He couldn't speak clearly. It was a bit unnerving seeing a normally burly and solid man be reduced to that. My sister cried too. Her shoulders rose and fell in short bursts that matched her sobs.

I began to ask questions.

"I'll get to that. Just let me finish," Dr. Stiff said matter-of-factly.

He pointed out the things that were wrong with the baby, who we would name Megan, which were much clearer on the 3D ultrasound than they were back in March. That was when the first ultrasound specialist said he was 98 percent sure everything was fine—98 percent.

We were blindsided. Thirty-five weeks and four days of what we were told was a normal pregnancy had come down to these few minutes with a doctor who had all the sensitivity of a bug.

"The physical abnormalities can be fixed," he said. "The club foot, the clenched fists and the defective heart, which you can see only has two chambers. However, she would need to be stronger to endure the heart surgery. But if she gains weight, her heart will have to work much harder, and she might not survive."

They admitted me to the hospital from there, once again along the winding back corridors, and scheduled an amniocentesis to find out exactly what genetic abnormality she had. It was Trisomy 18, a step beyond Down syndrome. We were all a mess of tears and tissues and sobbing—an inconsolable, uncontrollable sobbing.

It would be ten days before my daughter succumbed to the damage done to her body practically before she existed, a hairline fracture in her DNA when her twenty-three chromosomes were formed. There was nothing I did or could have done differently to keep any of this from happening. I know this. No amount of bed rest or extra sleep, healthier eating or exercise would have changed the outcome. Had we opted to do something to extend her life—which in hindsight, had I known she was such a fighter, I would have—we may have had more than ten days.

I wish I would have.

Valerie Lee Vierk • Ravenna, NE

Just South of the Moon

Sometimes when we look back on a precious experience, it's scary to think how close we came to missing it completely. This almost happened to me on the firefly night.

I'd been watching a good TV mini-series and so had missed my usual early evening walk along the west side of my little town. My route went along the ball field at the edge of town, turned south down a paved but little traveled strip of highway that passes by a little wood, a quiet creek, and a field on one side. After the movie, I debated whether or not to take my walk at ten p.m., but as it turned out I was very glad I went out instead of going to bed.

As I stepped out, I was greeted by a lovely full moon floating in the eastern sky, and a balmy breeze to keep the bugs away. I loved these nights with the warm breeze caressing me.As I approached the ball field, I noticed there were still people there, but as I passed and turned south, the lights and noise faded and it seemed as if I were entering a world of my own.

It took me about a minute to reach the little wood where several huge cottonwoods grew. It was a firefly night! That's what made it so magical, as only fireflies can. There were multitudes of them blinking their tiny lanterns on and off, and it reminded me of an enchanted forest in some European fairy tale, not a wooded area along a muddy creek in central Nebraska. It was the first night I had seen the fireflies that summer. It was June fifteenth, six days before the summer solstice, always a special day for me.

The fireflies were early this year; usually it was a day or two before the solstice when they first appeared.

Suddenly I remembered the wonderful storybook my mother had read to my brother, Steve, and me when we very small. It was titled *Little Squeegy Bug, Story of the Firefly*. I let my mind drift back in time; I was a little girl again in the summer of my childhood.

Little Squeegy Bug was what nowadays we'd call a generic bug, but they didn't call him that back in the 1950s. They called him a little nobody. Unfortunately, the other bugs were mean to him and he was depressed, but they didn't use that word either. They just said he was sad. There were other notable bugs though—Buzzer the Bumble (with a gun in his tail), Haunchy the Spider, Creepy the Caterpillar, and some other bugs with pertinent names that I couldn't remember. In the end, these kindly bugs made wings for Squeegy, put a little lantern in his tail, and he flew off into the sky to live by night "at the turn in the road, just south of the moon."

That was the most wonderful part for my brother and me. In our innocent, little minds it seemed such a fascinating place to live. Now at thirty-four, it still did. As I gazed up into the starry heavens, it seemed as if I was almost there myself.

I walked on, lost in thought, and enjoying myself immensely. In a hundred yards or so I found myself standing on the bridge over the creek named Mud Creek, and aptly so. By day it was a very slow-moving creek with brown water, but in the night, with the reflection of the moon shining on the water and the lamplighters blinking their green lights on and off, it was very pretty. I sat down on the bridge railing with the tree branches cascading over me.

After a few minutes, I walked on south another thirty yards or so to within a few feet of the railroad tracks. Usually, I never would be out here alone in the dark, but tonight I was euphoric—and brave. I would have crossed the tracks and continued on the rest of the half mile to the main highway, but I remembered my fifteen-year-old son, Teddy, would be coming home from a pizza party and might be alarmed if I was missing at ten thirty at night.

As I retraced my steps, I paused a couple more times on the bridge and by the enchanted wood. "The "squeegies" were still lighting up the night like a thousand flashing emeralds and I was reluctant to leave their world. I felt as if I'd been enchanted by their sparkling night.

When I walked up to our house, Teddy was sitting on the front porch steps. "Where were you, Mom?"

"Oh, I was at the turn in the road, just south of the moon," I quoted.

"Come on, Mom," my "cool" teenager said, obviously not sharing my whimsy. "I was starting to worry about you."

"I'm sorry. I was having a wonderful nature experience." I quickly explained about my magical walk among the lightning bugs and the book that his uncle and I had loved. "Did Grandma ever read it to you?"

"I don't think so," he answered. He'd grown up during the Star Wars craze, a couple galaxies away from my childhood of Roy Rogers and squeegy bugs.

The next evening after work, I went over to see my mother, Virginia. I needed very badly to see the actual little book again, because after thirty years, some details were fuzzy. I asked her if she could locate the book, and she gave me a knowing look. "Are you writing a story?" she asked. Through the years she'd learned that when I started quizzing her on a subject, it was usually for research for a short story.

I told her about the night before, then she promptly went into her "wisdom room" as Teddy had named it. In just a couple of minutes she emerged with the well-worn book. I was delighted because I had been afraid it would take her longer to locate it among her huge collection of treasures.

She sat back down on the couch; I was sitting in the rocking chair a couple of feet away. She held up the book so I could see the cover. There was little Squeegy with his skinny, curved legs and red shoes. He was a funny-looking little bug.

"Do you want me to read it to you?" she asked. I was shocked; after all, I was a grown woman now. I shouldn't have been shocked though because Mom had always read to us a lot when we were small. Yet I was deeply touched.

"Yes, please do," I replied.

In the turbulence of my married years, Teddy's early years, I had never taken the time to read the precious book to him, even when we were staying at my parents' house during one of the separations.

"I never read this to Teddy," Mom said a little sadly. That made me sad too. She started reading. I sat there looking at the lines that had grown in her face, studying her hands that were always chapped from hours in the dish pan. She was no longer the young mother who had read to me in the long-ago fifties, nor could I remember when she was young. That time had slipped away, was lost forever, like so many things are lost before we even realize we want them to stay. But, of course, I'd seen many pictures of my pretty, dark-haired, dark-eyed young mother. Now she had just turned sixty. Her hair was peppered with gray, and she wore glasses, but she was still the same dear mother she had always been.

I sat there watching and hearing her read and was taken back to that long ago time when my brother would sit on one side of her and me on the other. I heard again about the little bug who lived along a quiet brook. "He wasn't an ant and he wasn't a beetle and he wasn't a roach. He was just a little squeegy bug with no name and no mother or father."

One day Buzzer the Bumble Bee (with a gun in his tail) flew up to Squeegy, who was very impressed with the mighty Buzzer and wanted to be like him. When Buzzer said he lived "at the turn in the road, just south of the moon," Squeegy decided he'd like to live there, too, because it sounded like such a beautiful place. As Buzzer flew off, Squeegy decided that somehow, he would find the sky and go to that wonderful place.

But he had no idea how to find the sky so he just started climbing up a cattail. He was such a little bug and the cattail was so high that it took him three days to reach the top, and by then a thunderstorm was raging. He started to cry and Creepy the Caterpillar heard him and came out of his cozy home under a leaf, holding his lantern, and invited Squeegy to come in and spend the night with him.

In the morning Squeegy poured out his soul to Creepy about how unhappy he was and how he wanted to find the sky. Creepy recruited Haunchy the Spider, Yardy the Inchworm, and Sissy the Cutworm to help make silver wings for Squeegy so he could fly up to the sky.

Haunchy wove beautiful filmy strands, Yardy measured them into strips and Sissy cut the strips. Then Haunchy wove them together and fashioned wings for Squeegy and glued them with dew drops.

A few minutes after Mom began to read, Dad came in from the garage, peeked into the living room, listened for a few moments, and then went quietly away.

I knew Mom wouldn't be able to finish the book; I knew she would break down. I knew I would too. Almost to the end she choked up and could not go on. We both sat there a few minutes, weeping quietly.

Then brutally, yet perhaps mercifully, the phone began to ring. Still, I was angry that our special time back in childhood had been shattered. After a ring or two Mom got up to answer the phone in the kitchen, lifting her glasses to wipe the tears from her eyes.

"Oh, hello, Helen," she said, and I knew it would be a long time before she could extricate herself. I picked up the precious book and quietly let myself out of the house.

I went home and looked at the cover again. Bill and Bernard Martin were listed as the authors. I opened the book and noted the first printing—August 1945. I paged to where Mom had stopped and read the ending. Squeegy started to cry because even though he now had silver wings like Buzzer, he still didn't have a gun in his tail. Haunchy told him guns hurt people and instead reached out and took a lantern that was hanging along the Milky Way and fastened it to Squeegy's tail. Then he christened the nondescript little bug "Squeegy the Firefly, Lamplighter of the Skies." By day he could play with the other bugs along the brook, but by night he would fly up into the sky and light the way for the other little bugs. Best of all, at night his home would be "at the turn in the road, just south of the moon."

I cried again when little Squeegy bug flew off into the heavens. But there was a twist, a happy ending to this story. On the inside back cover, a blank page, I suddenly saw two little traced hands with the inscription in Mom's handwriting, *Teddy's hands, January 15, 1975*. She *had* read the book to him! He would have been three and a half. My spirits were lifted; it didn't matter that he hadn't loved the book as I had, only that Mom had read it to both of us. It was enough. A day or so later I returned the book to Mom and showed her Teddy's handprints.

I wrote the first part of this essay in June 1986, at the time of the incident. Mom died in July 2006, and a week or so later I was in the Ravenna library when the librarian, Pam, said to me, "We want to buy a book in memory of your mother since she served on the library board for many years. Do you have any ideas?"

I didn't hesitate a second and said, "Little Squeegy Bug, Story of the Firefly." I then added that it was a book from the 1950s and possibly not available anymore. Pam quickly began clicking on her computer and then said there was a new edition titled, *The Little Squeegy Bug*. I said that had to be it.

I went home and checked on Amazon to see if the original book was listed, and found several copies, but also saw the new edition by Bill Martin (now with Jr. after his name), Michael Sampson, and illustrator Patrick Corrigan. It was published in 2001. Then I found an article written by Bill Martin, Jr. shortly after the new edition was published. Martin said he had overtold the story in the original book and had shortened it up a little in the new edition. The new illustrator also modernized the sketches.

Now Squeegy was a blue bug and looked very different from the Squeegy I knew.

Dad died in 2009 and when I was cleaning out our parents' house, I ran across the beloved book. I told my brother about it and he asked if he could have it. Because it had Teddy's hands outlined in it, I was a little reluctant, but my brother is nineteen months older than me, and it was appropriate that it should go to him. But first I made a Xerox copy of Teddy's hands. Then I quickly went on E-bay to see if I could find another original one. I did.

In August 2021, when I was preparing to submit this essay, I did more research on the book and the author. I learned that back in 1945, Bill Martin's brother, Bernard, asked Bill to write a children's story that he could illustrate while he was recovering from wounds received in a military training exercise. Bill was also in the service, the Army Air Corps, and had joined shortly after the bombing of Pearl Harbor. The boys had grown up in Hiawatha, Kansas, along with three other brothers. There were no books in their house.

Squeegy was Bill Martin's first book. First Lady Eleanor Roosevelt bought it and read it to her grandchildren. Eleanor was so impressed with it that she mentioned it in one of her radio broadcasts and also in her weekly newspaper column titled "My Day." The book eventually sold over a million copies. It was a self-published book. Bill and Bernard had started their own publishing company called Tellwell, although that didn't appear in the copyright page.

Strangely enough, Martin could barely read when he entered Emporia State University. He had hidden this fact from his elementary and high school teachers! He did credit his fifth-grade teacher, Miss Davis, with reading to his class every day, which encouraged him to want to learn to read. In college, he somehow taught himself by staring at poems he had memorized and one of his professors had read in class. After he had the poems memorized, he could pick out the words on the written page. After graduating from Emporia, he eventually earned a master's degree and a doctoral degree in early childhood education.

Martin taught school for a few years and then was employed by Holt, Rinehart and Winston publishers as the editor in chief of the children's division. He went on to write over three hundred children's books, ten with Bernard serving as illustrator in the early years. Bill Martin was one of the first children's writers to tour schools and bookstores, where he read his books to the children.

Bill Martin, Jr. died in 2004 at his home in Commerce, Texas. He had delighted children (and parents) with his books that spanned a sixty-year career.

On August 10, 2021, I went to our public library to see the new Squeegy bug book that I'd never bought, or even looked at in our library, after Mom died. I asked the librarian, Joy, to find it for me, and she did. She pointed to a huge couch-like rocking chair in the children's section of our beautiful new library that was opened in 2018, a hundred years after our old Carnegie library was built in 1918. I sat down and opened the book. There on the inside front cover was the inscription in memory of my mother, Virginia, a past library board member, dated 2006. Bill Martin, Jr. had dedicated the book, "To my brother, Bernard, who made the first squeegy bug fly." Bernard had died in 1998, at age 86. He had studied at the Kansas City Art Institute and made a name for himself with his paintings, mostly of birds.

I read the book, but it wasn't the same, of course. The language was a little different, and Squeegy didn't go to live "at the turn in the road, just south of the moon," that magical place to me. Still, I now plan to buy the new version.

And one more twist. While adding to this essay in August 2021, I told Teddy about it. He immediately said, "I want to read it."

"Good," I replied. "You're in it." (How quickly and almost unbelievably my fifteen-year-old had come to be fifty!)

"I thought so," he answered.

Shades of his grandmother's perception? I think Mom is smiling up there and perhaps she has visited "the turn in the road, just south of the moon."

Short Stories

David Kubicek • Lincoln, NE

A Place of Their Own

The apartment smelled like an unwashed gym sock. Jennifer looked around at the graffiti-covered walls, peeling wallpaper, discolored blotches on the ceiling, and the naked lightbulb hanging down from the ceiling. Chris stepped into the bedroom, but Jennifer had seen enough. She had not pictured their first home together looking like this. She fidgeted under the steady gaze of the landlord who waited by the door. He was an old man wearing a black overcoat and hat, his breathing slow and forced.

Finally, her unease built up to such an intensity inside her that she couldn't stand still any longer. She began to move idly around the kitchen, and she noticed more problems. The floor would never be clean. Years, perhaps decades, of feet had stained the linoleum the color of weak lemonade, and the corners were black with packed dirt. The sink had only cold water. She turned it on, and a rusty stream gushed out, splattering in the deep porcelain sink. It took several seconds for the water to clear. She shut off the tap, but the faucet continued to drip. Behind her, the radiator snapped and started squealing.

Chris came to the bedroom doorway.

"Take a look in here," he said.

She wanted to rush out of this apartment, but that would embarrass Chris, so she went into the bedroom with him. Gray afternoon light from the window fell on the bed with a huge brown stain in the center of the mattress. A dusty gray blanket concealed the closet entrance. A rough-looking dresser stood against the wall on one side of the bed, and on the other side was a small stand with a telephone on it. Her eyes lingered on the phone.

"You got to go over to the phone company and tell them to connect it," the old landlord said, his voice crackling.

"What do you think?" Chris whispered.

"How could you ask that?" she whispered back.

"We've been looking since August. This is the first place we've found that we can afford."

"It doesn't even have a bathroom."

"Toilet's down the hall," the landlord said.

Jennifer felt heat rising in her face.

Nothing wrong with his hearing, she thought.

They followed the landlord down the hall. The bathroom consisted of two separate closet-like rooms, each behind its own padlocked door. They didn't go inside but examined the facilities from the hallway. One room contained a toilet and a sink; over the years it's dripping faucet had carved a rusty pathway down the side of the porcelain basin to the drain. The other room contained a bathtub and a wooden chair with dry paint drippings on the seat. The floorboards were gray with ground-in dirt, and there was an ancient roach motel in one corner of each room. Jennifer turned away, and the landlord padlocked the rooms. They returned to the apartment.

Chris drew her away from the landlord.

"Well?" he asked.

"Let's keep looking."

The radiator stopped squealing. The landlord's labored breathing was now the only sound.

"We've been looking for *two months*. We can't stay with my parents forever."

"We could afford to pay more than a hundred a month. What about that place on Folsom Street?"

"We'd be spending most of our money on rent. We've got other bills, and we need to save some for emergencies."

This place is *an emergency*, she thought.

"It's just temporary, honey," he said. "We'll only be here 'til graduation, if that long."

"There's probably more wrong with this place than what we can see."

She knew he was tired. She was tired too. Apartment hunting robbed them of study time. It robbed them of sleep. And it robbed them of time for each other. She'd lost count of the number of apartments they'd looked at over the past month. The nice ones were too expensive, and the ones within their budget needed work. Some of them needed lots of work. Living in the three-bedroom bungalow with Chris' parents and two younger sisters was stressing everyone out. On top of that, it was a thirty-minute drive to campus. They needed to live closer to school. They needed a place of their own.

"Okay," Jennifer said grudgingly. "Let's try it."

"You planning to stay at least six months?" the landlord asked. "I don't want people moving in and out all the time."

"Yeah," Chris said tightly.

The landlord went out into the hall and waited for them, then he pulled the door shut with a bam that echoed off the walls. They followed him down the long flight of stairs and along the sidewalk to his furniture store to pay the first month's rent.

~ ~ ~ ~ ~

The first night in their apartment, Jennifer woke up shivering in the darkness. Quietly she slipped out of bed. There was an autumn nip in the room. Wind gusted against the bedroom window, stirring up a chill breeze that made her shiver. Slowly she felt her way around the bed, her feet stepping cautiously on the icy floor. When she reached the other side of the bedroom, she held her hand above the radiator. Then she touched the cold pipes.

A rustle of bedsheets.

"Honey, what is it?" Chris asked.

"There's no heat."

"Maybe they turn it down at night."

"To forty degrees? I don't remember the radiator going on for at least two hours before we went to bed."

"Now that you mention it, neither do I," he said. "Better get out the quilt. We'll straighten this out in the morning."

When the alarm clock went off at 6:30, the radiators were sputtering and whining. Chris got dressed and went downstairs to see the landlord while Jennifer scrambled eggs and put on a pot of coffee. Ten minutes later, she heard the outside door open and heavy footfalls coming up the stairs and down the hall. Chris flung open their apartment door and slammed it behind him with a force that shook the walls and rattled the windows. Jennifer, pouring coffee, splashed a little onto the table.

"What's the matter?" she asked.

Grumbling under his breath, he dropped into a chair at the table. Jennifer put the coffee pot on the coffeemaker's burner and laid a hand on his shoulder, felt the tension in his muscles.

"The heat is set to go off at nine and come on again at six," he said. "We have no heat in this dump for nine hours."

"But we don't even have storm windows," she said. "Just screens."

"That old coot's got our money, so he doesn't care. He makes his living selling furniture. He only rents these apartments to profit off his empty space. 'Costs a hundred and seventy-five dollars a month to heat them four apartments,' he says. At least we didn't sign a lease."

"We can move back with your parents and look for something better."

He shoved his chair away from the table, slopping coffee out of his cup.

"We were so eager to find a place of our own. My mom will have her 'I told you so' ready and whip it out like an Old West gunslinger."

"You think staying here will prove her wrong?"

"My parents don't have to know. We can stick it out for a few months and be out of here before they ever come to visit."

"Last night was only a taste," she said. "Winter's coming."

"I know," he said, then more calmly, "I know."

~ ~ ~ ~ ~

The following Saturday, Jennifer and Chris drove out to her parents' house and brought back two boxes of books and the brown wooden bookcase her dad had bought for her when she was ten. They set the bookcase up against the wall across from the foot of the bed. Chris mixed some plaster and they patched the holes in the walls. Jennifer hung a wedding photograph of her and Chris over one of the repaired holes.

One kitchen wall was covered with graffiti. Nestled like a jewel among all of the lewd suggestions was a heart with an arrow through it. Inside the heart some former tenant had written in an elegant hand: Lisa + Chuck.

"Let's paint the walls," she said. "Those two cans of paint in the closet should be enough."

"That old geezer probably left them there as a hint," Chris said.

"You said yourself he doesn't care about these apartments."

"That won't stop him from raising the rent if he comes up here and sees the improvement."

"Forget about him. We'll probably be gone before he ever sets foot in here again."

"Seems like a lot of work for this rat trap," Chris said.

"We can do it next weekend. It'll be fun."

~ ~ ~ ~ ~

A week later, she was sitting at the kitchen table highlighting sections in her geology textbook with a yellow marker when a knock exploded against the door. She jerked upright, her heart racing. They had just finished the walls the day before, and a hint of fresh paint lingered in the air.

The knock came again, more gently. She got up and opened the door a crack but left the chain lock on. She peered out at the old man. He smelled sour, like old sweat clothes.

"I'm your neighbor," he said.

"Yes?"

"From apartment three." He pointed down the hall. "Did he tell you that the hot water in your bathroom comes from my hot water heater?"

"What?"

"Didn't he tell you? He didn't tell you." The old man shook his gray head, pulled on his earlobe. He held out a hand in front of him. "I told him to tell people that when they move in, but he never tells them. That's my hot water. I pay for it."

She could feel her heart drumming as she stared at the old man standing in the dim light of the hallway.

"You mean we don't have *any* hot water? What are we going to do for hot water?"

"Well," the old man said, tugging his earlobe and examining the doorknob, "the old man who lived here before paid me a dollar a month, and I was satisfied. It's the neighborly thing to do, don't you think? I mean, how would you feel if someone used your hot water and didn't pay you for it?"

She wondered briefly if the old man was trying to con her but brushed the thought away. He seemed genuinely embarrassed to be talking to her about this.

"We'll be glad to pay you for it," she said. "But there are two of us, and we use more hot water."

The old man shrugged.

"Then make it a dollar fifty. Five thirty-eight a month is what I pay. I have the receipts. You can see them if you want."

"That's not necessary."

The old man crooked a finger at her.

"Come," he said. "I'll show you. I'm not trying to cheat you. I don't need money."

"No, that's all right."

"Come. I'll show you."

She followed him down the hall. He reached up and tapped the pipe that came out of his kitchen and went into their bathtub room. Then he talked to her about the miserly old man they rented from and about there being no heat at night and about how cold it would get this winter. She listened politely while her mind screamed for freedom. It took half an hour to break away from him so she could retreat to the safety of her apartment where she double-locked the door, lay on the bed, and had a good cry.

~ ~ ~ ~ ~

The next day after work she went to a greenhouse and picked up a wandering Jew plant, an arrow plant, and a corn plant. She arranged the wandering Jew on the shelf above the refrigerator, put the arrow plant on the table with the phone in the bedroom, and the corn plant on the bookcase. She hoped the apartment wouldn't get too cold for the plants at night.

"We can get a space heater," Chris said.

"That will use a lot of extra electricity."

"This is one of the emergencies we're saving money for. It's not just for the plants. It'll help us survive the winter too."

~ ~ ~ ~ ~

Tuesday afternoon Jennifer went to Walmart. She bought a couple pyramids of solid, evergreen-scented air freshener, lamp shades to clip onto the lightbulbs that hung down on chains from the ceilings in the kitchen and the bedroom, and some heavy golden drapes for the windows. After class, Chris stopped at the hardware store to pick up a window insulation kit, and they put clear plastic sheets over the windows to hold back some of the cold. Then they hung the drapes, and they stuffed rags in the crack beneath the kitchen door that opened out onto the roof of the furniture store.

On the first of the month Jennifer went down the hall to pay the hot water bill. The old man's TV talked loudly in his living room. He didn't answer the door right away, so she hammered harder, and he came to let her in. His apartment smelled as if it had been closed up for years. It smelled of dust. It smelled of last night's supper. It smelled like the old man.

"Did I disturb you?"

"No. That's all right. I've got nothing to do."

She dug a dollar bill and two quarters out of her jeans pocket.

"I came to pay for the hot water."

He took the money from her and held it absently as if it was not important.

"How are you getting along?" he asked.

"Fine."

"Good." He nodded and opened the door a little wider. "Do you want to come in for some coffee?"

"Don't go to any trouble."

"It's no trouble. I always make coffee in the afternoon."

She went in to have coffee with the old man. He told her about his wife, whose name was Mary. He had moved here after she'd died of cancer ten years ago. He told her about his son and his grandchildren. He told her about the other tenants who lived above the furniture store, and he told her about the tenants who had once lived here. They were mostly older people like himself who had retired or were about to retire. Jennifer remembered the heart among all of the graffiti on the painted-over kitchen wall.

"Do you remember Lisa and Chuck?" she asked.

He thought for a moment, shook his head.

"Were they friends of yours?"

"They lived in our apartment, I think."

"Must have been before I came here."

She told him that Chris was working as a custodian in a medical clinic, and she was working in a fabric store while they were in school. They were majoring in business at the university where they had met two years ago in a business law class. They would graduate in the spring.

"You two are just starting out in life," the old man said. "Mind if I ask how old you are?"

"Twenty-one."

He nodded.

"Yes," he said. "You're just starting out."

~ ~ ~ ~ ~

On the twentieth, Chris went down to pay the second month's rent, and the landlord said nothing the whole time. He silently took the check and silently handed Chris the hand-written receipt.

On Thanksgiving it got down to twenty degrees outside. They went to Jennifer's parents' home for dinner and later in the afternoon stopped in to see Chris' family.

"I really ought to get in and scrub out the toilet and bathtub rooms," she said one night while they were doing dishes.

He washed a cup and put it into the rinse pan on the chair beside the sink. She fished the cup out, wiped it, and set it on the table.

"Don't bother," he said. "We won't be here that long."

"It won't be easy finding another place we can afford right now. And besides, we're too busy to look. We'll probably be here all winter and maybe even a little while after graduation. I get sick every time I go into those rooms."

"The vent leaks. Water'll come in and mess up the floor again."

She knew the rooms were dirty. She knew they leaked. She knew that they weren't *really* a part of this apartment, like outhouses weren't *really* a part of farmhouses before indoor plumbing made its way to rural areas. But she knew she would feel better about the apartment if all of the rooms were clean.

"I want to try to clean them up," she said.

"Suit yourself."

He dropped a fork, ploomp, into the rinse water.

The next morning she wore out two mopheads scrubbing the rooms. Then she used some industrial strength bowl cleaner that Chris had brought home from work and scrubbed the rust and dirt off the sink, toilet, and bathtub. She used a pumice bar to eradicate the most stubborn stains. Then she sprayed the fixtures with glass cleaner and polished them until she could see herself in the chrome. Since she had just drawn a bucket of fresh soapy water, she mopped the kitchen floor again and wore out another mophead in the process.

On December first, she went next door to pay the coming month's hot water bill.

~ ~ ~ ~ ~

One night a winter storm blew into the city. When Jennifer got home from work, there were four inches of snow on the ground. Roads were snow packed and slick. Snowplows struggled to keep them open. The wind whipped the snow around, and she couldn't tell if it was still coming down or just drifting.

She decided to wait up for Chris. She wasn't a bit tired. There was a strange energy coursing through her body. She felt the same sense of excitement that she'd often experienced as a young girl at the first snowfall of winter.

She sat at the kitchen table and read a novel for pleasure, something she hadn't done in ages. She was so involved in her reading that she didn't notice when the heat went off. When a gust of wind blasted the window, she became aware of the chill in the room. She brought the space heater into the kitchen, and it took the edge off of the cold.

Occasionally, she got up and turned off the light and peered out into the darkness to watch the snow swirling down out of a black sky. It piled in white drifts on the furniture store roof and ticked against the windows. The wind made a lonesome moaning sound as it howled around the building.

At twelve thirty, the outside door opened far below and the suction shook the apartment door. Heavy footsteps tromped up the stairs and down the hall. She pulled open the door just as Chris was fumbling his key out of his pocket.

"I didn't expect you to be up," he said.

She took him in her arms and kissed him. His face was cold and red and a little damp. Droplets of melting snow glistened in his hair.

"Come in and warm up," she said. "Get that coat off. I've got water on for cocoa."

"It's warm in here," he said, stepping into the room and rubbing his hands together.

"I've got the heater on."

"So I see."

The teapot on the stove started whistling. While Chris slipped out of his coat and overshoes, she poured their cocoa and dropped several miniature marshmallows in each cup.

"Car almost didn't start," he said as he sat down. "I thought I'd have to call for a tow. Streets are terrible."

He sipped his cocoa, and she sipped hers. She watched the streamers of steam rising from the cups. She breathed in the sweet aroma. She took another sip and savored the rich chocolate flavor.

"It's great to be home," he said.

She looked around them at the scrubbed kitchen with its freshly-painted walls and pyramid of air freshener and wandering Jew plant on the shelf. In the next room was a bed with soft, newly-laundered sheets and enough thick quilts to keep them warm on the most bitterly cold night. There were pictures on the walls and a clock radio to gently coax them awake in the morning and the golden drapes that glistened in the daytime sunlight and held back some of the nighttime cold.

Thinking about these things and the work they had put into this apartment over the past couple of months, she was a bit surprised that she no longer considered it as only a pitstop until they could find something better. For the time being, at least, this place was home.

"Yes," she said. She sipped her cocoa and felt it's warmth all through her body.

"It's great to be home."

Rob Czaplewski • Grand Island, NE

First Rock Thrown

A bullet whistled over the trench from a distant fortification. Moments later, a gun mounted within a wood parapet returned a volley across the bleak landscape. The blasts interrupted a flock of birds singing from a nearby tree. After a few seconds of inactivity, their chirping began again. The war continued its dormant existence, as it had for years.

The scorching sun baked the trench, making the shovel-dug walls as hard as concrete. The crunching of boots pounded over the dirt as the soldier stumbled towards the commander's bunker. His footfalls were heavy and irregular like the awkward cadence of a drum.

Private Dove's arm muscles twitched as he struggled to carry the heavy wood crate the last few yards to his destination. The messenger's burnt skin glistened as sweat rolled off his face and dripped onto his dust-covered uniform. The soldier's sprint finally ended as he burst through the fabric door flap of the commander's dugout. He dropped the load onto a chair positioned next to a table covered with documents.

"For God's sake, where have you been?" growled a faceless shadow from the corner of the room.

"Sorry, sir, they unloaded the sandbags and ammunition first. This was the last box on the supply truck."

"Damn fools," muttered the officer appearing from the darkness and standing below a dangling light bulb.

Another soldier rushed in, brushed next to the tired messenger, and crisply saluted. "Major Blasé, the enemy has fired their noon volley and we returned fire, sir!"

The major nodded his approval and turned toward a man sitting at a desk. "Colonel Hawke, the noon volley has been reported."

The gray-haired man scratched a tally mark with his pen into a book. "It has been recorded." The colonel stood, took a step toward the table, and scooped up the scattering of papers.

Private Dove pried open the crate he had carried and emptied the contents onto the cleared table. He unfurled a large white linen and let it float gently down over the surface. Momentarily, a delicate tea set sat before the officers. The bone-white porcelain tea pot, cups and saucers were trimmed with royal blue scrolls and a gold lion's head in the center of each piece. The final task of the private was to place sterling silver spoons and a box of flavored tea packets onto the table.

Colonel Hawke surveyed the arrangement. "And the chicken?"

"I saw the cook from the mess hall a few yards behind me when I was running through the trench," said Private Dove. "It should be here soon, sir."

The door's flap flopped open, and an out-of-breath cook rushed in with a large tray. He placed two plates on the table, both full of potatoes, corn, and fried chicken. The sweaty soldier stepped aside and stood arrow-straight, throwing up a salute.

Colonel Hawke sat down and motioned for the major to join him. Meals were always a formal affair for the commander. Even though the colonel's quarters was cramped, just a fifteen-foot-square room dug into the side of a hill, he made sure it was prim and proper. His taut-made bunk was tucked in the far corner. Sitting on top of the bed were two books: *The Bible* and *Catch-22*. He read both nightly. He claimed one put a smile on his face and the other profoundly irritated him. He never specified which book caused which feeling.

On the wall next to his desk hung a wrinkled map with red pins marking the enemy's positions and blue pins indicating the location of his forces. The pins never moved. They weren't supposed to. This was a gentlemen's war. It was managed by politicians staring at each other across long, polished conference tables hundreds of miles away. It was a war of the minds, a chess game where the pieces moved, but nothing was captured and certainly no blood spilled.

"Anything else, sir?" asked Private Dove.

"No. Please return after lunch with tomorrow's plans."

Private Dove turned quickly and exited. The sun blinded him as he left the darkness of the commander's bunker. Numerous trenches spread away from the officers' dugout in various directions.

He looked down one of the adjoining trenches and saw the sentries leaning against the sandbagged walls, eating beans off tin plates and drinking warm water from dented canteens. He wiped his forehead and hiked past them on his way toward the rear of the line. He stepped over soldiers taking naps, saw groups playing cards, and a few men were washing their shirts in discarded oil drums filled with dingy water.

Zigzagging through endless trails of dugouts, Private Dove finally reached the Intelligence Center. He entered a courtyard surrounded by ten-foot-tall sandbag walls with a shelter squatting at the far side. In the middle of the enclosure stood a crooked oak with gnarled limbs spreading above three cast iron tables. An officer occupied each table. One read a newspaper, another smoked a pipe, and a female captain scribbled a letter.

"I've been expecting you," Captain Bungle said casually, folding his newspaper in half. "The crucial day is almost upon us, isn't it, Private Dove?"

"Yes, sir," the private quietly responded, wiping a river of sweat off his face.

"The End of the End," shouted Captain Bungle, throwing his arms wide and smiling. He stood and walked into the shelter. In a few moments he returned with a black leather satchel that was secured by a padlock.

"Tea?" the officer offered, gesturing to a drink cart a few feet away.

"No, sir. Colonel Hawke is expecting this right away." The private spun and kicked up dirt as he left. As he made his return journey to the commander's bunker, he thought about his years of service in the army.

Growing up poor, Private Dove never envisioned going to college. He needed money, easy money, that he could send to his parents to help them pay the bills and raise his sister and brother. Volunteering for front line duty made him eligible for "combat pay" and increased his monthly paycheck. Even though there hadn't been a battlefield-related casualty since the war began, combat pay was guaranteed.

His first assignment was like every other infantryman; he stood at his post and stared across the open field at the enemy—who stared back, never maneuvering, never shooting, and never fighting. But after months of that duty, he got bored, very bored. Even in a stagnant conflict, he needed to feel useful, and he requested to be reassigned as a messenger.

At first, he embraced his new role as it allowed him to interact with people, get exercise, and keep his mind busy. In time, however, his daily visits through the network of trenches began to tear away at his sense of duty and honor. The enlisted men were constantly subjected to the heat and cold, rain and snow, and the food was far from the cuisine he helped deliver to the officers. The pay was good, but the chance of promotion was slim since the opportunity for battlefield accommodations didn't exist. Officers retained their commands while enlisted men remained in their lowly status of ordinary soldiers.

Private Dove not only began to question his service but wondered why his government even needed an army at all. What were they protecting? What was the threat?

He met soldiers whose fathers served along the front lines, and their fathers before them, and their only duty was to stare at the enemy across the field for hours, weeks, months, and years. Generations of soldiers stood and defended. But what were they defending? Would they eventually win? If they won, how would they know?

Private Dove wound his way back through the maze to the commander's post. The officers had finished their meal and an orderly was removing the plates and linens. Colonel Hawke snatched the satchel from the private's grip and unlocked it with a key he took from his front pocket. He removed a white cloth, a short gold-handled ceremonial bayonet, an inkwell, a black fountain pen, and a rolled scroll. He reviewed the document, tersely nodded, and placed the contents back inside.

“The day of victory is upon us. We’re ready,” Colonel Hawke boasted. Major Blasé shrugged an approval and Private Dove stared at his commanding officer but said nothing.

~ ~ ~ ~ ~

“The Day of the Great Surrender” was scheduled every year during the summer solstice. It was the only day military action was allowed by the army. The operation required the commander, accompanied by his officers, to march under the white flag of truce to the midpoint of the field separating the two armies. The commander would officially ask for the enemy’s surrender. If the request was accepted, although it never had been, they would be victorious.

The humid morning broke with a cloudless sky. The bugle sounded the morning wake-up call and the troops stirred excitedly. This was the day each year everyone wanted to be a witness to history.

After breakfast, Private Dove entered the command post. “The men have assembled for your briefing, sir.”

Colonel Hawke straightened his tie, placed his cap over his thinning hair, and grabbed a walking stick with an ivory lion’s head handle that his grandfather had used when he was the commanding officer a half-century before him. “Major, bring the satchel.”

Major Blasé snatched the case from the desk, but the leather handle snagged on a nail and he dropped it. He ordered Private Dove to pick up the contents that had spilled on the floor, acting as if it was the private’s fault. With a red face, the major gripped onto the satchel, “Ready, Colonel.”

With a scowl aimed at his junior officer, Colonel Hawke strode through the door and was greeted by lines of soldiers standing at attention on each side of the trench.

The colonel addressed his men. "We gather on this special day, during wartime, not to seek bloodshed but to pursue honor. I promise, with the dedication of our leaders and the wisdom of our politicians, that victory will be ours!" The men answered with three coordinated cheers.

The colonel stepped onto an observation platform that towered above the trench line. He scanned the one-hundred-yard gap between the two deadlocked camps. "It's time, major."

The major opened the satchel and took out the white cloth and attached it to a pole. With the flag of truce blowing in the breeze, the major stood beside the colonel and was joined by four captains and six lieutenants. In one fluid, harmonized movement, like a line of ants, they descended a set of steps and marched towards the enemy's position.

The crunching of their boots ceased at the midway point between the trenches, and they waited in the awkward silence. Eventually, a few paces in front of them, a white flag rose above the horizon line followed by several officers. The enemy slowly approached and stopped within arm's length of Colonel Hawke's group.

The enemy's commander, General Stagnant, stepped forward with his staff officer. Colonel Hawke confidently approached his nemesis, stood with one leg slightly forward and he waved his hand, "Major, bring me my orders."

Major Blasé opened the satchel, took out the scroll and handed it to his commander. The major took out the inkwell and held it firmly in one hand as he searched in vain for the fountain pen. Colonel Hawke's face grew a deep crimson as he grunted out of the corner of his mouth, "How can I ask the enemy to sign the surrender document if we don't have the pen?"

In the trench, Private Dove witnessed the commotion and realized the pen must still be in the command post, having fallen out when the satchel was dropped. He scurried inside and found it under the table. He rushed over the top of the trench and sprinted toward the group of officers. The major swiped it from his grasp, "Only officers are permitted at this ceremony!"

Private Dove smirked and slowly turned to return to the line. He purposely went at a snail's pace so he could overhear the proceedings.

Colonel Hawke regained his composure and read the scroll, "On this glorious day, our grand army stands proudly upon this battlefield, knowing with full measure that we have bravely protected our land from invasion of the enemy. And now, we triumphantly ask for your unconditional surrender." He dipped the pen in the ink well and offered it to his counterpart.

"No."

"Is that your final answer?" Colonel Hawke inquired.

"Yes."

"The war continues!" Colonel Hawke exclaimed loudly, and he began to pack the scroll into the satchel.

Private Dove, who was only a couple steps away from the confrontation, spun around and shouted, "That's it? This whole 'The Day of the Great Surrender' is over in a few seconds after one question?"

Colonel Hawke pointed at the private and screamed at Major Blasé, "Discipline that man!"

Private Dove stomped up to his commander, “For what? Asking why we continue this war? This meeting is a joke! Why are we even here?”

“We are protecting our country,” the colonel responded, the veins on his temple pulsating.

“From what? Why did this war ever start?” asked the private. “Does anyone know?”

A stalky, mustached lieutenant stepped around Major Blasé and cleared his throat, “I’m the army historian. This conflict started one hundred and twenty years ago.”

“One hundred and twenty? I thought it was ninety-five years ago?” asked one of the lieutenants.

“No, it’s been like three hundred,” responded one of the enemy’s officers.

“My dad told me it started when he was a boy so it could only be about seventy years,” offered a captain.

“So, no one even knows when this war began?” asked Private Dove. “Can anyone tell me why we’re fighting?”

The officers from both armies looked at each other timidly. Each one offered a reason.

“Taxes?”

“Trade?”

“Farmland?”

“Gold?”

“Oil?”

“Religion?”

“Revenge?”

After a few more suggestions were tossed about, they looked at Colonel Hawke for the answer, but he did not utter a word.

Finally, General Stagnant motioned toward his fortification and an officer rushed forward. The enemy commander cleared his throat, "Gentlemen, if I may interject. This is our historian who may be able to help us."

The older man looked sheepishly at everyone staring at him. "If I may, General. Before I answer, I'd like to go to my quarters and find something. I'll be back in a few moments." The man left and the group stood impatiently waiting for his return. Finally, he lumbered across the field toward them.

He held a brittle, yellowed piece of paper. "I found this at the bottom of an old trunk last night. I believe it is the original declaration of war that our forefathers created."

"That's amazing," uttered the enemy general. "What does it say?"

"In this year of our Lord, 1645, we proclaim war upon our enemy for having heaved a rock at the king's horse." The officer cleared his throat and looked up at the ensembled men. "That's it."

Private Dove smiled. "So we're done. We can go home."

"Why?" the general asked.

"Because you can't expect us to keep fighting over a 400-year-old rock-throwing spat!" The private approached his commander. "Declare this over, sir!"

"You will not speak to me that way, soldier! This is not over!" He spun around and faced General Stagnant. "Surrender your army!"

"No. You surrender," the general responded.

"No. You surrender," the colonel replied.

"No. You," the general stated again.

"No," Colonel Hawke stomped his boot into the dirt.

"For God's sake!" shouted Private Dove. "You surrender, we surrender, who cares? Let's go home." He grabbed the pole with the white flag that had been carried by Major Blasé and began waving it high in the air so his fellow soldiers in the trenches could see it.

"Put that down!" ordered Colonel Hawke.

"They've surrendered!" boasted General Stagnant and a cheer went up from the enemy's fortification.

"We have done no such thing!" The colonel drew his sidearm and pointed it at Private Dove. "Drop the flag or I'll shoot."

Private Dove continued to wave the flag of truce. Major Blasé darted toward him, but the private spun away and sprinted toward the enemy's trench.

General Stagnant raised his arms in victory but a shot pierced the air, and he sank to the ground with blood staining his uniform.

Private Dove stopped running and looked at Colonel Hawke, "You've killed him!" Private Dove's shout was heard by both trenches.

An eruption of guns, tanks, cannons, and missiles burst across the trench line, heaving up mounds of dirt, splinters of barbed wire, and broken body parts.

Private Dove, holding the flag, twitched violently as bullets riddled his body. He stumbled backwards and fell beside his commanding officer. Their blood-streaked faces were inches apart. The colonel's eyes closed.

Private Dove's grip on the pole weakened and as he took his last breath, the white flag fluttered down and covered him and the dead face of Colonel Hawke.

And the war continued.

William L. Smutko • Blair, NE

The Short-Lived Joy of Tommy Nelson

"Hey, fat dummy," a kid hollers as he darts in and smacks second grader Tommy Nelson across the back. The ball Tommy was tossing into the air falls to the ground.

"Stop it. Leave me alone," Tommy hollers at the kid as he bends over to pick up the ball.

Another kid swoops in, smacks Tommy as he's bent over and taunts, "Can't pass a simple spelling test. Dummy."

"Leave me alone," Tommy shouts.

A third kid scoots in and yells, "What's four plus four, dummy?" as he hits Tommy.

"Please, stop it," Tommy yells, his face turning red.

The first kid attempts another pass but gets too close. Tommy lets go of his ball, reaches out and grabs the kid by the shirt collar then by the belt, and throws him ten feet across the playground.

The teacher on playground duty runs up to Tommy and shouts, "Mr. Nelson, what have you done to that boy? I think you need to see the principal."

"Hold on a minute," says the school custodian as he walks up to the scene. "Those kids were hitting Tommy and calling him names. Tommy kept asking them to stop and let him alone. Tommy was just defending hisself. The kids think cause he's big, he's fat. Looks to me he's all muscle."

"I saw it, too, Mrs. Johansen," says fifth grader Harry Sigurdsson. "It happened just like Mr. Andreasen said."

~ ~ ~ ~ ~

The center drawer in his dad's dresser has always held Tommy's attention, especially the oblong blue box with the gold lettering. Now that he's eleven, his long-held fascination with the box has gotten the better of him, and he's opened the drawer and removed the box. He lifts the lid, which is hinged on one end. Inside rests a red ribbon with white and blue stripes down the middle attached to a heavy brownish metal star.

"Tommy, what are you doing in your father's stuff?" his mother asks, looking in the door.

"What's this, Mommy?" Tommy asks, holding up the box with the medal in it.

"That's a Bronze Star for Valor. Your father was awarded it for his actions during the battle for Monte Cassino in World War II. Your dad doesn't talk about it, but he was a very brave soldier. You need to be proud of him."

~ ~ ~ ~ ~

Tommy's dad drives the tractor pulling the hay wagon and fourteen-year-old Tommy picks up the eighty-pound alfalfa bales with one hand and throws them up to his older cousin, Anders, in the back of the wagon.

"Slow down," Anders says to Tommy's dad. "Tommy's throwing them up here faster than I can stack them out of the way."

Later, as they unload the hay at the barn, a delivery truck from the co-op drives into the farmyard.

"I've got a thirty-gallon barrel of grease for you," the driver says to Tommy's dad.

"Take it to the shop next building over," Tommy's dad says.

"Looks like my tailgate lift isn't working," says the driver when he gets to the shop.

"That's OK. I'll get it," says Tommy as he grabs the two-hundred-fifty-pound barrel off the tailgate and carries it into the shop.

~ ~ ~ ~ ~

Ducks and geese fill the bright blue sky, and the oak trees along the drives of the Palmyra cemetery are a brilliant red.

"Earth to earth, ashes to ashes, dust to dust. May the Lord bless and keep our brother Nels, the Lord's favor shine on him with grace and mercy. May the Lord look upon him with favor and give him peace. Amen." The pastor finishes and looks at the honor guard.

"Squad, attention! Present, arms!" says the commander of the firing squad. "Ready, aim, fire! Ready, aim, fire! Ready, aim, fire! Order, arms!"

After "Taps" plays, Tommy asks his dad through a quivering chin, "Why are there so many people here? And why the guns and bugle?"

Tommy's dad wipes his eyes and says, "Your Uncle Nels was respected by all these people because he was a good man. The military part is because he served his country."

~ ~ ~ ~ ~

It is nine o'clock on a Wednesday night in mid-May. A soft rain gently waters the corn and soybeans Tommy's father planted and the vegetables in the large garden his mother takes care of. Inside, Tommy's mother is helping him study for an American government test that he needs to pass in order to graduate high school the following week.

"Start by reading the questions at the end of the chapter," his mom says.

Tommy reads the ten questions.

"Now start reading the chapter. One paragraph at a time," she says.

He reads the first paragraph and says, "This doesn't answer any of the questions."

"What does it tell you?" she asks him.

Tommy and his mother stay at it into the night.

At one a.m., Tommy yawns, stretches, and says, "I'm pretty sure I can remember enough to pass. Thanks, Mom."

"Mr. Nelson, you received a C on the test. Did you cheat?" asks his teacher.

~ ~ ~ ~ ~

The Monday after graduation, Tommy drives to the army recruiting office in Waukesha and enlists. He wants to serve his country like his dad and uncles. The lowered intellectual standards in place because of Secretary of Defense Robert McNamara's Project One Hundred Thousand lets him.

Two weeks later, he's at Fort Bliss, Texas, starting basic combat training. The desert is hot and dry with no trees or grass, only concrete, gravel, and sand. The concrete and gravel make it hotter and reflect the blinding sunlight. This desolate place is very, very different from the green of Wisconsin. The wind blows dust and sand through the cracks in the barracks walls, leaving a coat of dust and fine sand on everything. Tommy can never get his fill of water.

~ ~ ~ ~ ~

Staff Sergeant Alvarez has been to Vietnam twice and has a Silver Star and a Purple Heart to prove it. He's been given the job of making sure that all the members of what he calls his "escuadron imbecil" pass their tests on first aid, the Uniform Code of Military Justice, and all the other classes.

"Nelson, what is the first general order?" Alvarez barks.

"Drill sergeant, my first general order is, I will guard everything within the limits of my post . . ."

"What's the rest of it, Nelson?"

"Drill sergeant, I can't remember."

"Nelson, you are estupido, a fucking imbecil. What makes you think you can be a soldier?"

It takes Tommy two weeks of constant drilling to finally learn the general orders, but first aid proves even more demanding. Tommy and the others have to know what a sucking chest wound and a crushed trachea, among many other injuries, are and how to treat them.

"Private Nelson, front and center," shouts Alvarez.

Tommy reports to the front of the platoon formation. "About face!" commands Alvarez.

Tommy faces the platoon.

"Nelson doesn't know how to treat a sucking chest wound," Alvarez says. "Do you want this guy in combat next to you if he can't help you if you are wounded?"

"No, Drill Sergeant!" they all shout in unison.

Tommy stands there shaking, looking at the ground.

~ ~ ~ ~ ~

Tommy got put back two times before he graduated from basic. But he did win the Physical Combat Proficiency Test award for his company. He earned the maximum five-hundred-point score, and his time in the overhead ladder and his number of push-ups in two minutes broke the school records. He's been at Fort Lee, Virginia, for advanced individual training as a general warehouseman about two weeks.

It's Wednesday evening after chow. He and the rest of his squad are hanging around the barracks.

"Hey, Tommy, want some Oreos?" One of the guys in his squad points the open bag at Tommy.

Tommy's eyes light up. He grins from ear to ear and says, "Yes, please."

"Thank you," he says as he takes two. He bites into the first one. It's filled with toothpaste, not icing. All the guys point at him and laugh. His shoulders droop and he leans forward a little but swallows the cookie anyway and, to hide his sadness, starts laughing too.

~ ~ ~ ~ ~

Tommy stands in formation at the replacement depot in Long Binh in late June. Vietnam is hot, as hot as it was in basic training, but his sweat doesn't evaporate here like it did in Texas. His shirt sticks to his back.

"Barnhart, Johnson, Kennedy, Longworth, Nelson, Olson, Ralston, Turner, Upson, and Wilson, you're going to Dong Tam to the 9th Infantry Division. Grab your gear and get your asses on the first bus," says the sergeant.

At Dong Tam, Tommy is assigned to the Maintenance Supply Platoon of Headquarters and Headquarters Company of the 709th Maintenance Battalion. Jimmy Roberts occupies the bunk beneath him, and across from Jimmy is George Winchell. Both got into the army because of McNamara's rule. The three bond immediately. They get each other's jokes; they understand the pain of being labeled dummy. They become inseparable, not only bunking together but also eating together and sitting together at the weekly movie night. Where one of them is, the other two are close by.

The morning air is foul with the smell of diesel and burning feces. The water table in the delta is so high that in-ground latrines can't be dug. So waste has to be burned.

"Nelson, Roberts, Winchell, I want you three to unload the deuce-and-a-half tires and stack them at location four-two-one on the west side of the warehouse. Then report back to me," says Lieutenant Brooks, their platoon leader.

An hour and a half later, the three friends report back to the office. "LT," Tommy says, "we're finished with the tires."

"Good job, guys," says Brooks. "Now I want you to use the rough terrain forklift and move the two jeep engines sitting in front of the warehouse door to location oh-seven-three on the east side of the warehouse."

Jimmy gets into the cab of the forklift, starts it, maneuvers the forks under the crated engine, picks up the engine, and starts moving to the new location. The right front tire of the forklift drops into a washtub-sized hole, and the crated engine starts to fall off the forks. Tommy reaches out and grabs the four-hundred-pound engine and pushes it back onto the forks.

"LT, you should'a seen what Tommy did out there," says Jimmy when they're back in the office. "He lifted a crated jeep engine back onto the forks and kept it from falling off the forklift. He's one strong dude."

~ ~ ~ ~ ~

Tommy and this big guy from the Engineer Battalion are facing each other across a narrow table. Their elbows are on the table and their hands are locked in each other's grip. They've been at this almost two hours. An open-sided tent covers them and is surrounded by the bleachers used for the Bob Hope show last month. The winner of this match wins the title of 9th Infantry Division Arm Wrestling Champion and a three-day pass to the R&R center at Vung Tau. Shouting soldiers fill the bleachers and cheer on their favorite.

The bulging muscles on the arms of the two contestants look as hard as granite. Sweat is pouring off both of them, and they're gritting their teeth so hard one of them might break a tooth.

Twenty minutes into the third hour, the other guy's arm breaks with an audible crack. The stress his muscles were putting on his arm was too much for the bone.

The commanding general brings a trophy to the table and hands it to Tommy whose strength is so sapped he almost drops it. The general puts the trophy on the table and pats him on the back. The members of Tommy's company lift him up on their shoulders and carry him all the way back to their dayroom.

~ ~ ~ ~ ~

"Nelson, front and center," barks the first sergeant.

Tommy reports to the front of the company formation. Lieutenant Brooks steps forward and announces, "PFC Nelson is now Specialist 4 Nelson," and pins Tommy's new rank on him. "Let's have a loud hurrah for Tommy."

The company explodes with a deafening "Hurrah!"

"Congratulations, Tommy," says Lieutenant Brooks. "You earned it."

~ ~ ~ ~ ~

Tommy and his two buddies are in the dayroom shooting pool on a hot, dusty Sunday afternoon in September. Two Doughnut Dollies—Red Cross girls—walk through the door all smiles and perfume in their pale blue uniforms. Debbie Cosgrove is tall, slim, and blonde. Amy Strong is small and has auburn hair and a smile that's fatal inside ten feet.

Amy starts "Proud Mary" on her guitar and asks them to join in. When the song's done, Debbie starts laying *Playboy* centerfolds on the floor. After they all have a good look, she turns them over and has them playing a homemade game of Concentration.

After about a half hour, Debbie starts asking each guy his name and where he's from. Tommy gets up when it's his turn and says, "My name is Tommy Nelson and I'm from Palmyra, Wisconsin." Amy flashes a wide grin, runs over to him, and gives him a big hug.

"I know Palmyra well," she says. "I'm from Whitewater only eleven miles away."

The guys all laugh, and Tommy turns red from head to toe.

They play charades and end the visit with a loud "We Gotta Get Out of this Place." The girls ask Tommy and another guy to walk them back to their hooch.

"What I wouldn't give to be waterskiing on Trippe Lake right now," says Amy as she walks beside Tommy.

"I'd like to be up to my chin in Blue Spring Lake. And grilling burgers on the beach after," replies Tommy.

"It's hard to believe, but there'll be snow there in a few weeks."

"I remember using the tractor to plow the lane after that big storm winter before last."

"I have a good friend in Palmyra. Her name's Ruth Sigurdsson. Know her?"

"I don't know her, but I know her brothers, Gunnar and Harry."

They get to the girls' hooch, and Amy leans so close to Tommy he can see the little beads of sweat on her upper lip and all he can smell is her perfume. She gives him a kiss on the cheek and says, "Thanks for walking me back. It was nice talking to someone from home."

Tommy's in a high hover. He runs all the way back to the company dayroom, grinning like he's won the Irish Sweepstakes. George and Jimmy are full of questions about what happened on the way to the girls' hooch. All Tommy can do is smile.

The next day Lieutenant Brooks has Tommy, because he's strong enough to manhandle them, stacking heavy equipment tires against the outside of the warehouse on the river side. George and Jimmy are helping. The aroma of rotting vegetation drifts in from the Mekong.

"Hey, Tommy! Watch where you're going. You almost ran that tire into the ditch," George yells. "You could get hurt."

"Set your mind on the tire instead of Amy. Pay attention," Jimmy says. "We got a lot a work to do."

Tommy's dripping with sweat as he rolls the six-foot-tall tire up against the side of the warehouse.

Without warning a rocket propelled grenade roars in from the tree line across the river with the sound of a large piece of cardboard being dragged across a concrete floor and explodes on the forklift tire.

~ ~ ~ ~ ~

Ducks and geese fill the bright blue sky, and the oak trees along the drives of the Palmyra cemetery are a brilliant red. The smell of spent gunpowder lingers as two men in uniform fold the flag that had shrouded Tommy's casket. The senior of the two presents it to Tommy's mother as the bugler blows "Taps."

Shoshana Sumrall Frerking • Eagle, NE

The Mulletheads

The mulletheads across the street were at it again. They were painting something in the driveway. They were always painting something, and the godawful fumes would get you if that blaring, whiney, heavy metal emo music didn't. The big one—the punk with the leather vest and beard bleached to match his mullet—he was the one that actually lived there. The skinny bastard with the tattoos and the greasy one with the pointy boots, they just hung around, smoking and talking loud, watching the paint dry like it was the eighth wonder. It had started up a couple of years ago when Bleach moved in.

Forgetting about the list he had been mentally constructing a second earlier, Jake slammed the front window down and prowled through the living room into the kitchen to crank some real music—Zeppelin or Skynyrd—anything to drown out the crap over there. Wasn't there some kind of ordinance about noise pollution? Or chemical fumes within city limits? Dane had known about all that kind of thing.

Last September, Dane had pulled the truck into the driveway, and they'd all been out there, bent under the hood of a brown El Camino. Tattoos had stepped out into the street, a cigarette hanging out of his mouth, raised a hand as Dane slammed the driver's side door. Jake had barely spared him a glance. He knew what they probably thought—what lots of people thought—when they saw him and Dane out together. He wasn't about to give them a chance.

"Either of you know anything about gauge lights?"

Dane had ambled down the driveway, Jake staring after her. "Getting dim on you, are they?" And they'd been off, talking candlepower and modeling paint. Bleach shook Dane's hand, offering her a Pabst. Jake had gone into the house without looking back.

The mulletheads kept their distance when he was around. They knew he was onto them. When he tried to talk to Dane about it, she just smiled and gently kissed him. He'd started on countless occasions to barge out the door and start it up with them over whatever new stunt was disturbing his peace. But some women have got that sixth sense. Right then, Dane would always yell from somewhere in the house or garage: "Babe? Where's the half-inch socket?" "Sweetheart? Give me a hand with this level. I can't see the bubble." Or, softly: "Jake, darling . . . let us repair."

"Let us repair" meant *meet me in the bedroom and don't make me tell you twice.*

He knew all her little tricks and didn't mind one bit. She was always the one to pull him back from whatever mess he'd been about to get himself into. From his irritations, of which there were many (such as the way Bleach always raised his beer in salute whenever Jake pulled into the driveway; Jake was not intimidated). From stupid bragging contests. From the shadows around the corner and imagined slights. She knew exactly how to put all mulletheads into perspective.

Even now, as he reached for the stereo knob under the cupboard above the sink—the knob that would fire the Bose speakers, blasting the Skynyrd loud enough to let the world know he was Not Intimidated—that voice, like sweet steel in his head, slowed his hand. *Really, Jake? Because if this is going to be a big-wang match, I've already got you all beat, game over.*

As his hand fell to the counter, thunder rolled quietly in the southwest. And reminded him, inexplicably, that he was making a list. Damned fumes had made him lightheaded. "Dumbass," he muttered to himself, yanking out the junk drawer and rummaging through expired coupons and questionable batteries until he came up with the creased notepad with Tigger chasing his tail on the pink cover, thinking:

1. *Goodwill*
    a. *Coats* (the winter one—check pockets for her coolant tester; the fall/spring one—found discarded in a pile of drywall scrap, but it had cleaned up nice)
    b. *Shoes* (one pair of Timberlands for work; one pair of Zappos for everyday; the Adidas were gone now, partially melted by the lightning)
    c. *Clothes* (not much there; most of the shirts and jeans, they'd both worn)

He fished out a chewed pencil and started to write *Goodwill*, but the lead was broken off. Everything he touched these days seemed to be broken. Everything slowly winding down, approaching its end of usefulness.

A bolt of electricity strobed outside the window, and thunder stalked the hills to the west. From the driveway next door, a hotrod engine howled in reply, its primal scream dissolving in a series of backfires that ricocheted off the fronts of houses. A drunken cheer followed, and Jake ground his teeth as he dug around in the drawer, hunting for some other writing thing while trying to hold the list in his head. He was never any good at all that kind of thing. And who the heck didn't have spare pens and pencils in their junk drawer? He slammed it shut.

The crank sharpener was fastened in the kitchen entryway next to the fridge. He stuck the defective pencil in and turned the handle. It rattled around but nothing caught. His back coming to rest against the opposite face of the entryway, Jake stared at the battered old sharpener with the pencil hanging limply from the hole.

She'd picked it up at the summer flea market on a Saturday, years past. It worked poorly at best, but at some point one of the rollerblades inside (*barrels*, she'd corrected him) had come loose and fallen into the bottom of the case. Dane wouldn't let him throw it out.

I'll fix it, she'd say from time to time. *When I get a minute.* It reminded her of the one in her grandparents' house that had gotten gummed up with crayon guck and they'd made her take it apart and clean it herself at age seven. It was one of her best memories. It was at the top of the second list he was laboring to remember.

2. *Storage*
    a. *Pencil Sharpener* (drywall putty for the screwholes)
    b. *Power Tools* (Dane had fixed things. Jake had other people fix things.)
    c. *Music* (They'd shared many things. Her passion for Glen Campbell and Hank Williams Senior was not one of them.)
    d. *Bike*

The mountain bike had minimal damage; Dane had just dismounted and was walking it toward a rest area to wait out the worst of the storm. He knew, because she'd just told him so, the last time he would ever hear her speak, when the lightning crash drowned out all else, and then there had been only silence on the line, smooth and final.

For two weeks after that, the mulletheads had gone quiet. Then one evening, there'd come a knock on the door. A couple minutes passed and the knock came again. Later that night, Jake had peeked outside. On the corner of the doorstep was a bottle of Crown Royal. He'd examined it under the sink light. The seal on the lid was intact. The next day, the racket across the street had started up again.

He was seeing the sharpener sitting there on a folding table littered with animal saltshakers and all that kind of mopey shit you see at flea markets, feeling the sun beat down on his neck as she reached out to pick it up with a little cry of delight, when thunder crashed, shattering the memory of that long-ago Saturday. This time, the windowpanes trembled, and he saw that the afternoon sky had gone the color of a cigarette stain.

He turned and jerked the drawer open again. With the number three Phillips, he carefully removed the self-tapping screws that held the sharpener to the wall. The displaced rollerblade clattered around inside as he took down the little machine. It was dented, veins of rust tracking through the flaked yellow paint. Jake gently laid the sharpener on the counter and turned to the liquor cabinet.

He broke the seal and unscrewed the cap on the bottle of Crown, staring at the west window, seeing all of the years to come, countless years filled with unmitigated mulletheads. "Please come back," he whispered. But nothing answered.

His arms slowly rose, crossing to fold around him, as far as they would reach. He closed his eyes, rocking slightly. First left.

Then right. Tiny movements. He began to turn himself slowly, still rocking. Lightning produced faint red strobes across his eyelids, and he could feel Dane's chin resting lightly on the top of his head as she led him in those gradual, barely-moving circles, like she'd done for years, always in just this place, by the end of the counter. The thunder became one constant, rolling entity, swallowing up the revving motor across the street, until the two were indistinguishable.

This morning he'd awakened in a kneeling position, his head on the floor. Just to his right, a darkness leading into something unknown, some awareness that had watched over him, whether in love, pity, or indifference, was just closing, like a door in the wall, leaving a hint of green, of flowers. By the time he was fully awake, there'd been nothing there, and for a moment its vanishing left such a vacuum in the room he could hardly breathe. He uncurled his cramped body, pulling himself up to sit on the edge of the bed. By the dull throb in his back and limbs, he'd been in that position for hours. Had he been watched the entire time?

He'd looked over at her pillow, then down at his feet. The broken-handled hairbrush he'd fallen asleep holding every night for almost a year now had landed beside him on the floor. Slowly, he stood and walked out of the bedroom, down the stairs, through the shadowed living room, and out onto the front porch, where the barking of the mulletheads' terrier—which, even muffled, had been what awakened him—now leapt into bright clarity, jagged as the new sunshine.

"Shut the hell up!" he yelled at the stupid dog and hurled a futile beer can across the street. It fell several feet short of the fence. Pointy-Boots had wandered out of the garage, cigarette dangling from his lip. Raising his eyebrows in mild curiosity, he'd offered a small wave, which Jake did not return. Didn't anyone have a job anymore?

Now, on this late afternoon, Jake opened the back door and stood on the wooden deck they'd designed and built together in '01 (after wrangling with the city over a BS piece of paper for a good month when he knew damn well the neighbors on both sides had added on without even applying for a permit first; knew how people looked at Dane, and his blood pressure escalated every time). The sky had lowered, now a sinister mattress of gray, shot with pulses of green light.

He set his Crown and Coke on the railing and pulled a small garden shovel out of the barren soil in the flower pot next to the screen door. He walked down the steps, crossed the grass to where the cedars grew in a line along the west edge of their property. The first fat raindrops hit his neck as he knelt in the small place where the trees parted. He plunged the blade into soft earth, plowing steadily until the hole was maybe a foot deep. Then he stared into the hole for several minutes, thinking about how she had loved a good storm, feeling her large, strong hands covering his own.

At last, he straightened, unlocking his knees and turning his face into the cold, steady beat of the rain. He went back into the house, retrieved the pencil sharpener, came back out, and sank down in the sodden grass by the hole, holding it in both hands. "Ah fudge!" she'd said when the rollerblade came loose that last time. And insisted—time and again—that she'd fix it. When she got a minute.

When she'd fixed things, she always rolled up the cuffs of her old jeans, looking like some lanky cowboy with a workshirt hanging off her shoulders as she snaked the sink or rebuilt the lawnmower's ancient motor for the umpteenth time. Once—just once—that day seventeen years ago, she'd worn a pretty, cotton dress, to the courthouse. Light green, with pale flowers.

In his mind, he put his head down on the pile of dirt with the little broken yellow thing cradled to his chest while the hole filled with rain. Instead, he bent and laid the sharpener and its three oversize screws in the bottom of the hole. He pushed the loose soil in with his hands until the hole was filled again. Then he rose and pressed it down flat with the sole of his boot.

He looked down at the small patch of dark earth and the rain hammered nails. White lightning erased sight for a second, thunder rocketed over the fields, and at last he turned, remembering his overflowing glass.

Tammy Marshall • Neligh, NE

Mr. Collins and the Lost Sense of Humor

Mr. Collins had lost his sense of humor.

He had it on Monday when he gave his students an actual pop quiz and asked them to name the sodas for each brand label.

He had it on Tuesday evening when he jumped out at Mrs. Collins from the darkened laundry room as she passed and yelled "Under where? Under there!" before pelting her with fresh-from-the-dryer wadded up underwear. (Little had he known, though, that Mrs. Collins knew what he was up to, and she was prepared for his shenanigans with a basket of rolled up socks that served as the perfect-sized grenades in a counterattack to his underwear assault.)

He still had it yesterday, Wednesday morning, when his boss, Principal Fitzsimmons, stopped him in the hallway to give him his class's quarterly progress reports. She smiled and slapped him on the back. "Keep up the good work, Mr. Collins," she said. Mr. Collins whistled all the way back to his fifth grade classroom where he greeted his students with an extra-enthusiastic, "Hello, boys and girls!" Then he shared the good news with them, and they celebrated with ten minutes more of recess that afternoon.

But, today, Thursday, Mr. Collins awoke feeling blue and listless. He lay in bed for a while trying to figure out what was missing.

He knew he'd lost something, but he couldn't put his finger on it. He couldn't ask Mrs. Collins because she'd already left for her job at the hospital.

He arose and looked at the cat, but the cat simply stretched and then meowed for his breakfast.

Mr. Collins continued to be puzzled while he fed the cat, sipped his morning coffee, showered, dressed for work, and even as he drove to the school.

Still confused, he entered the building and ran into the janitor, Mr. Quigley. Mr. Quigley was a grumpy man, but he always stopped to hear one of Mr. Collins' jokes, so he paused in anticipation, but Mr. Collins just walked right past Mr. Quigley. The older man scratched his head, shrugged his shoulders and returned to sweeping the floor, grumbling loudly about the dirt Mr. Collins was tracking in, but Mr. Collins didn't hear him.

Mr. Collins stood looking glumly out the window as his students began to file into the classroom. "Hello, Mr. Collins!" many of them enthusiastically yelled in greeting as they were accustomed to doing each day, but on this day Mr. Collins didn't turn around with his usual goofy grin to greet them in return.

Instead, he remained with his back to the students as they slowly took their seats, looking with confusion at each other.

The ringing of the first bell finally caught Mr. Collins' attention, and he turned around to face his students. "Hello, boys and girls," he said in a dull monotone.

Billy, an outspoken boy, suddenly blurted, "Oh, I get what you're doing, Mr. Collins. You're pretending, aren't you?" He smiled up at the teacher from his seat in the second row.

Mr. Collins simply gazed back at him with a blank expression on his face. Then he turned to the board and began to write out the day's math problems.

The students all looked at each other, shrugged, and then began to copy the problems into their notebooks.

Normally, Mr. Collins would add an occasional smiley face to the zeroes in the math problems or he'd add a top hat and cane to the eights or he'd make all the numbers either extra fat or super towering—anything to catch the students' eyes and to keep them interested in math. Today, though, Mr. Collins wrote his numbers in perfectly straight lines, perfectly boring straight lines.

Gabriela, a spunky girl who regularly told her parents, "Mr. Collins is the BEST teacher ever!" finally blurted, "What's wrong, Mr. Collins?"

Mr. Collins blinked at her from behind his glasses. Then he did something no student had ever seen him do—Mr. Collins frowned!

The entire class gasped, and one shy girl named Hailey suddenly burst into tears.

Mr. Collins surveyed his classroom of confused fifth graders. "I feel like I've lost something, but I don't know what."

Billy's hand shot up even as he yelled out, "Ooh, ooh, is it your keys?"

Mr. Collins shook his head as he patted his left front trousers' pocket. Everyone could hear the jingle of Mr. Collins' keys.

Billy started to lower his hand, and then it shot back up as he shouted, "Ooh, ooh, I know. Your wallet! My dad always loses his wallet."

Some of the students nodded at Billy's suggestion, but they quickly stopped as Mr. Collins drew forth his well-worn leather wallet from his right back trousers' pocket. He waved it above his head for all to see before replacing it in his pocket.

"Now, get to work on these math problems, and remember to show your work," he said as he scowled at the students.

Their momentarily joyful expressions all fell as they quickly got to work on their math equations.

Mr. Collins wandered among their desks and pointed out errors as he saw them, but at no point did he offer up a "Good job" or a pat on the back as he usually did.

The students stole worried sidelong glances at each other.

Mr. Collins' odd demeanor continued through their mid-morning spelling lesson and their grammar quiz.

Then, thankfully, it was time for recess. The students rushed to line up at the door where they waited as patiently as possible for Mr. Collins to exchange his dress shoes for his tennis shoes because he normally took part in a friendly kickball or basketball game with them. But today Mr. Collins simply marched them down the hall to the side door of the school.

Instead of rushing outside to play, the students slowly trudged out and stood around for a bit, unsure of what to do and how to behave without Mr. Collins' guidance.

Mr. Collins stood near the school looking up at the sky. He seemed lost.

Hailey hesitantly approached him and tugged on his shirt sleeve. Mr. Collins slowly looked down at the small, shy girl.

"I know what you lost, Mr. Collins," she timidly said.

"You do?" His bushy eyebrows shot up in surprise.

She nodded seriously up at him. Mr. Collins leaned down to peer into her face. "What, Hailey? What did I lose?"

She gave him a small smile and answered, "Your sense of humor, Mr. Collins."

Mr. Collins stood up straight and stroked his chin. "You might be right, Hailey, but if that's what I lost, how can I possibly find it?" He looked back down at Hailey, but she just shrugged.

Suddenly, a flock of small birds flew overhead. Mr. Collins turned his face upward to watch them pass over him.

Splat!

Sploosh!

A glob of bird poop landed square on Mr. Collins' forehead and began to slide down toward his prominent nose. He quickly pulled out the handkerchief he always kept in his right front trousers' pocket and wiped at his forehead.

As he pulled the dirty cloth away from his face, he saw that every fourth-, fifth-, and sixth-grade student had stopped what they were doing, some in mid-stride even, and they were all staring at him with wide eyes.

A smile began to tug at the corner of Mr. Collins' mouth, then it spread across his lips into a grin, and finally those lips parted to show all his teeth before he opened his mouth wide and started to laugh loudly. Soon every student on the playground joined in with their own laughter.

The end-of-recess bell rang, and as the students filed back into the building, Mr. Collins yelled out for all to hear, "I sure am feeling POOPED! How about the rest of you?"

Students laughed and rushed off to tell everyone who missed it what had happened to Mr. Collins during recess.

As they entered his classroom, Mr. Collins smiled at his students who, in turn, smiled back at him and gave each other relieved glances.

He winked at Hailey as he told the class, "Just as one 'little bird' was telling me what I'd lost, another little bird flew over and gave it back to me." He paused before saying, "And in a very disgusting way, I might add."

The students laughed, and a couple looked like they might get sick when Billy pointed out that Mr. Collins still had a small chunk of bird poop lodged in one of his bushy eyebrows.

Mr. Collins wiped it away with a clean corner of his soiled handkerchief. “Kids, let this be a lesson to you all. Never lose your sense of humor. If you do, you’ll end up with poop on your face!” He grinned at them, and they smiled back.

“Now, who’s ready for lunch?!” he yelled out to them with a devilish gleam in his eye.

The fifth graders groaned in disgust at the thought of eating after what they’d just witnessed.

“Hey, Mr. Collins,” Billy shouted across the room, “my grandpa told me that in the Philippines they eat bird nest soup? Maybe we could get even with that bird who pooped on you!”

The entire class roared with laughter as they swarmed toward the door to line up for lunch. Mr. Collins smiled down on them all.

Susan Baron • Omaha, NE

You Don't Say

My Uncle Ralph calls me a chip off the old block. My mother says I'm a pain in the neck and I should be careful in this day and age. She scolds me that it isn't all fun and games and if I take after Uncle Ralph I'll be in a jam in no time and come to no good end. And that, she says, is nothing to sneeze at.

Uncle Ralph is my father's brother, and my mother makes no bones that she has no use for him. Mother thinks Uncle Ralph always has some cock-and-bull story and is always trying to pull the wool over your eyes.

Father says his brother is just a horse of a different color and tends to think outside the box.

Mother reminds Father, "Time and time again you have bent over backwards to help Ralph and what do you have to show for it? Ralph is just the same old same old."

"Now, Mother," says Father, "Ralph just gets down on his luck. It's true Ralph has his trials and tribulations, but to the best of my knowledge, Ralph has a kind heart."

Mother says Father's bleeding-heart attitude beats all, and she would bet her bottom dollar it will only be a matter of time before Ralph gets himself or someone else into hot water. And that's what happened.

You see it all started when Uncle Ralph showed up at our door around suppertime a while back. "Down at the heels again," Mother says. Then she laid down her fork and quickly followed

Father out to the porch where Uncle Ralph was waiting. They pulled the door closed, so I couldn't hear their conversation.

Soon they came back to the table and Mother looked madder than a wet hen. She said, "It boils down to this, Ralph. How long do you intend to stay? "

Uncle Ralph says in a very nice voice, "Why, Ethel, no longer than I have to, come hell or high water."

"Now, Mother," (Father always says "Now, Mother" when he is trying to calm her down) "charity begins at home. Let's go the extra mile for Ralph here. Give him a chance."

"Sure thing, Ethel, I'm just temporarily between a rock and a hard place, but I'll be out of your hair in no time and you'll hardly notice I was ever here."

So, Uncle Ralph stayed, but Mother had the last words. "Mark my words this won't be a case of all's well that ends well."

After supper I went out to the porch where Father and Uncle Ralph sat smoking. Mother was in the kitchen washing up and I could hear her banging the pots around more than I thought necessary. Father knew Mother was about to blow her stack so he tried to pin Uncle Ralph down.

Ralph is rocking away while he smokes a cigar and blows smoke rings in the air. "Well, John, here's the thing. I say there's no sense in crying over spilt milk and, needless to say, I'm not going to leave any stone unturned to make the best of a bad situation. You know what I'm saying?"

Father didn't look like he knew at all what Ralph was saying, but he nodded agreeably.

Uncle Ralph went on. "So, here's the long and short of it. I'm one to live and let live and I'm going to make hay while the sun shines but," and here he took another puff on his cigar, "I don't intend to leap before I look."

Gee, but my Uncle could sure turn a phrase.

Father looked down at his feet. "Does that mean you'll be looking for a job come morning?"

Uncle Ralph looked shocked. "Sure, John, if you think I should. But I don't want to put the cart before the horse. I mean, I won't let any grass grow under my feet, if you get my meaning." Father looked like he thought Uncle Ralph was as clear as mud.

Uncle Ralph jumped to his feet. "What say I take a little turn around the town and check things out. Don't you worry a bit, John. I'm chomping at the bit to make things happen, but I need to play my cards close to my vest at first. Don't want to put all my eggs in one basket." Father looked bewildered. "Hey, Squirt," and he motioned to me. "Come along and keep your old uncle company." And so, Uncle Ralph and I strolled toward the downtown of our small village.

Once we were out of sight of the house, Uncle Ralph peppered me with questions. I'm only eleven so I didn't know a lot of the stuff he asked me about: who was rich or not, who was the sheriff and was he around a lot. Uncle Ralph pushed his hat back on his head. His eyes danced and he asked me, if he was to need my help with some little thing, could he count on me.

"Sure," I say, "Blood is thicker than water," and every fiber of my being meant it.

Then he says him and me was birds of a feather and need to stick together. He winked and held out his cigar, offering me a drag. I felt over the moon with happiness.

~ ~ ~ ~ ~

True to his word, Uncle Ralph was up and out of the house right after putting away one of Mother's big breakfasts. "Thank you, Ethel, for the fine meal. I'll be home in time for supper."

Mother watched him saunter away. "There goes trouble."

I moped around the house, sorry not to go with Uncle Ralph. Finally, Mother told me to find something to do or she would find something for me to do. I skedaddled 'cause I had no intention of spending the day beating the dust out of rugs or pulling weeds in the garden. I climbed up in the old silver maple in our front yard and watched for Uncle Ralph.

Come suppertime, Uncle Ralph came strolling down the street in a casual way. He was smoking a cigar and he seemed happy as a lark. He looked like a man who had hit pay dirt.

I almost fell out of the tree, I climbed down so fast. I ran to him and he caught me. "Hold your horses, young man. Where's the fire?" I had been on pins and needles all day, hoping Uncle Ralph would find a job and stick around. I had crossed my fingers so much they ached. "Did you get a job? Did you get a job?"

Uncle Ralph laughed. "Tell you what, I'll give you the dope if you can do a little something for me first."

"Sure thing, Uncle Ralph. I'd do anything for you."

"Uncle Ralph needs a little pick-me-up, you see. You know where your father keeps his whiskey?"

Yes, I did know. It was in the sideboard in the dining room, but it only comes out on very special occasions, I told Uncle Ralph. "I'll just ask Father for it." Uncle Ralph's hand was kind of hard on my shoulder as he jerked me back.

"Now wait just a second. Didn't you say, didn't you promise you would do anything I asked?"

I didn't remember it quite like that, but I wasn't about to hem and haw about it.

"I don't want you bothering your father. I just want you to do this little something for me without asking a lot of questions. You see," and he got down close to my face, "this is a test to see how well you take one for the team. It's a test to see if you got guts. No guts no glory. You want to have guts, don't you?"

Of course, I did.

"You just go grab that bottle, hide it under your shirt, and bring it out to me here behind the tree. If your father sees you, I'll explain to him it's a drill, a way to test you."

At supper I began to feel a little let down because Uncle Ralph didn't have any news about a job. He had plenty to say. He assured Father and Mother he was willing to be low man on the totem pole and put his nose to the grindstone at the first opportunity. He hadn't found just the right opportunity, but he had high hopes.

Father said they were hiring at the mill. Did he go there?

Most assuredly, said Uncle Ralph. And he thought they would call him back for a second interview.

Mother said she wasn't aware they had interviews at the mill. They either hired you or they didn't.

Uncle Ralph looked right at Mother. "Now, Ethel, don't jump to conclusions. Patience is a virtue and the man who—" Uncle Ralph stopped talking and stuffed a big piece of Mother's pot roast in his mouth. "Ethel, this pot roast just melts in your mouth. Melts in your mouth, I say."

Mother murmured just loud enough for me to hear, "Slippery as a snake."

~ ~ ~ ~ ~

The next morning Uncle Ralph and I walked by the stores on Main Street. Uncle Ralph said he needed some more cigars so we were gonna stop in the drug store. I told him there was a cigar store, but he said, no, the drugstore would do just fine. We would go to the cigar store another time. "We're gonna play a funny trick on the owner, see?"

I had my doubts. Mr. Gibson, the pharmacist, was a pretty serious man.

Uncle Ralph assured me Mr. Gibson would get a kick out of it. Uncle Ralph had this old watch and it didn't work so good anymore. What he was gonna do was get Mr. Gibson to show him some cigars in the front of the store and I was to slip Uncle Ralph's old watch into the watch case located in the back of the store. I knowed about the watch case 'cause I had looked over that case of watches lots of times.

I sniggered. That would be a keen joke all right.

"Oh, and one other thing," adds Uncle Ralph, "take one of the new watches while you're at it."

Wasn't that stealing?

"No." Uncle Ralph says, "It's just a joke. When Mr. Gibson sees that old watch with the new ones, well, then won't he be surprised, and we'll get the last laugh when we return the watch."

Okay. I had my doubts, but I had promised before to be all in.

That night we had fried chicken and potato salad for supper. The new watch glinted on Uncle Ralph's wrist as he reached for second helpings. I wondered when Mr. Gibson would notice the trick we had played on him.

Father cleared his throat. "How's the job hunting, Ralph? Ethel tells me you were out most of the morning with the boy here."

"Yes, yes, we were. We stopped at the drug store." Uncle Ralph gave me a wink. "I had a nice chat with Mr. Gibson. He didn't need any help, but he gave me some good tips that I will get right on tomorrow."

Mother looked up from her plate. "What kind of tips? Sam Gibson isn't known to be helpful unless it involves money."

Uncle Ralph bobbed his head in agreement. "True. Mr. Gibson is a man of few words. For sure. But I say nothing ventured, nothing gained, so a man just has to put his best foot forward and seize the day. By the way, Ethel, you have outdone yourself with this fried chicken. I can't remember when I've had any so good. And your potato salad is out of this world." Uncle Ralph kissed his fingers and flicked them in the air like he was French or something. Gosh, Uncle Ralph could sure talk.

Mother muttered, "Slick as a whistle."

~ ~ ~ ~ ~

The next morning Uncle Ralph asked me to go with him. I pleaded with Mother to let me go, and she finally said I could, but she wasn't pleased as punch about it. I skipped and bounced next to Uncle Ralph as we headed downtown. Uncle Ralph carried a small leather case with the initials RG in fancy gold script. I asked him about it and he told me it belonged to a very famous man named Ralph Greenleaf.

I said, "That's funny 'cause that's almost your name: Ralph Greenwood."

"Well, yes," says Uncle Ralph, "except Ralph Greenleaf is a very famous pool player who won the World Pocket Billiards Champion at least a hundred times! And this here is his very favorite pool cue that he gave me on his dying bed and it's worth a fortune."

"Wow," I say.

"There's just one problem though. You know I'm a little down on my luck in this dog eat dog world and I might have to sell it. Maybe you could help me do that?"

I nodded my head up and down. I was just an eager beaver to help Uncle Ralph.

"It ain't hard, my boy. You just have to remember what I just told you about old Ralph Greenleaf and if anyone asks you if it's true, why you swear on a badge of honor it's the truth. Can you do that?"

I crossed my heart and hoped to die I could. I would make it crystal clear that Uncle Ralph was telling the truth. "It goes without saying, your problems are my problems and I'm no fair-weather friend," I promised.

Uncle Ralph stopped and shook his head. "Well, I never. You, my boy, are tops. I tell you, men like you are few and far between."

Uncle Ralph had called me a man. I would have gone to the ends of the earth for him. "I'm in. I'm your man," I assured him.

The pool room was dark and cool. I was a little scared 'cause I was pretty sure Mother would bust a gut if she knew where I was. She said only drifters and no-goods hung out in pool rooms. But I wasn't about to be a baby and say that to Uncle Ralph.

We took a seat near the pool tables. I got busy looking around the room. I might never get a chance to be in an actual pool room again and wasn't going to miss a thing. Soon Uncle Ralph stood up and motioned for me to stay put. He was watching the men shoot at the balls and pretty soon they asked him to play. He took a pool cue off the wall. I started to remind him he had his own cue, but he gave me a look that would kill, so I bit my tongue and kept quiet.

Uncle Ralph ordered beer for himself along with a shot glass full of whiskey. I munched on potato chips and drank root beer and felt like I was a kid in a candy store, only it was so much better. I was a kid in a pool hall.

From the way I saw it, Uncle Ralph wasn't doing so good. He was losing every game. Pretty soon he came back to the table and opened up the case. He carefully screwed the pool cue together and gave me a wink. "Watch and learn, my boy."

From then on, all the games went Uncle Ralph's way. The men were slapping down their betting money on the corner of the pool table and Uncle Ralph's pile kept getting bigger. One of the men got angry. "Why are you some kind of a pool shark or something?"

Uncle Ralph apologized. He said he couldn't help it. It was this pool cue he used.

The men stopped playing and moved to get a closer look at the stick. Uncle Ralph told the story about Ralph Greenleaf. He motioned for me to bring the case over and show them the gold initials and at the bottom of the case was a real signed picture of Ralph Greenleaf. Uncle Ralph laid it on real thick and said he thought the cue had some kind of magic. The men were impressed. Uncle Ralph wouldn't let them touch it, but they could look all they wanted. One of them asked if Uncle Ralph would sell it. "No," Uncle Ralph said. "It would break my heart to do that. But I might have to."

All the men leaned a little closer. "My boy here needs an operation and I don't have the money, so I am at my wits end on how to raise it."

One man asked, "Whaddaya want for it?"

Uncle Ralph thought for a long minute. "I don't rightly know. It's a very special cue. One of a kind. What would you give for it?" One man offered ten dollars and then the other men started bidding.

Uncle Ralph whistled as we walked back home. A big wad of cash bulged in his pocket.

"Can I ask you a question, Uncle Ralph?"

"Certainly, my boy."

"Why did you tell them I needed an operation?"

"Why, to get them to buy the pool cue. And it worked, didn't it?"

"I guess so, but aren't you sad, Uncle Ralph?"

"Sad about what, my boy?"

"You sold the magic pool cue that Ralph Greenleaf gave you on his dying bed."

"Oh that. That was just another trick we played, my boy. Ralph Greenleaf is alive and well far as I know and there's plenty of pool cues out there you could say once belonged to him. This is about the sixth one I have owned."

I was shocked. "Do you mean you lied, Uncle Ralph?"

Uncle Ralph stopped so quick you'd think he's been shot. "You really are a babe in the woods. You see, son, all's fair in love and war, and a man's gotta do what a man's gotta do. I don't want you to go thinking I'm a bald-faced liar or something. That would break my heart. No, siree, it's just a trick I play, and I guarantee you when people figure it out, they'll laugh their heads off." He patted me on the head and handed me a quarter. He said it was for all my help and told me I was a force to be reckoned with.

I liked that and it almost made me feel better.

At supper I didn't feel like eating even though Mother had made my favorite, meat loaf with fluffy whipped potatoes and garden peas. Mother put her hand on my forehead. "It's not right for a boy not to eat." She glared at Uncle Ralph. "Did you let the boy eat a bunch of junk that has gone and made him sick?"

Uncle Ralph stopped his forkful of meatloaf in midair. "Why no, Ethel. I don't know what the boy eats when I am not looking. Which reminds me." Uncle Ralph leaned back and dug into his pants pocket and came out with a dollar bill. "I might not have been watching him when I was working at an odd job I picked up today. I only made a dollar and a half, but I want you and John to have most of it for letting me stay here and all." He laid the dollar in front of Mother.

Mother forgot all about me as she stared at the dollar. It looked like the cat had got her tongue.

I was speechless myself. There seemed to be no end to the stories Uncle Ralph could tell. They just rolled off his tongue like warm honey.

Mother eyed Uncle Ralph suspiciously. "I hope you earned this money honestly."

"Why, Ethel, you hurt my feelings. I'm a man who believes in an honest day's pay for an honest day's work."

I could almost could hear her say, "In a pig's eye."

~ ~ ~ ~ ~

The next morning my mother made pancakes just for me. She brought over the warm maple syrup and sat down in the chair next to mine. "Are you feeling okay, son?"

"Ya, I guess," I mumbled. "Thanks for making me pancakes."

Mother looked thoughtful. "Is anything bothering you? Anything happen you want to talk to me about?"

I wondered if Mother knew the tricks Uncle Ralph and I had played. I really wanted to tell her, but somehow, I got the feeling Uncle Ralph wouldn't like it. I hunched over my plate and buried my eyes in the pancakes. "No, nothing."

Mother sighed. "You can tell me if something happened. I won't be mad. It's just sometimes a boy doesn't always make the right decisions if he's not in the right company. Things are not always plain as day. Life can be a tough row to hoe when a young boy is finding his way."

This was my chance to tell Mother, but I chickened out. It was a can of worms I didn't want to open.

Uncle Ralph was as cheerful as ever when he entered the kitchen. He gave Mother a bright smile and a cheerful hello. "Ethel, I think I will skip your delicious breakfast this morning." He patted his belly. "Your cooking is making me fat as a hog. Little sonny boy and I will just get going. It's full steam ahead, time for me to get a leg up and get in the thick of things. I'll just have a sip of coffee."

Mother set the cup of coffee down in front of Uncle Ralph with a thump. "Ralph, now that you mentioned it, time is a wasting. Isn't it about time you were moving on?"

"I'm glad you brought that up, Ethel. I almost have all my ducks in a row and I'm ready to knock it out of the park. I surely am grateful to you and John for this opportunity to get back up on my feet, but yes, mam, the worm has turned and my moment in the sun is coming." Uncle Ralph pushed back his chair and grabbed his hat. "You coming, boy?"

I didn't really want to go with Uncle Ralph, but I didn't know how to get out of it. The bloom on the rose of Uncle Ralph was beginning to fade. At first Uncle Ralph was fun, but I was having my doubts. He had such a funny way of saying things. I could never figure out just what he meant, but I sure had a good time listening to it. So I went with him downtown and surely wished I hadn't.

We was walking along like we always do and he says I got a new trick you and me can play. Truth be told I wasn't in the mood to play no more tricks. I was starting to feel bad about taking my Father's whiskey, and Uncle Ralph didn't seem anywhere close to taking that wristwatch back to Mr. Gibson. I was still trying to figure out the pool cue thing. These tricks of Uncle Ralph's seemed to be something else entirely.

I screwed up my courage, "I don't much feel like playing tricks today, Uncle Ralph."

Uncle Ralph was surprised. "Now, buddy, you're my right-hand man. Why, you're the real deal. I'd be up a creek without a paddle without you by my side. The naked truth is I'm only kicking up my heels to entertain you. It's gotta be terrible dull for a boy like you living in a place like this. Nothing to do except what your momma tells you. Ain't I right, boy?"

"Yes," I say. "Now that you put it that way. The summer days do get terrible long 'specially when Mother puts me to work."

"Now you're talking, sonny. This trick I got in mind will be just the thing to perk you up." And so I listened to him explain what I was to do.

~ ~ ~ ~ ~

There was no supper for me that night. I got sent to my room. Uncle Ralph had disappeared and Mother was so mad she was fit to be tied. I could hear the sheriff with Father and Mother down in the kitchen.

"John, we knowed it weren't your son's doing to steal that money. Other mischief has come to light: a watch went missing right after the pair of them was in Gibson's pharmacy; a famous pool cue that weren't nothing but an ordinary one got sold for way too much money." The sheriff laughed. "The boys at the pool hall weren't none too happy when I explained to them they'd been had."

Father said he didn't know what had got into me. They hadn't raised me like that.

"It weren't your boy, John. You know it was your brother, Ralph Greenwood. Why, every time he comes to town, there's a crime wave. Putting your son up to stealing money from Perkins' hardware cash register was just the last of it. Your son got caught with his hand in the till for real. But I knowed you and Ethel have raised a good boy so I'm going to give him a clean slate. Let bygones be bygones, as it were."

Mother spoke up. "Thank you, Sheriff. You're a kind soul for giving our son the benefit of the doubt. It's a fine kettle of fish Ralph got him into, but the boy knows better. I won't beat around the bush here. His father and I believe that if we spare the rod you spoil the child. He'll get what's due him."

I gulped when I heard that and could almost feel the switch being applied to my behind. Mother would be the one to do it, Father being too gentle a spirit. I knowed this time she wouldn't be saying this hurts me more than it hurts you. I will lick my wounds and take my medicine.

I learned a lot of lessons here. The first one being some friends is not friends. They is just like a pig in a poke and not what they pretend. Second, a boy can't do wrong if he listens to his Mother. And finally, make sure you're wearing two pair of pants when you're expecting a whipping.

Johnnye Gerhardt • Omaha, NE

Evolution of a Prairie

(*A Lesson in History*)

Undulating grasslands anchored by a hill lay undisturbed on the Midwestern plains. A migration begins and thunderous hooves pound the earth as thousands of buffalo run by, dwarfing the obstructive mound in the center of their race. They pass by the eruption in their path and disappear into distant foothills. It is quiet once again. The prairie grass sighs with increasing wind.

~ ~ ~ ~ ~

A Sioux warrior leads his dog and blue-eyed painted pony to the base of the hill. Both animals drag a travois to the top. The dog's travois is piled with poles and buffalo hides. The pony pulls the body of an elderly Sioux male and his belongings. The warrior constructs a burial platform from the timber and hides that the dog has brought, then hoists the body and its treasures onto the platform. He sits cross-legged on the ground and chants. The sun sets; the scene disappears into the dusk. Only a few trinkets from the burial remain on the hill. An oak grows from an acorn hidden among the remains of the platform. The Sioux elder has become one with the earth, its creatures, and perhaps part of the tree itself.

~ ~ ~ ~ ~

Years pass as sunlight reveals a well-worn trail in the grass. Hundreds of lighter hooves accompanied by the slapping of leather reins against hide and the clatter, creaking, and clank of covered wagons override any natural sounds. A wagon train passes in the distance. One wagon turns toward the hill. It stops at the base. A sod house surrounded by scrawny cattle replaces the wagon.

A sullen, sour-looking man in woolen pants with suspenders over a dull white shirt sits on a poorly crafted homemade chair in front of the sod house. His weather-beaten, sad-eyed, undernourished wife slumps nearby on another chair in worse condition than her husband's. On a moth-eaten horse blanket lying at her feet five children, two smiling and three emotionless and blankly staring ahead, sit with their hands in their laps and their backs straight as their mother commands. A sway-back horse stands in a hastily laid out cemetery on the east side of the house. A photographer stands behind his camera tripod and takes their photograph. The image fades as a prairie fire destroys the now abandoned sod house, leaving a lump barely discernable in the tall grass. The crosses marking the graves are blackened, trampled, and broken. No one will ever know they were there. Only the hill with its lone oak remains. The prairie grass returns.

~ ~ ~ ~ ~

Iron hammers hitting metal spikes echo against the hill. They morph into the shrill scream of a locomotive's whistle. Black smoke, a billowing snake, from the engine dissipates long before it reaches the hill. The grass hisses its distaste as the wind blows the sooty cloud away.

Creatures are anxious over the exuberant voices, hammers-on-nails, and the clatter of lumber traveling on the wind. A town erupts and spreads out onto the plains. The wild grass surrounding the hill whispers fearfully.

~ ~ ~ ~ ~

A wagon pulled by four horses carries building supplies to the top of the hill. Workers lay a foundation and erect the frame of a Victorian-style house next to the oak. Remnants of the Indian burial are scattered and covered by centuries of dirt from western bluffs. The tree shades the west side of the house. A carriage pulls up to the front door. A well-dressed Victorian gentleman assists his bride out of the carriage and carries her into the house. The constant wind drives the man mad and he releases his insanity onto his wife. A locket is ripped from the woman's throat and falls through a crack in the floor. His supremacy is established.

Resigned, the woman stands on a chair and hangs a framed photograph from the picture rail near the ceiling. The picture is that of the family in front of the sod house. The husband doesn't want it there. The bride insists, saying it is his heritage and he should be proud of it. Without his grandfather's sacrifices the man wouldn't have the land, she tells him, the now very valuable land, surrounding the hill. And won't it be nice to be the king of that hill. He concedes.

A baby is born to the couple. Then another. That one dies. It is buried next to the oak. Another child is born, then another. They succumb to the wilderness. Worn from grief the woman dies. The man buries them unceremoniously by the oak.

Lightning sparks a grass fire that consumes the prairie and the wooden structures in the town. It circles the hill. The man, his house, and his land are reduced to ashes and charcoal. The flames respectfully pass by the oak.

~ ~ ~ ~ ~

Modest early twentieth-century homes with their ample plots populate the tamed grassland surrounding the hill. The blackened landscape again turns golden. In time a silver ribbon slices through it and multicolored automobiles travel along its length. No one stops to mourn or pay respects to the bodies buried on the hill or next to the sod house that is now a small, unnoticed rise on the prairie. They're forgotten.

~ ~ ~ ~ ~

A tidy group of men and women with shovels, picks, and trowels survey the hill. They talk about the tragedy rumored to have happened there a hundred years or more ago. They disturb the earth with their instruments. They guess the oak to be at least three hundred years and a curiosity since there are no others for hundreds of miles.

Carefully scraping and brushing the dirt away, the locket glimmers in the sun for the first time in a century. Excitement disturbs the quiet work. Remnants of the Indian burial surface close by as do skeletal shards from the children and the woman.

In a college auditorium, a professor displays the artifacts in a slideshow and presents the conclusion. The family that once lived there had been killed by Native Americans, probably Sioux, who proceeded to burn down the house. The fire spread to the town below, killing everyone.

~ ~ ~ ~ ~

History is often just a point of view.

William L. Smutko • Blair, NE

Death of a Warrior

It's after two a.m. The noise from the merrymakers in the bar across the street has stopped. The full moon shines down and reflects off Lake Michigan, illuminating the city of Chicago. Harry Sigurdsson lies in bed wide awake, in physical pain from lack of sleep.

That mother's grief has drained me.

He and Hank Keller had been to visit Mrs. Roger Guthrie to inform her that her son, Roger Jr., died in combat in Vietnam. She was shaking and had tears welling up in her eyes when she answered the door. She collapsed when Harry gave her the formal notification of her son's death. Mrs. Guthrie is a widow. Her husband, Roger Sr., had been killed during the battle for Okinawa.

The alarm on Harry's bedside table clangs like a firehouse bell. He opens his eyes and looks at it.

I should get up, but I can't move. It's like I'm tied down by a thousand spider webs.

A small bit of awareness that recognizes the need to get up fights against the tethers holding him down. Bit by bit, it gains ground. An hour later he manages to shut off the alarm and roll out of bed onto the floor.

Come on, ranger. You can do it. Just start moving.

From the carpet next to the bed, he fights his way upright and to the bathroom.

Harry has overslept again, which shouldn't matter. He's a short-timer with only thirty-five days of active duty left to serve.

Damn it! This is the second time this week. I've got a job to do. I can't let this get to me.

The detachment commander, Major Bartimaeus "Bart" Johnson is shouting as Harry arrives, "Where the hell is Sigurdsson? Is he getting a short-timer's attitude?" A career officer whose myopia has kept him from serving in any of the combat branches, Johnson trained as a mortician before joining the army.

Harry's tardiness irritates Johnson. "We have a job to do. A soldier's family has the right to a timely and dignified notification of their son's death," he says.

Harry's an hour late. "Sir, I apologize for being late. I just couldn't get out of bed. Hank, I'm sorry," he says.

First Lieutenant Henry Keller, a Lutheran chaplain, has been working with Harry for only four months. When making an official notification, Harry gives the family the bad news. Hank then offers what comfort he can to the grieving family.

Except for his three months of airborne and ranger training, all of Harry's two years of active duty has been served with the US Army's Family Notification Detachment. His older brother, Gunnar, was killed in an ambush while serving with the 4th Infantry Division in Pleiku, Vietnam. As a sole surviving son, Harry cannot be sent to a combat zone.

As senior officer of the team, Harry picks up the information on the three notifications they have to make today. Mr. and Mrs. Abraham Wilson, Chicago, Illinois; Mr. and Mrs. Tobias Brock, East Chicago, Indiana; Mr. and Mrs. Thomas Nelson, Palmyra, Wisconsin.

Oh shit! Not Tommy.

He collects maps of Chicago and East Chicago and a 1969 Rand McNally road atlas. Then he and Hank plot out a route to the Wilson house in Chicago and to the Brock house in East Chicago.

They load their maps and paperwork into the staff car and head for their first encounter. Harry urges the '64 olive drab Rambler through the Chicago traffic south to Englewood. At Sixtieth and South Aberdeen, he slows down to reconnoiter the area and locate the target house.

Back off. Let me do my job.

The overwhelming sadness is assaulting him.

He locates the house, circles the block, and parks in front. Dressed in their forest green class A uniforms, the brass insignia and buttons shining in the bright sunlight, the two men approach the white clapboard house that sits wedged between two large row houses. Harry rings the front doorbell, and they wait. A couple of minutes pass before a slight woman in her late forties wearing a house dress answers the door.

I recognize the dread in her eyes. I've seen it hundreds of times.

The walls of the front room are painted sky blue, and the room is furnished with a floral print living room set.

"I'm sorry, Mrs. Wilson, I'm here to inform you of the death of your son, Robert," Harry says. She collapses into a chair.

Keller takes over. "Is there anyone I can call for you? Your husband? A pastor?"

They wait for Mr. Wilson and the family's pastor to arrive.

Back off. Go away. Leave me alone.

The sadness charges again as they wait.

Thinking about her seems to keep it at bay.

Out on the sidewalk, several young children are walking with their mothers in the beautiful fall weather. They are all giggles and laughter.

Go away.

Back in the staff car, Harry retrieves a swagger stick from his bag. Carved to look like a rolled-up scroll, the stick measures twenty-two inches long and about an inch in diameter. The scroll part is covered with shallow notches in neat rows, evenly spaced, following the axis of the stick. Harry takes a pocketknife from his right front trouser pocket, opens it, and carves another notch into the scroll.

That's number 726.

Keller takes the wheel for the next encounter. "Harry, it's a beautiful day, isn't it?" he asks. "Those children sure were happy, weren't they? Nothing quite as enlivening as children's laughter, is there? The Wilson's pastor sure seemed good at giving comfort, didn't he?" He talks the entire trip to East Chicago. Harry just listens, nods his head occasionally, and does battle with the sadness.

Leave me alone. Go away.

In East Chicago, they recon the neighborhood and park in front of the house on the corner of 138th Street and Carey Road. The red brick house features a white front porch and stained glass in the window of the front door.

They exit the vehicle and approach the house without talking, their backs ramrod straight and their eyes locked on the front door. Again, the doorbell is answered by a woman. Mrs. Brock is in her late thirties or early forties. Her eyes show anguish and fear brought by the two men in uniform who stand on her front porch.

Here we go again.

She collapses onto the couch in tears as soon as Harry starts the official notification. Hank again takes over. He calls her husband and her sister, both of whom are soon at the house, which smells of apples, cinnamon, and cloves. Mrs. Brock had taken an apple pie from the oven just before she had answered the door.

What's that smell? It just confuses things.

Back in the staff car Harry pulls the swagger stick from his bag and cuts another notch into it.

727.

It is almost two o'clock when they find a place to have lunch, which they eat in silence.

The drive through the colorful fall countryside of Wisconsin perks Keller up a bit but brings no joy to Harry.

I'm not looking forward to this at all. I wish there were some way to avoid it.

It is four thirty when they find the Nelson house on West Marsh Road. The white farmhouse looks recently painted and is surrounded by a quarter acre of well-kept lawn, a large vegetable garden, and lots of flowers. Harry turns up the long gravel drive to the house.

Back off!

The sadness is attacking again.

Mr. and Mrs. Nelson, a stout farm couple in their mid-fifties, are both at the door waiting for Harry and Hank when they reach the front porch.

She's holding her stomach; her eyes are full of panic. He glares at Harry, his eyes and face tight with anger.

Tommy had arrived late in their lives and was a little slow witted. But he had been passionate about serving his country as his father had. Defense Secretary McNamara's Project One Hundred Thousand lowered the requirements so that he had been able to enlist. He had served proudly as a warehouseman for HHC 709th Maintenance Battalion.

The sadness attacks again with more vigor.

Shit! Won't you please leave me alone?

Harry is barely able to repulse it.

I was three years ahead of Tommy in school.

Back in the staff car, Harry digs out the swagger stick, pulls out his pocketknife, and carves another notch into the scroll.

728. That last cut fills the scroll. There is no room for anymore.

On the trip back to Chicago, even Hank is quiet. "Harry, you're going to have to carve a new swagger stick," he says.

~ ~ ~ ~ ~

It is six a.m. and Harry's awake. He spent the night repelling attack after attack of the sadness.

It kept coming after me all night.

He slowly sits up in bed, swings his legs over the edge, and stands up. He has the next two days off.

Hiding in this castle keep while the sadness lays siege to it has no appeal.

He showers, shaves, puts on a pair of Levi's 501s, a cotton flannel shirt, and a pair of black Converse sneakers. In the kitchenette he puts the electric coffee pot on to perk and opens the refrigerator. A half-empty bottle of milk and the box containing the pizza left over from last night's dinner are the only occupants. Harry removes the box and sets it on the table. A few minutes later, the coffee stops perking. He pours himself a cup, picks up a slice of pizza, and starts halfheartedly nibbling at it.

He sees the Chicago phone book lying on the table.

Maybe an adventure will help keep the sadness at bay.

He picks it up and flips through the yellow pages, chewing the cold pizza.

This pizza has no taste. It's as if my taste buds are turned off.

He finds what he's looking for, a business that rents canoes. His whole life he has been told how beautiful the Horicon Marsh is, especially when it's full of migrating birds as it will be now.

It's only three hours up there, and the canoe rental place is on the way.

Harry leaves the apartment at seven o'clock. He's at the rental place by seven thirty when it opens. He rents a ten-foot aluminum canoe and a rooftop carrier that hooks to the rain gutters over the windows of his '64 Chevy II Nova coupe. The canoe comes with a paddle and life jacket. He puts them in the trunk and ties the canoe to the roof rack and the front and rear bumpers.

He's on I-94 headed for Milwaukee by eight thirty. Once out of Chicago, he cruises at eighty-five miles per hour, pushing his car to its limit.

See if I can leave the sadness behind.

In Milwaukee, Harry picks up US 41. Ten miles out of Milwaukee, it changes from a four-lane highway to a two-lane road with a third central "suicide" passing lane. The Chevy II spends a lot of time in the suicide lane as he passes slower vehicles.

At Wisconsin State Road 28, he turns off toward Mayville.

I'm almost out of gas.

In the village of Theresa, he turns off the road to a country store with a gas pump. A young man comes out of the store.

"Fill it," Harry says to the boy and goes into the store.

I didn't bring anything to eat or drink.

Harry purchases four tins of Crown Prince sardines in mustard sauce, a box of Premium saltines, and a six-pack of Leinenkugel beer. He pays for the gasoline and heads south to Mayville. The sadness finds him and starts a reconnaissance in force.

Back off. Leave me alone.

In Mayville, Harry checks the road map and turns onto County Road TW, heading north to Dyke Road where he turns west and heads to the west branch of the Rock River.

At ten o'clock a.m., he reaches the pull-off where Dyke Road meets the river. The sun is shining in a cloudless sky with the temperature in the low seventies, and a ten-mile-per-hour breeze out of the south. The leaves on the poplar trees at the turn-off have turned a brilliant yellow. The grass is an emerald green from a recent rain, and the cattail leaves are golden in the sunlight. Ducks, geese, cranes, and swans fill the brilliant blue sky.

Focus on the mission.

Harry unties the canoe from the front and rear bumpers, unhooks it from the rooftop carrier, and lifts it down off the top of the car and carries it to the water. He gathers the provisions from the front passenger's seat, then goes around to the back of the car, opens the trunk, and collects the paddle and life jacket. He loads everything into the center of the canoe and pushes it into the water. He climbs into the stern and pushes off the bank. The light current and south wind fight with each other for control of the vessel. Harry pulls the paddle from in front of him and starts paddling upstream toward the center of the thirty-two thousand acres of cattail marsh. The wind at his back helps the canoe move upriver. As he gets farther into the marsh, the current becomes more of a suggestion than a force.

Under the blue sky and bright sunshine and amidst all the flying birds, the sadness attacks.

Action will push me away from it.

Harry digs in deeper and faster with the paddle. An hour of intense paddling pushes him farther into the marsh. The sadness is not far behind.

Man am I thirsty, and hungry too. I need a break.

He paddles to a small grass-covered island with a lone white birch tree and beaches the canoe. He pries the cap off one of the beers and opens a tube of crackers and two tins of sardines. Harry puts the bottle to his mouth and sucks down half of the amber liquid. He digs a sardine out of its tin, puts it between two crackers, and wolfs it down, looking over his shoulder for the sadness. He devours another sardine cracker sandwich and drains the beer. All the heavy paddling has left him feeling almost starved. He eats both tins of sardines and drinks three beers.

It's coming after me. It won't leave me alone.

He gathers up what is left of his provisions and trash, puts it in the canoe, and pushes off into the marsh.

At two twenty-seven p.m., a cold front drops down from Ontario across Lake Superior and into Wisconsin. The wind blows out of the north, and the temperature drops twenty degrees to the mid-fifties. At two forty-two, a thunderstorm pops up with high winds and heavy rain. Harry's soaked to the skin, and he starts to shiver. He paddles harder. The shivering becomes more intense.

It's attacking again. I don't think I can hold it off any longer.

Harry succumbs to the 728 cuts. Shivering with cold and intense sadness, he curls up into a ball in the stern of the canoe.

By four o'clock, all movement has ceased in the canoe caught in the cattails.

~ ~ ~ ~ ~

The rising sun shows the canoe free of the cattails and floating in open water. The oboe-like calls from a family of loons fill the morning. Six swans flank the canoe, three on each side, and swim with it as it floats into the morning mist.

Originally published in *The Deadly Warriors Patrol,* Vol. 13, Fall 2017, pg. 2.

Leopold J. Kovar • Brainard, NE

At the Auction

Annie Cantor couldn't avoid it. She had to go to her sister Ruth's auction. Every auctioneer knew Annie by sight and knew what she was interested in. If she stayed home, everyone would think that the feud was on again. Annie figured that if she skipped Sunday Mass, no one would notice, but if she didn't show up at this sale, there'd be talk. She promised herself she'd go to be seen and then slip out as quietly as possible. She knew Ruth was selling all her junk. The good stuff Ruth had already weeded out and sent to her kids, probably as Christmas and birthday presents.

Ruth took her position as older sister as a justification for telling Annie how to raise her kids, how to bake the best pies, and who she ought to vote for in the local elections. There was no obvious reason for the breakup. It was just several years accumulation. Annie could never object without an argument or a dismissive wave of the hand from Ruth. One day Ruth criticized Annie for parking crooked in the space in front of the bank. That did it. For eighteen years after that, they hadn't exchanged a word or a Christmas card. When the diocese finally allowed Saturday evening Masses, Ruth chose to attend those. Annie never did. Sunday still meant Sunday in her book.

Both women were addicted to bingo, but they always sat at tables far apart. In that lull between high school football and basketball seasons, the Burgess Knights of Columbus moved their bingo schedule from Thursday to Friday, rightly guessing that they'd pick up some of those people accustomed to going somewhere on Friday evenings. One November Friday, Annie arrived at the KC Hall to find the hall packed. Having driven twelve miles from Haugers to Burgess, she was in no mood to turn around. She felt the numbers were with her this evening. She looked up and down and noted with dismay that the only seat available was next to Ruth. She decided that was her seat and slid in without comment. Just that quickly, the feud was over.

As she combed her hair this morning, she thought, if there'd been, at that time, casinos across the Missouri that sucked away the bingo crowds, Ruth and she still might not be speaking. As it was, they exchanged a word if they happened to meet. They never went through the trouble these days of avoiding one another.

Annie knew she'd have to make a show of pawing through the tables and boxes of Ruth's discards. After that she'd be able to buy a cup of coffee and a kolache at the PCCW table and chat with a few friends. There'd always be someone she hadn't seen in five or ten years who decided to come out of the woodwork. Sometimes they were women from out of state just visiting and deciding to take in a sale. These women never bought anything but they showed an interest.

Ruth was right there at the front sidewalk, greeting people like it was some official function. Even half a block away, Annie could hear her.

"Well, yes, I'm moving into a small house in Burgess. This house is too big for one person. My daughters wanted me to come live with them, but I just couldn't do it. They need to live their own lives and not have their old Ma just hanging around. It's not fair to the younger generation. They have a life too."

Annie recognized that Ruth was a master at making herself look generous.

"Hello, Annie. I suppose you've seen just about everything here, so there shouldn't be any surprises for you."

Ruth made it sound so good so that a stranger might think they were on good terms when, in fact, Annie hadn't been in Ruth's house for ten years. They had coffee once on the front porch after their bingo reconciliation, but Ruth's opinions were as strong as ever.

Annie looked through all the Guy Lombardo and Henry Mancini records. Ruth had no ear for music. These must have belonged to her husband Art's nephew, Clarence. They suited his goopy taste. After over twenty years in the military, he still retained that sad sack quality, but Ruth was proud of him. Annie had forgotten that Art Pommel smoked a pipe. There were at least a dozen of the smelly things displayed. At every sale there were a couple old record players. They'd bring a dollar at the most. Annie had to make her presence look good so she got a number from Mary Cowles, the auction clerk. She was so well known she hadn't had to show her driver's license in years.

"That'll do it, Annie," Mary said.

Annie slapped the number to her blouse just below her right shoulder, then looked at her watch to gauge how long she'd have to stay. She had only a momentary breather before she saw Orieandra Molluak bearing down upon her. Annie glanced frantically around her, but it was too late. At every public event or auction, Orie zeroed on a single person and hung on.

"Hello, my name is Orieandra Molluak." The woman with thick glasses and a head full of small tight brown curls poked her hand toward Annie.

For ten years, ever since she and her husband moved to Haugers, Orie greeted everyone this way. She always acted as if she were meeting a person for the first time, never looking directly at a person. She would immediately begin to reel off the story of sad life and subsequent triumphs, her philosophy of life. It did no good to remind her that you'd heard it all before. Orie never listened. She took it as her mission to enlighten her chosen companion again and again. The trouble, Annie knew, was that everyone was too kind. No one wanted a confrontation so women resigned themselves to a spoiled day.

"I don't suppose you know my story," Orie began. "My Daddy came from money. But that drink. It just got a hold of him and wouldn't let go."

Annie did her part by continuing to nod her head long after she stopped listening. She now and then added a "Mmm." Annie looked around to see if some kind soul would rescue her. That didn't happen often because Orie was like flypaper, ensnaring the Good Samaritan in her goo.

"My first husband beat me. Course, in those days, you just took it. That's what we were taught to do. Who could fight a man? It just wasn't done."

Annie spotted her daughter, Melody, and made a beckoning plea by twisting her neck. Melody shook her head. Annie's anger subsided when she realized she'd have done the same thing. The amplified auctioneer's patter sometimes drowned out but did not alter Orie's spiel. Annie inwardly sputtered that eager buyers were bidding so much for Ruth's tacky salt and pepper shakers. Some people just can't help themselves.

Annie realized she had to rescue herself. "Oh," she cried. "Ruth isn't keeping the picture of *The Last Supper*. I can't let that go."

"Don't worry about that," an Orie alerted that she might lose her prey. "I have an extra one at home that is much better."

"But that one was Mother's," Annie said, fully aware she'd have something to add to next Sunday's confession.

The bidding rose to ridiculous levels. What should have cost five dollars was now up to twenty-five and people turned to stare in disbelief at the bidders. Even the auctioneer was shaking his head. Annie, defeated, let it go at thirty dollars. That was ten dollars more than she had in her wallet.

A stronger force than Orie barged into the scene. "Are you out of your mind? You barely have enough to eat and yet you bid on that old picture."

Orie confronted Ruth. "That was your mother's. How could you? *The Last Supper* is sacred."

Ruth looked at the two women and understood and then she pulled Annie away.

"We have to talk," she said in her sternest tone.

When they had moved away, Ruth whispered, "You did a good job."

"Thanks for saving me. I still wasn't sure I could get away."

"Do you know who got the picture? Her husband. He's as crazy as she is."

"But they already have two at home."

"Then," Ruth smiled, "they're triple-blessed."

Katherine Wielechowski • Lincoln, NE

Roommates, Accidents, and a Cannibal Love Song

"My father wasn't terrible, but I certainly preferred my mother. Although looking back, I may have just overcooked him."

"What the hell are you reading to me?" Gab rolled over so he could see his roommate, Benji, from his loft bed.

Benji grinned. "It's the first lines of the short film I'm writing. *Ode to a Cannibal Love Song*. What do you think?"

Gab blinked once, then again, unable to think of a single thing to say.

Benji and Gab had met in Speech 101 the first week of classes their freshmen year and quickly became friends, even though Benji was a weird theater/film kid and Gab was a weird science kid. This was their second year rooming together and they had made plans to find a house or an apartment off campus for their last year at U of M.

"Well?" Benji nearly vibrated with excitement.

"It's . . . interesting." Gab attempted a smile that he was sure looked more like a grimace.

"Just wait, it gets better!" Benji propped his feet up on his desk and turned back to the script in his hands. "Good ol' Daddy was my first. I had never attempted to cook man before, which was probably why he was tough and dry. It took some practice to get the cooking process just right. Plus, it helps if the person you're cooking is a little younger with a little more fat on them. It helps with the flavor." Benji glanced up at Gab. "And this is where the song 'Flavor of Man' goes. Mattie is still helping me with the tune but I can read the lyrics if you want."

Gab's hand shot over the edge of the bed, stopping Benji. "Wait. This is a musical?"

Benji nodded enthusiastically.

"A musical about a cannibal."

Benji nodded again.

Gab went back to his textbook. "You need help, man."

"Actually, yes, I do. There are some technical anatomy stuff in the 'Butchering Song' that I want to run by you. Plus, I'd like your help with set design for the Locker—it's what I'm calling the cannibal's work room." Benji did air quotes around "work room." "I'll need help mainly with the equipment that would be used to dissect a human body. I'm picturing something like an emergency room from an 80s movie: green tile on the walls, terrible florescent lighting, swinging doors, trays of scalpels and saws hanging around, etc. I want to do some close-ups on the tools, so I need them to be correct." Benji pulled a legal pad out of a desk drawer and picked up a pen. "What would you use to cut up a human? Probably standard hospital tools and the like?"

Gab's jaw dropped open as he stared at his roommate. He scratched his head in disbelief. "You need professional help, man. Like from a head doctor. Not me."

Benji scoffed. "It's not like I am actually going to become a cannibal. In fact, the thought repulses me. But I have always been interested in the psychology of serial killers, cannibals specifically, so I'm combining projects. Professor Lake and Dr.

Argentin are allowing this one project to be my final for both my film production and my criminal psychology classes."

Gab was impressed. "How did you manage that?"

"I'm a fast talker." Benji grinned. "Plus, it doesn't hurt that I'm pretty."

"You're pretty something," Gab muttered.

"I'll let you be in it." Benji held out the offer like a treat for a dog.

Gab rolled his eyes. "Dude, I don't have time to be in a movie. Midterms start next week and I am already behind."

Benji tapped his fingers on the desk, waiting for the right moment to play his trump card. "Paige is helping me."

Gab slowly turned his head to stare at his roommate. Paige was the girl he had liked since freshmen English and had made exactly zero progress with. Benji also knew how Gab felt about her. "You're a dick."

Benji laughed. "So you'll help me?"

"Yeah, I'll help you," Gab growled.

Benji punched the air. "Yes!"

"I'm not playing the cannibal," Gab warned.

Benji shook his head. "No, of course not. My friend Heath is."

"Hot Heath? Star of the theater department, played Macbeth and the Phantom and Long John Silver and Roger, showing vast range for dramatic and musical performances, not to mention action sequences and high emotional roles? That Heath?"

"Yes, that Heath. Think he'll work?"

Gab shrugged. "Yeah, he might."

Benji laughed. "Well, I'm glad he has your approval."

"What is Paige doing?" Gab regretted the words as soon as they left his mouth.

"She's doing the costumes," Benji paused a moment and gave his friend an evil smile. "And acting."

"Oh, really?" Gab tried for casual, but failed miserably. "What role?"

"She's the cannibal's victim."

Gab's mind immediately jumped to Paige, lying on a steel dissection table in torn clothes, covered in fake blood, struggling to escape, while Hot Heath stood over her with a bone saw in his hand and hunger in his eyes. "Who wins in the end? Does the cannibal kill the damsel in distress or do the cops get him first?"

"A little of both. The cannibal dies in a shootout with the police but the victim gets caught in the crossfire first. That is where the cannibal's final song 'Beautiful Meal/Last Supper' happens. It's a lament that finishes with a harsh, metal swan song."

"I see." Gab was quickly regretting his decision to help, but his desire to spend more time with Paige overruled his common sense. "What role are you thinking for me?"

"Deputy #2."

Gab raised an eyebrow. "I don't even get a name?"

"To be fair, nobody in the film has actual names. They're just Cannibal, Victim, Sheriff, and so on."

"So why can't I be the sheriff?"

Benji toyed with his pen, not meeting Gab's eye. "Because you're not an actor."

Gab closed his textbook and sat up. "So Deputy #2 is a non-speaking part?"

"Yes."

"Thank goodness." Benji's head shot up in surprise. "With midterms and applying to internships, I don't have time to memorize a bunch of lines."

A knock on the door cut off Benji's response.

"Are we expecting company?"

Benji nodded as he got up to answer the door. "The core group is meeting here at three."

"A heads up would've been nice."

"I was going to mention it like twenty minutes ago, but you kept asking questions about the film, and they're early." Benji opened the door and stepped back as a 6'5", ginger-bearded, built like a football player Hot Heath entered the room followed closely by Mattie. The half-Korean girl was dwarfed by the film's star even though she was average height, but her habit of wearing all black and curling in on herself didn't help.

"Hey, Gab," Heath rumbled as he held out his hand.

"Hi, Heath." Gab took the giant's baseball mitt of a hand, then waved at Mattie. "Hi, Mattie."

She nodded to him, then perched herself on the filing cabinet next to Benji's desk. She stuck an AirPod in her ear and pulled out a notebook. Her head bobbed slightly to the music.

"I heard you're going to be in the film too," Heath said as he settled into the armchair in the corner of the room.

"Yeah," Gab frowned at him. "But how did you hear? I just agreed to it ten minutes ago."

"Oh! Shannon and Paige are here!" Benji called from the door ignoring the glare Gab threw at him.

"That's Sheriff Shannon to you." The five-foot-nothing ninety-five-pounds-soaking-wet blond was proficient in multiple martial arts and sword fighting and was the best fight choreographer U of M's theater department had ever had. She playfully punched Benji in the stomach (playful or not, he still doubled over), then climbed the ladder to Benji's loft. "Gab! My right-hand man, how are you?"

Gab grinned at Shannon's infectious enthusiasm. "I'm good, Sheriff, how are you?"

"Freaking awesome." She slid until she was hanging half off the bed so she could see under it. "Hey, Heath, almost missed you."

"I've never heard that before." Hot Heath lit up the room with his million-watt smile.

"Hi, everybody." Paige waved to the group.

Gab's stomach flipped when her gaze paused on him. He tried to smile but he wasn't sure if he succeeded or not. Paige's honey brown hair was pulled back in a ponytail and she wore a floral sundress with sandals.

She pulled the strap of her leather messenger bag over her head and set it on the floor next to Gab's desk. "Hey, Gab, do you mind?" She gestured to his chair.

"No, help yourself." He glanced at his messy desk and realized his anatomy diagrams and notes were spread across it. "Sorry about the mess."

She glanced at the pictures. "Oh, are you helping us with the film?"

"Yeah, but those are for my anatomy class."

"I'm sure they'll come in handy with this too."

"Hopefully, not too handy. They're diagrams of the human reproductive system." He felt his face go hot.

"Oh." Paige laughed. "No, probably not so helpful with Benji's movie."

"Nope, unless the cannibal is a fan of long pig fries."

Paige tilted her head in confusion. "What is long pig?"

"Another term for human flesh as food."

"Wait, wait, wait," Benji burst in. "Long pig is human meat? How have I never heard of that before?"

Gab shrugged. "No idea. I heard it on a show years ago."

"Mattie!" Benji dropped into his chair next to his writing partner. "We have to use long pig somewhere."

Mattie flipped through her notebook. "We've been trying to come up with a song for the opening montage when Cannibal is finally giving into his urges."

Benji snapped his fingers. "Long Pig, Forbidden Fruit."

Mattie nodded as she started scribbling. "I can make that work."

Gab shook his head in surprise. "That's the fifth song that I've heard mentioned. How long is this movie?"

"Aiming for sixty- to seventy-minute runtime." Benji clapped his hands to get everybody's attention. "Ok, now that everybody is here, let's go through roll. Mattie is the co-composer and assistant director, Shannon plays the Sheriff and is combat advisor, Heath is starring as Cannibal, Paige is doing costumes and plays Victim, Gab is our newest technical advisor and is playing Deputy #2, and I'm writing, co-composing, set design, and directing. Let's get to work."

~ ~ ~ ~ ~

"Hey, how are you doing?" Gab crouched down next to the steel table that Paige was strapped to.

It was nearly midnight on their fourth and last day of shooting and it was freezing in the old warehouse where they had built the set for the Locker. They only had three hours left to get the film wrapped before they had to start tearing down the set and vacate the property so Benji was pushing everybody hard to get it right. At the moment, he was going over last-minute script changes with Heath and Mattie.

Paige didn't have it too bad action-wise. She just had to lay on the table, writhing and screaming once in a while, but what little of her costume that wasn't shredded was covered in fake blood. "Well, it's not the most uncomfortable table I've been strapped to." She laughed at his shocked expression. "Kidding. No, it sucks but it's not horrible. My hands are really cold though."

"Oh, I can help with that." Gab stood and leaned over, taking her hands in his to warm them, causing their faces to come within inches of each other.

"Careful, don't get any blood on your costume yet. The squibs will do that for you."

"I still can't believe Benji decided to kill me off. And where the hell did he get squibs?" Gab was hyper-aware of the small packets of explosives and fake blood taped to his chest.

"I made them." Paige grinned at Gab's gaping expression. "I got a lot of practice when we did *The Lieutenant of Inishmore* last year."

"I saw that, it was really good."

Paige smiled. "Thanks! It was fun to work on."

"Hey," Gab started, unsure how to continue, especially considering their proximity and Paige's inability to escape since she was physically strapped down. "Would you want to go out with me sometime?"

Paige got a strange look on her face. "You asking me out on a date, Deputy #2?"

"Yes, Victim, I am."

"Well, then yes, I'll go out with you sometime."

Gab was stunned clear down to his toes. "Seriously?"

Paige laughed again. "Yes! I've had a crush on you since freshmen English."

"Me too! I just never had the guts to do anything about it."

"I'm glad you found the guts now." The pair shared a moment that was rudely interrupted when the rest of the cast and most of the crew started serenading them with 'Cannibal's Love Song.'

Gab shot up, his face on fire. Paige giggled at his reaction.

"Ok, while I'm happy you two finally figured your shit out, love and horror don't mix." Benji broke in. "We're going to start at the bridge for 'Cannibal's Love Song.' Heath, you're standing over Paige lovingly caressing her with a knife while you sing. Paige you're unconscious until the last line. Start waking up at 'how can I eat what I love/how can I not.' Got it?"

Paige nodded.

"Ok, places everybody!" Benji clapped his hands and took his seat behind the cameraman.

"Good luck," Gab whispered before he ran behind the swinging doors to watch through the window for his cue. Even though he knew the knife was fake and Heath was definitely not a serial killing cannibal, it still made him uncomfortable to watch the scene, especially now that he had a personal stake in Paige staying alive.

"Hey, you and Paige, eh?" Shannon teased Gab with an elbow to his ribs as she joined him at the door.

Gab grinned. "Yeah, who knew?"

Shannon rolled her eyes. “Literally everybody. There’s a pool. I won, so thanks for that extra fifty bucks in my pocket.”

“I hate theater people.”

“No, you don’t.” Shannon stood up on her toes to see through the window.

“Need a box, Sheriff?”

“Shut it.” She glared up at him, then stepped to the side to lean against the wall with her arms crossed.

“What’d I miss?” Brandon, a.k.a., Deputy #1, joined them at the door.

All three of them were dressed in matching uniforms: black pants, black button down shirt, badge, and gun belt, with one difference: Shannon’s had ‘Sheriff’ embroidered in gold thread above her badge. When their cue came, Shannon would lead the charge into the Locker with her two deputies hot on her tail

“Nothing,” Gab answered without looking away from the scene unfolding in the Locker.

“You’ve got something black on your neck.” Shannon gestured to where it was.

Brandon furiously rubbed at the spot. “Lipstick,” he answered with a huge grin.

Gab and Shannon looked at him with suspicious expressions. “Mattie?” Shannon asked, slowly, naming the only Goth wearing black lipstick on set at the moment. Brandon nodded.

“I thought she was a lesbian,” Gab said in confusion.

Shannon shook her head. “She’s bi.”

“Oh,” Gab said, then turned to Brandon. “Aren’t you gay?”

“Excuse you, I’m pan.”

"Right. Sorry. I'm just going to go back to watching for the cue." Gab turned back to the window. "Oh, it's almost time. You both ready?"

Shannon pulled her fake pistol from the holster on her belt and took Gab's place at the door. Brandon and Gab took their weapons in hand and fell in line behind their sheriff. Gab peeked through the window over Shannon's head and saw Heath raise his knife over Paige's struggling body. "Go now!"

Shannon burst through the door, yelling like SWAT breaking up a hostage situation. Brandon followed and Gab brought up the rear. Heath snarled at them and threw his knife before picking up a pistol from the table and turning it on the trio. He backed away from the table as Shannon and Brandon followed him, everybody furiously pulling triggers and yelling.

Gab rushed to the table and began unbuckling the straps that held Paige down. He got one of her arms and the torso strap undone before his squib exploded. The force knocked the wind out of him and he threw himself back like Benji told him to. A second squib exploded, making his ears ring. Then a third and he fell back, but he misjudged how far he had stumbled from the table and toppled into a cart that held the Cannibal's tools. He followed the cart to the ground with a loud clatter as the stainless steel hit the concrete floor.

His chest felt like somebody had stomped on it, his ribs felt battered where he had landed on the edge of the cart, and there was searing pain radiating from his thigh, but Gab stayed still, pretending to be dead. He didn't want to ruin the shot for Benji and have to go through it again. He heard Heath bellow and one last shot, indicating the scene was done. There was a long quiet moment and Gab silently begged Benji to yell cut so he could move from the uncomfortable position he had landed in.

"Cut!" Benji screamed into the silence. "That was amazing everybody! I'm going to watch it real quick to make sure we got everything we need but I think that's it."

The cacophony of crew rushing to reset things and actors coming back to life rose on the set and Gab allowed himself to roll over onto his back. He sat up and blindly reached out to rub the spot on his leg that was on fire when his fingers touched metal. He looked down to see a scalpel sticking out of the meat on the outside of his thigh. Gab managed to resist every instinct to pull it out and calmly scooted back until he rested against a tool chest.

"We got it!" Benji called, walking onto the set. "That's a wrap, everybody!"

The cast and crew clapped and cheered, happy that the grueling four-day shoot was over.

Benji walked over to squat next to Gab. "Crashing into the cart like that was inspired! I didn't know you had it in you." He held out his hand to pull Gab to his feet but Gab shook his head.

"Do you have a set medic?"

Benji laughed. "I barely had enough money to pay for the warehouse, no way I could afford a set medic. Wait, why do you need a medic?"

"I seem to have stabbed myself when I fell on the cart." Gab pointed at the knife sticking out of his leg with a grimace.

"Oh, holy shit! We gotta get you to the ER. Heath! Can you get Gab up?" Benji turned back to his roommate. "I have to supervise tearing down the set. Are you ok with somebody else taking you?"

"Yeah, that's fine. Do what you gotta do."

"What happened?" Shannon called from where she was helping Paige unbuckle the rest of the straps.

"Gab's been stabbed," Benji announced.

"What?!" Paige exclaimed. The rest of the set went silent.

"Come on, Deputy #2, how'd you get stabbed in a gun fight?" Brandon asked, nonplussed where he stood with an arm wrapped around Mattie's shoulders.

Heath walked over, his face white, and he looked like he was going to throw up. "Did I throw the knife too hard? Benji, you assured me it was fake and wouldn't do any damage when I threw it!"

"Wasn't you. I found a scalpel when I fell that was a bit more real." Gab again pointed to the metal sticking out of his leg as the rest of the cast and crew gathered around him. "Can you help me up?"

"Of course!" Heath effortlessly pulled Gab to his feet and helped steady him.

"I'm taking him to the ER," Paige announced, sliding under Gab's arm to help him walk.

"That's a good idea." Benji patted her shoulder in thanks.

"Can somebody grab my clothes and phone?" Gab asked as Paige and Heath turned him for the door.

"On it," Shannon called as she dashed off the set toward the dressing room.

"Everybody, I know the wrap party is traditionally right after wrap, but is everybody ok with putting it off a couple of days so Gab can be there?" Benji asked. Everybody still there murmured their agreement and Gab smiled his thanks as he was slowly walked out of the building.

Shannon ran up as they got to Paige's car. "I grabbed a towel, too, so you don't get blood all over."

"You're an angel," Paige thanked her as she took the towel and spread it on the seat before Heath lowered Gab into the car.

"Let me know if you need anything else," Shannon offered as she stacked Gab's clothes on his lap. "I've been hurt loads of times on sets and stages, but I've never been stabbed by a real scalpel. You're handling it like a champ."

"Thanks, Sheriff." Gab waved as she shut the door and Paige started the car.

~ ~ ~ ~ ~

"Jesus, what happened to you two?!" The doctor stopped short when he entered the curtained-off area the nurse had escorted Paige and Gab to.

Paige looked down at herself, realizing for the first time that she looked like she had gone through a wood chipper. "Oh, no! Most of it is fake. We were working on a movie when he got stabbed."

"Stabbed? Nobody said it was a stabbing. I'm going to need to file a police report."

"He did it to himself," Paige explained before the doctor left.

The doctor blinked. "What?"

"His character got shot and in the process, he fell over a cart that had a bunch of real medical tools on it. In the fall, a scalpel got him in the leg."

"Well, I've seen stupider injuries." The doctor put on gloves and examined Gab's leg. "Does he talk?"

Paige nodded. "He kind of passed out. I accidently hit it when I was helping the nurse cover him in a blanket."

"I see." The doctor examined the wound and decided the scalpel didn't hit anything vital and ruled out surgery. He numbed the area, removed the blade, cleaned everything, and got the cut sewn up.

Gab came to around the time the scalpel was removed and nearly fainted again, but he managed to pull through enough to watch the process, announcing that if he was going to medical school, he had better get used to it.

When the doctor finished, he ordered a tetanus shot just in case and left for a nurse to finish up. When the nurse was done, Gab signed a mountain of paperwork and Paige helped him back to the car.

"Do you want me to take you to your dorm or should we head back to the set? I texted Mattie and she said they were still working."

"Let's go back to the set. You have to go there anyway to get your clothes and I'm in the mood to make Benji feel guilty in public." Gab grinned as Paige laughed and pulled out of the parking lot and headed towards the warehouse. "This is not what I had in mind for our first date."

Paige shrugged. "It's probably the most expensive date I've ever been on."

Gab snorted. "And the bloodiest."

Paige waved her hand back and forth. "That's a toss-up."

"You've had a bloodier one?"

"I can't really say if it was bloodier since it was tough to tell what on you was real and what was fake, but I've definitely had another pretty bloody date."

Gab shifted in his seat so he could see her better. "I've got to hear this."

"The one and only time I went out with a college jock, he took me to the batting cages. I was there to watch him and not actually participate." Paige rolled her eyes. "Didn't seem to matter that my softball team in high school went to state two years in a row but whatever. He was showing off and cranked the machine as fast as it would go, and then didn't duck when it shot a ball at his face. Ended up in the emergency room with a broken nose, a concussion, and no second date."

"Wow."

"Yeah." Paige pulled into a parking spot and turned off the car. "Ready?

Gab half nodded, half shook his head, and braced himself for the pain he knew was coming when he pulled himself out of the car. They entered the warehouse to see the set was nearly all torn down with just two walls and the table left standing. People started cheering as they noticed Gab's entrance, leaning heavily on Paige. He was embarrassed by the attention but appreciated that it meant he was now part of the tight-knit theater group that Benji had gathered around him.

Paige escorted him to a chair and helped him sit, then went off to get cleaned up and changed so she could help with the final tear-down.

"Look at those pants! Those were rented!" Benji pointed at the large hole the doctor had cut in the fabric to get to the wound. "I'm going to have to take that out of your pay."

"How about you just deduct it from the workman's comp payment you're going to give me."

Gab and Benji stared at each other for a long, silent moment. Benji's eyes narrowed slightly. "How about we call it even."

Gab nodded. "Deal." He held out his hand and Benji shook it before they both laughed.

Benji pulled over a folding chair and sat next to his roommate. "How're you doing?"

"Better than you'd think. It hurts like crazy, but no permanent damage, and I've got a good story from it." The pair sat in companionable silence for a minute. "Hey, Benj."

"Yeah?"

"When you win an Oscar, or a Tony, or a hotdog eating contest, you have to mention me in your speech."

Benji nodded. "I can do that."

"So, you think your professors will like the movie?"

Benji grinned. "A plus, baby. A plus. And they're going to love the story of you getting stabbed."

Gab nodded and settled deeper in his seat. "Glad I could help."

Tammy Marshall • Neligh, NE

The Horses of Miller Creek

Felicity stared up at a hawk lazily circling the sky near the canyon rim as she walked toward a grouping of large boulders. She squinted a little, attempting to ascertain if it were indeed a hawk or if it were some other type of large bird of prey. She shook her head in defeat as the bird disappeared from her view, admitting to herself that even if the bird had been nearer, she probably wouldn't have known its specific breed. Hawk, eagle, vulture, duck—those terms were the best she could do. Duck. She giggled a little at the thought of a duck circling this desert canyon looking for its next meal.

As she slipped into the shade behind the largest rock, Felicity eased her backpack off her shoulders and leaned her sweaty back against the dark stone. It didn't provide the relief she had hoped for, but it was a relief, nonetheless, to be away from Gina for a few minutes.

After taking a long drink from her water bottle, she pulled off her bright orange company-logoed cap and fanned herself for a minute. Suddenly, Gina's demanding voice startled her as it bounced off the canyon walls, and Felicity dropped her water bottle onto her foot and watched it bounce from there to the red canyon floor.

Swearing as she stooped to pick it up, Felicity wiped the dust from the still-open spout and noticed a few swallows of her precious water disappearing quickly into the dry earth.

"Hurry up, Felicity!" her boss yelled.

"I'm trying!" Felicity yelled back, and then she stifled the oath she wanted to add. The small group of advertising executives could be heard milling about near the trail she'd abandoned to relieve herself behind the rocks. Gina had been miffed with her for asking for a moment of privacy. Felicity didn't care that they were all women on this "company bonding experience" from hell; she wasn't about to pee in front of other people, no matter their genders.

In reality, though, she simply wanted a few moments of peace, so she called back, "Go on ahead! I'll catch up!"

There was a pause, followed by some muffled discussion. "Okay, but hurry up! We'll only go as far as the river which is just around the next two bends!"

She pulled her ponytail through the back slot of the cap and repositioned it on her head. "I'll be right behind you! Just finishing up here!"

Looking up, she saw the hawk, or whatever it was, circling again. Then it swiftly dropped into a dive, heading for the canyon floor in front of her. In disbelief, she watched as the bird extended its talons, grabbed a snake, and flew to the top of a large rock. She pushed away from the boulder where she'd been leaning, her eyes darting around the floor near her. She'd completely forgotten about the rattlesnakes that lived down here. Even though she suddenly had the urgent need to actually relieve herself, she decided it was time to catch up to her group. Maybe peeing in front of others who could watch for snakes while you peed wasn't such a bad idea after all.

As she swung her bag onto her back again and stepped into the sunlight, Felicity felt the ground start to shake a little. At first she thought it was just herself shaking from the fear that the sight of the snake in the hawk's clutches had instilled in her, but then she realized that a low rumble was coming from the canyon behind her, away from the river.

The rumble intensified, and the noise bounced off the canyon walls. She stared at the nearest outcropping of the wall, uncertain where to go because she didn't know what was making that noise. It had become so loud that its own echoes had been swallowed up into one thundering continuous well of noise.

She quickly hid herself on the sunny side of the large boulder and peeked around it to see what was coming. It sounded like a stampede, but she couldn't imagine that was possible since this canyon was part of the Arizona state park system, and Gina certainly wouldn't have brought them into this canyon if there were a large herd of livestock down here.

She suddenly remembered Gina and her team of advertising executives who were at this moment heading toward the river and probably oblivious to their imminent peril. She needed to warn them. Taking a quick step away from the shelter of the rock, Felicity just as quickly darted back to its safety as the first animal flew past her.

Gaping, she stared in awe as hundreds upon hundreds of wild horses rushed past her and charged around the bend. They were followed by men mounted on tamed horses who rode by, shouting and waving their hats at the animals. As the last man and horse disappeared from her view, Felicity pushed off the rock and ran after them.

Breathless, as she came around the second section of canyon wall and into the expansive area, she dreaded what she might find—her co-workers all lying bloodied and mangled on the canyon floor—so she stopped in utter amazement and disbelief when all that greeted her eyes was wide open space and the tiny figures of Gina and the rest of her team in the distance.

Felicity stood there panting as she shook her head and rubbed her eyes. Had she hallucinated the entire thing due to being in the sun too long, or from lack of water, or from being poisoned by a couple bug bites she'd suffered that morning during their descent into the canyon?

Turning in a full circle, Felicity noticed the lack of swirling dust and hoofprints in the floor of the canyon that would have marked the passage of a herd of wild horses. Again, she shook her head and wondered if she'd had some sort of a heat stroke. She felt fine, though, and all her body parts seemed to be under her control, so she pulled her cap low over her brow and trudged off after her coworkers who were now gathered next to the river.

As she drew nearer, she could see Gina standing with her hand shading her eyes and peering back toward Felicity. When Gina spied her, she raised the same hand to wave frantically at Felicity who waved weakly in acknowledgement as she rolled her eyes.

"Yes, Gina, I can see you. Everyone for a mile in all directions can see you and every single one of us down here wearing these silly orange caps and bright yellow shirts," she mumbled as she trod onward. Gina continued to beckon and now her words were reaching Felicity's ears.

"Hurry up, you big slowpoke! We're waiting for you, so we can do our power circle before we eat." Gina now stood with her arms akimbo and fists planted firmly on each hip, so Felicity increased her pace a little.

The others milled around near the river, and Sandria, the heaviest of the group, was lying down and appeared to be napping. Gina nudged her with her foot, and Sandria reluctantly began to rise as Felicity arrived next to her and plopped her backpack down next to Sandria's. She extended a hand to Sandria and tugged her to a standing position. The other woman clapped her on the back affectionately.

Felicity smiled at her. Sandria was the only member of the group that she really liked. It was probably due to the fact that they'd both come from places outside of Phoenix and were, thus, seen as outsiders by the other advertising execs. Sandria came from the Bronx, which made her the more exotic of the two since Felicity had lived her whole life in North Dakota, a distant foreign land that none of the group could begin to imagine.

Gina called the women together, and they quickly made a small circle and joined hands. Felicity grimaced a little at how sweaty Sandria's hand was, but she didn't break hold of her grip.

"Ladies, we've come here to draw strength from this canyon," Gina began. Felicity shut her eyes as she saw other women doing the same. "It's a place untouched by modernity and civilization, yet it has so much to teach us if we can only listen." Felicity opened one eye a crack and looked at Gina to see if she was joking, but Gina's face was a mask of placidity. Her boss continued, "We ask that the spirits of this sacred canyon speak to each of us and give us wisdom and strength to . . ."

Felicity lost the rest of Gina's words amid the roar of hooves thundering behind them. She released her grip on the hands of the two women on either side of her and spun around, her eyes searching the expanse for signs of the horses and their pursuers. The canyon was empty.

"What the hell?" she asked the empty expanse.

"Excuse me, Felicity, but I could say the same to you. What the hell are you doing?" Gina asked behind her.

Felicity rubbed her eyes and looked again. The canyon was still empty. She slowly turned to face the group of women who all wore similar looks of confusion on their faces.

"You okay?" Sandria asked.

Felicity shrugged. "Honestly, I don't know. That's the second time today I've heard horses stampeding through this canyon. The first time, I actually saw them too."

All the women except Sandria gasped. Anna Maria, a dark-haired woman, solemnly said, "Dios mio, the horses of Miller Creek." She then made the sign of the cross and looked skyward.

Gina stepped toward Felicity. "Can it be true? You actually saw the horses of Miller Creek?" She gazed in awe at Felicity.

Felicity frowned while Sandria raised questioning eyebrows at her. Shrugging, she said, "I don't know anything about Miller Creek or its horses. I just know that I saw and heard a bunch of wild horses stampeding past me, and I had to jump behind a big rock for protection."

Gina chuckled. "You aren't going to need protection. Legend says that those who actually see and hear the horses will be blessed for the rest of their lives."

Felicity scoffed. "Legend says. Do you hear yourself, Gina?"

Gina scowled now. "I'm being totally serious. You'll see." She turned away from Felicity. "Let's eat, ladies."

The others gave Felicity odd glances as they spread out along the riverbank to unpack their light lunches. Felicity slowly followed and sat down beside Sandria.

"You don't believe that nonsense, do you?" she quietly asked Sandria.

Around a mouthful of sandwich, Sandria mumbled, "You never know. Hey, when we get back, let's go buy a couple lottery tickets together, okay? See if you really are blessed."

Felicity smiled wryly and gave Sandria a playful shove. "Yeah, sure." Then she opened her backpack and removed her lunch bag. As she pulled it free, she heard a tiny clink from the depths of her pack.

She set her lunch bag down next to her and opened the backpack as wide as it would go. She peered into its depths and then reached in, felt around, and finally pulled out a long chain necklace with a locket dangling from it.

Immediately, her eyes welled up and she placed a hand over her mouth in shock. Sandria noticed it and asked, "What's that?"

With shaking hands Felicity opened the locket to reveal two aged photos inside. Whispering, she said, "Those are my grandparents. I thought I'd lost this necklace years ago." She looked down into the backpack in disbelief again. "I have no idea how it found its way into this bag or how I didn't find it earlier during all those times I carried this backpack to the gym."

Sandria looked at her with her eyebrows raised as far as they could go. "The blessings begin, my friend, so it seems."

Sandria seemed about to announce Felicity's discovery to the group, so Felicity stopped her by grabbing her arm. As she shoved the necklace back into the bottom of the bag, she said, "Don't say a word about this." Sandria gave her a reluctant look of acquiescence, and they both began eating their lunches in silence.

After a few minutes, Sandria quietly said, "I won't tell anyone if you promise to get those lottery tickets with me when we get back to town."

Felicity held back a guffaw and nodded. "It's a deal." Then she cocked her head and listened intently.

Far down the canyon, she could hear a herd of horses running wild, and she felt the tremor from their pounding hooves vibrate her bottom where she sat. She slyly looked around at the other women to see if anyone else had heard or felt anything. There was no change in anyone's demeanor.

She cleared her throat. "So, are any of you going to tell me the story behind these horses?"

Gina glanced at her watch and scowled a little, but then she looked around the circle and noticed the expectant faces on most of them. Sighing, she nodded. "Anna Maria, you know it best. Would you like to tell Felicity the story?"

Anna Maria finished the last bite of her sandwich and wiped her mouth with the back of her hand. Then she rose and walked to where Felicity and Sandria were sitting and calmly sat down near them. The rest of the group all stopped their conversations and leaned in to better hear the tale even though it was well known to them.

After waiting for silence from the other women, Anna Maria began, "My great-great-grandfather was one of the few men who took back his cattle from Bart Miller and lived to tell of it. Miller had been stealing livestock and land from ranchers for years, and anyone who tried to fight him ended up dead, or"—she paused to look skyward again—"those he loved ended up dead." She crossed herself once more. "My great-great-grandmother was Miller's last victim. Ever."

Felicity quietly said, "I'm so sorry."

Anna Maria dismissed her words. "It was a long time ago." Her eyes burned a bit brighter, though, as she continued the story. "However, my great-great-grandfather wasn't going to roll over like every other rancher had before him. He wanted vengeance. So, he and his sons and a few other brave ranchers banded together to put an end to Miller's reign of evil.

They knew that there was a large herd of wild horses that lived in and around this canyon, and just outside the canyon is where Miller's land began and where the stream that feeds this river runs." She pointed to the slow-moving river that hugged the canyon wall.

"Miller Creek?" Felicity asked, and Anna Maria nodded.

Then Anna Maria continued, "After a few weeks of planning and getting the wild horses comfortable with their presence, the men guided them into the canyon and then whooped them into a stampeding frenzy heading right toward Miller's land and his fancy house he'd built along the banks of the stream he'd named after himself. By the time the horses—the thousands of horses—rounded the final bend in the canyon and barreled out onto Miller's land, there was no stopping them.

They broke down his fancy fences, they ripped up his wife's large garden, and they slammed into and tore down his barn, his corrals, his sheds and even half of his magnificent house. When the dust settled, there were seventeen dead wild horses and five dead Millers."

Felicity covered her mouth in surprise. "The horses trampled them?"

Anna Maria shrugged. "That's what the official medical examiner's report from that time says, or something to that effect." Then she smiled ever so slightly. "Of course, by the time the wild horses made it to the Millers' property, my great-great-grandfather and his sons had already been there." She leaned closer to Felicity. "But when you're stomped on by over a thousand horses, there's really no evidence of foul play left for any coroner—especially a coroner way back then—to find."

Felicity watched Anna Maria stand up, but before she moved off, she asked her, "So, why is it good fortune to see the horses of Miller Creek?"

Anna Maria looked up at the sky for a moment, and then she said, "Shortly after the stampede, my great-great-grandfather had a dream in which his dead wife visited him and told him to find the wild horses again. She said that the place where they were grazing would bring him untold riches."

Anna Maria rubbed her arms as though she were fighting off a chill. "He and his sons went out the next day in search of the horses. It took them about a week, but they found the herd roaming freely over a large area of sparse grass but near a few watering holes. My great-great-grandfather dismounted and went to fill his canteen at the nearest hole, but when he took a swig of the water, he immediately spit it out."

Felicity frowned. "Why? Was it tainted or poisoned?"

Anna Maria nodded. "It contained a high concentration of crude oil."

There was a collective gasp, and then Gina piped in with, "She's an Ortega. Of Ortega Oil."

Anna Maria bowed slightly. "At your service, ladies."

Sandria blurted, "Jesus, you must be rich. Why are you creating ads for a living when you could be living it up on some yacht?"

Anna Maria rolled her eyes. "I actually like working and earning my own way in life, thank you very much."

Felicity interrupted, "So, are you saying I'm going to strike it rich? Find some oil? Just because I saw those horses stampeding through the canyon?"

"I can't say how your luck will run, but I can say that there have been many stories over the years of people who saw or heard the Miller Creek horses one day and had something wonderful happen to them shortly after," Anna Maria said as she bent down to retrieve her pack.

The other women took the cue from her and began gathering themselves and their packs to continue the hike. Sandria stepped closer to Felicity. "What are your plans for the next few days? Care if I tag along? I could use some good luck." She snapped her fingers. "Hey, let's go to Vegas!"

"Oh, you," Felicity said as she playfully shoved her friend and coworker. Then she hefted her bag high on her back and squinted up toward the canyon's rim. Her mind returned to the lost locket she'd found in the depths of her bag.

Her grandmother—the woman in the locket—had bequeathed Felicity the contents of a safe deposit box in a bank in Fargo over a year ago, but Felicity hadn't been back to North Dakota since her grandmother's funeral. She'd returned briefly for the service and burial, and then she'd hurried back to Arizona on the first flight out of Fargo. A couple months later, she'd received an official letter from her grandmother's lawyer informing her of the bequest.

Until today, though, she'd actually forgotten all about the safe deposit box. Now she found herself wondering if it might contain something truly valuable.

"Felicity!" Gina yelled, snapping Felicity from her reverie. "Come on!"

Felicity trotted to catch up to Sandria who immediately said, "My lucky numbers are twelve and fifty. How about yours?"

"What?" Felicity was still lost in thought about her grandmother and the mystery of the bank box.

Sandria sighed. "The lottery, girl, the lottery. With your new luck, we're a shoo-in to win. Now, come on, what are your lucky numbers?"

Felicity laughed. "I'm not playing the silly lottery," she began, but then she suddenly stopped. Stopped talking and walking.

Sandria turned and paused as well. "What's wrong?"

Felicity's mind was racing, remembering the letter from her grandmother's lawyer. Quietly, she asked, "What numbers did you say, Sandria?"

"Twelve and fifty. Why?"

Felicity saw with total clarity the line in the letter that read, "Box number 1250 in the Fargo branch of the American Liberty Bank." She gasped and put a hand to her mouth.

Sandria took a couple steps back toward her. "What is it?"

Felicity grabbed Sandria's wrist with both of her hands. "My grandmother."

Sandria tugged to release her wrist from Felicity's firm hold. "What about her?"

Suddenly, Felicity knew what was waiting for her in her grandmother's bank box. She started to laugh, and then she spun in a circle and did a little jig. Finally, she faced Sandria and announced gleefully, "Forget Vegas! You're coming with me to Fargo."

Sandria scowled. "Fargo? Where the hell is that?"

The two women started to walk, hurrying to catch up with Gina, Anna Maria, and the other women. "It's in North Dakota. Jeez, learn a little geography, girl."

Sandria slapped her on the back. "I know where it is. Why the hell would I want to go there though?"

"I need a witness."

"For what?"

"I'm a rich woman. All this time I've been a rich woman and I didn't even know it until these horses and that locket reminded me."

Sandria was getting breathless as she tried to keep up with Felicity's pace. She was the only smoker in the group of women, and it was starting to show. "Slow down and tell me what you're talking about."

"My grandmother owned stock in a bunch of companies. Young companies all over the country. Most of the companies didn't amount to much, and my grandfather always used to grumble that he'd rather she just went to the casino and threw her money away on slots instead of buying all that worthless paper as he called it.

When she died, there was a lot of fuss among my dad and his siblings concerning where my grandmother had put all those proofs of stocks she'd bought over the years. I remember that they went on and on about how they were certain she owned a bunch of stock in Ortega Oil."

Sandria whispered, "As in Anna Maria's Ortega Oil?"

"Exactly," Felicity said. They were now close behind the group of women, so she lowered her voice to continue the story. "I didn't much care about the stock or where my grandmother might have put those papers, but now I do."

"Why is that?" Sandria was practically panting now, so Felicity put a halt to their walk.

She retrieved Sandria's water bottle from her pack and handed it to her. As the other woman drank deeply from the bottle, Felicity said, "I know where they are."

Sandria lowered the water bottle. "Fat lot of good that will do you." She stopped talking as a big grin spread across Felicity's face. "Unless, of course, your grandmother willed them to you."

Felicity nodded. "She willed the entire contents of her bank box to me." She paused for effect. "Bank box number twelve fifty."

Sandria dropped her bottle and then swore as she bent to retrieve it. When she stood up and faced Felicity, she said, "You're just messing with me now."

They heard Gina yelling for them to "stop dawdling," so they started walking again. "I'm being totally serious," Felicity said in a tone that matched her statement. "I'd forgotten all about the bank box until today when I found that locket, and Anna Maria told her story and mentioned Ortega Oil, and you told me your lucky numbers."

Sandria asked, "But are you sure the stocks are in that box?"

"No," Felicity admitted, "but I'm pretty damn certain of it. My uncle tore my grandmother's condo apart looking for them before they sold the place." Suddenly, she laughed. "I remember that about a week after I received the key to the bank box, he emailed me and offered to give me five bucks for it to 'take it off my hands' as he said." She kicked at a red rock. "Son of a bitch! I'll bet he had a feeling the stocks were in there, and he pretended to be solicitous toward me, going on about how it would be silly of me to have to fly back up there for what was certainly a few old coins and my grandparents' wedding certificate."

"Did you reply to him?"

Felicity shook her head in disgust. "Yeah, I did. I told him thanks for the offer, but I'd hang onto the key for the time being, and I'd let him know what was in the box someday when I had time to return."

"Still going to do that?"

"Not a chance." Felicity smiled and squinted up at the bright sky. Another hawk was circling, and she pointed it out to Sandria. "What kind of a bird is that?"

Sandria shaded her eyes with her empty water bottle, peered up and then shrugged. "Beats the hell out of me. A big one?"

They both laughed and started the ascent up the trail that would take them out of the canyon and back to civilization. When they reached the halfway point, Felicity turned to look down into the canyon one last time.

The rock outcroppings behind which she'd hidden from the ghost horse stampede were far in the distance now, and she could see a few tiny hikers milling about near them. From around the bend behind the tall rocks, Felicity could also see the dust from an approaching stampede. She pointed it out to Sandria who was leaning against the canyon wall and trying to catch her breath.

Sandria followed Felicity's pointing finger and stared hard. Then she looked at her friend and shrugged. "Sorry. I don't see anything except the canyon and those big rocks."

Felicity dropped her arm and stood in wonderment as the horses of Miller Creek charged through the canyon followed by mounted men—Anna Maria's great-great-grandfather and his sons—who were driving the horses toward their destiny. As the last horse and rider disappeared around the far bend of the canyon, Felicity smiled.

"Fargo, here I come."

William L. Smutko • Blair, NE

My Tho

Merchants in white shirts, pressed trousers, and loafers haggle with pajama-clad farmers wearing rubber sandals and unloading rice, shrimp, fish, and vegetables from their boats along the canal in My Tho, a sprawling city of eighty thousand in the Mekong Delta. Sun-browned villagers on tri-cycle motorcycles with pickup beds haul their goods into the city past vendors squatting under umbrellas next to their wares. They are hawking everything from conical straw hats to homemade soap. Fifteen-foot by fifteen-foot one-room general stores line the streets and sell just about anything you could want: cigarettes (everyone smokes), coloring books, fish sauce, Coca-Cola. The French influence is visible in the local architecture, especially the Catholic churches, convents, and orphanages. Government buildings are all still sandbagged up four feet with razor wire across the top of the bags, a reminder of the Tet Offensive.

Dong Tam, the US military compound five miles to the west of My Tho, is home to the US 9th Infantry Division, the 3rd Surgical Hospital, and other support units and has a population of about fifteen thousand.

The mission of the surgical hospital is to provide hospital facilities to the 9th Infantry Division and that part of the province and to provide MEDCAP (Medical Civil Action Program) operations to the area.

~ ~ ~ ~ ~

The operating room in the 3rd Surgical Hospital smells like a butcher shop so The circulating nurse dabs oil of wintergreen on First Lieutenant Colleen Cleary's mask to cover the abattoir smell of the operating room. Lieutenant Cleary, an orthopedic nurse, her surgical gown stained with blood, is prepping a soldier to have both his lower legs amputated. She places a tourniquet on the soldier's right leg, just above the tourniquet the medics put on in the field. She does the same on the left leg. Both lower legs are only attached with a little skin and muscle. The bones below the knees of both are shattered. She applies an Ace bandage to the left thigh just below the new tourniquet and keeps wrapping it tightly around the leg, forcing any residual blood from the leg. She repeats the procedure on the other leg.

The soldier on the table is the fourth multiple amputation today. She will pray for all four later, after her shift.

Once the surgeon is finished, she wheels the table to the intensive care unit and helps transfer the soldier to a bed.

"This guy wouldn't have made it in WWII or Korea," says the ICU nurse.

~ ~ ~ ~ ~

A crucifix hangs above Colleen's bed and on the perpendicular wall to the left hangs a picture of Mary. Below Mary is a small table with several votive candles and a metal .50 caliber ammunition box with a small slit cut in the top. The ammo box with the slit cost her two bottles of Jim Beam. She pulls four Vietnamese coins from a blue Crown Royal bag full of them and drops the four coins into the ammo box, lights four candles, kneels on a cushion in front of the table, and crosses herself. "Holy Mother, please intercede to help these boys heal and help me discern what I firmly believe to be my call to become a nun."

~ ~ ~ ~ ~

A little boy sitting on the steps to the school catches Lieutenant Cleary's eye. She and a team of four medics are at the orphanage in My Tho on a MEDCAP. The boy is about three years old and sitting by himself, not joining with the other children running and playing in the courtyard. His eyes are empty, and he emits an aura of complete hopelessness.

"Who is that little boy?" she asks gray-habited Sister Mary Nguyen Thi Nug, who is serving as their interpreter.

"We call him Yên Tĩnh. He was brought here two weeks ago by a long-range reconnaissance patrol, the sole survivor of a small Viet Cong village on the Cambodian border."

The orphanage, an old French provincial building with a mansard roof of red tile and off-white stucco walls pockmarked by bullets and shrapnel from the Tet Offensive, is run by the Sisters of St. Paul De Chartres. Colleen and her crew set up their stations on the worn and bleached wooden floor of the infirmary under the watchful eyes of a crucified Jesus and Pope Paul VI. The smell of disinfectant lingers as they work with the sisters to dispense antibiotics for sore throats and ear infections and to make sure the children are all current on injections for measles and mumps and that any unhealed wounds are cleaned and bandaged.

Sister Mary has Yên Tĩnh by the hand as she walks up to the table where Lieutenant Cleary is sitting. Colleen reaches out and grabs hold of both of Yên Tĩnh's hands and pulls him close. "Tên tôi là Colleen. Bạn tên là gì? What is your name?"

The boy points at the black bar on Cleary's shoulder and says, "Bạn là một trung úy."

"Yes, I'm a first lieutenant, but my name, tên, is Colleen. Trung Úy Colleen. What is your name?" she says pointing at him.

"His name is Tran Chi Duc, but we call him Yên Tĩnh because he is so quiet," Sister Mary says.

"Ask him what he would like me to call him?"

"He asks if you would call him Duc."

Colleen lifts the boy up onto her lap, sticks her otoscope into each ear, has him open his mouth so she can examine his throat, and uses a reflex hammer to check the reflexes in his legs and her stethoscope to check out Duc's heart and lungs. His skin is dry, so she rubs body lotion on his torso, arms, and legs and notices a shoe-shaped birthmark on the inside of his left thigh. As she rubs lotion on his back, Duc leans in and cuddles up to her and starts sucking his thumb. Able as she is to control her urge to hug other children at the orphanage, an instinctive movement has her cradling him in her arms. She starts rocking and singing, "Twinkle, twinkle little star. How I wonder what you are. Up above the world so high. Like a diamond in the sky." Duc falls asleep in her lap.

Sister Mary says, "He hasn't been sleeping well. But you're the first person he's done that to." A deep reluctance—almost to the point of refusing to let Duc go—fills Colleen when the sister picks him up and takes him off to his bed.

Tears fill Colleen's eyes on the jeep ride back to Dong Tam.

Kneeling in her personal chapel, Lieutenant Cleary says Compline, her evening office, before going to bed and adds a special prayer for Duc.

~ ~ ~ ~ ~

Colleen is washing her short army-length hair during her morning shower. Duc creeps into her head as she rinses the soap out.

She sees Duc sitting on the orphanage step as she takes a bite of her fried duck eggs and toast.

She feels the warmth of him sleeping in her arms as she checks the medical supplies in the operating room.

He has been on her mind the whole day, when she's not been involved in caring for a soldier's wounds. She sees his sad eyes and feels his body snuggled up against hers. She knows he'll be fed and clothed and have a safe place to sleep but worries he won't get the attention he needs in the orphanage, that his emotional needs won't be met.

~ ~ ~ ~ ~

"Father, thank you for taking the time to talk with me," Colleen says to the division's Catholic chaplain as she enters his office.

"Please sit down, Lieutenant. How can I help you?"

She sits down in the chair in front of his desk and says, "I feel strongly that I have received a call to become a nun."

"I see," he says, making a tent in front of his chin with the fingers of both hands. "How long have you felt this way?"

Colleen fidgets a bit and says, "It was on my first duty station at Madigan Army Hospital in Tacoma, Washington, a year ago that I felt I received the call. I come from a family of very faithful Irish Catholics, so I wasn't surprised."

He drops his hands to the desktop and asks, "Have you seen any signs or had any visions to back up this feeling?"

Colleen sits up straight in the chair and says, "It was a Saturday night. I had been to Mass that evening because I was going to be on duty on Sunday. I was in bed in that gray zone between wakefulness and sleep. I saw myself in a nun's habit. It wasn't really a dream as such. I don't know what to call it. A vision maybe?"

"A vision's a good possibility. How have you been praying about it?"

"I've been saying Matins, Vespers, and Compline every day since I've been here and asking for guidance after each. But I've met this boy."

"Oh"

"It's not what you might think, Father. He's only three years old and an orphan, but I can't seem to get him out of my mind. I think I might want to adopt him."

"Lieutenant, the Holy Spirit will give you the answer eventually. Keep praying and it will come to you."

~ ~ ~ ~ ~

At the end of her shift, Colleen drops six more coins into the ammo box—it's starting to get heavy—and kneels before the picture of Mary. *Dear Mary, help me. Am I to take the veil as I thought and planned for or take on this boy?*

The motor pool smells of diesel and grease, and the air is full of the omnipresent black Mekong dust. She checks out a jeep for her own personal MEDCAP to help her forget the six severely wounded soldiers she worked on today.

Duc is sitting on the steps, the same place she saw him the first time. Colleen parks the jeep and calls him over to her. She checks out the skin on his legs and arms, then hands him a coloring book and crayons. He gives her a perplexed look.

She realizes Duc's probably never seen a coloring book or crayons before. She pulls a crayon from the box, opens the coloring book to the first page, and starts coloring a picture of Mickey Mouse. She hands the book and crayon to Duc. He takes them from her and continues what she started. The weight of the six severely wounded soldiers eases and a feeling of warmth, protectiveness, and affection flows in as she watches him color. A smile forms on her lips.

Sister Mary comes out to meet her. "What can I help you with?"

"I just came out to see how Duc is doing," she says, turning her attention to Sister Mary. "Have you got a few minutes? I'd like to talk to you a bit."

Duc runs up and shows them the picture of Mickey he has finished.

"Did you give him the crayons and book?" Sister Mary asks, the smile leaving her face.

"Yes, I did. Is that a problem?"

"We have thirty children here. It seems unfair to the others to single one out and give him more attention. Doesn't it? Perhaps next time you can bring something for the others."

"I'm sorry. I didn't think. I just acted. Duc has awakened something in me I've never felt before. I have compassion for the soldiers I treat, but this is different, more primal."

"There is something about young children that brings that out in most of us." The sister's smile returns.

"I wanted to ask you, Sister, how long have you been a member of this order?"

Sister Mary puts her hand to her chin, thinking about the answer, and says, "I started as an aspirant when I was sixteen, six years ago. I'm now a solemnly professed sister. Why do you ask?"

"For some time now, I've been thinking about joining an order when I'm released from the army. I've been doing Vespers, Compline, and Matins every day for the ten months I've been over here."

"Trung úy, trung úy," Duc interrupts with a second colored picture.

"It's beautiful," Colleen says and Sister Mary translates.

Colleen looks at her watch and says, "Well, I'd best be getting back. Thanks for the talk." She waves goodbye to Duc, afraid to hug him.

~ ~ ~ ~ ~

O God, come to my assistance; O Lord, make haste to help me; O Lord, thou wilt open my lips: and my mouth shall proclaim thy praise . . .

Matins said, Colleen heads for the shower and breakfast.

~ ~ ~ ~ ~

"I'm starting a collection for the orphanage we service in My Tho. I think the kids could use a little emotional uplift. I want to provide crayons and coloring books for them," Colleen says, holding a large manilla envelope toward the ward nurse on duty. "They have just enough to survive. A little personal enjoyment would be nice."

She collects from all the doctors and nurses and raises seventy-five dollars.

Colleen wheels the last patient from her shift to the ICU and heads to her room where she drops three coins into the ammo can, kneels in front of her picture of Mary, and says a prayer for the three wounded soldiers. She notices the ammo can is getting very heavy with the coins she's deposited almost every day. She takes the money she's collected and the ammo can and walks to the motor pool.

In My Tho she buys twenty-nine more coloring books and boxes of crayons.

In the orphanage courtyard, Duc is sitting in his normal spot but looks up when she drives in. When she parks, he runs over to her, waving his coloring book and shouting, "Trung úy, trung úy."

Sister Mary comes out to see what's going on.

"I've brought more coloring books and crayons for the other children and a couple more soccer balls for them to kick around," Colleen says to the nun. "I've also brought you this." She lifts the heavy ammo can. "There's over one hundred dollars in it. I've been dropping coins in for over ten months. Use it for whatever you need for them: food, clothing, blankets." She lifts Duc onto her lap, hugging him close, and looks at his coloring.

"Thank you but we now have thirty-seven children here."

~ ~ ~ ~ ~

A few days later, Colleen again pulls into the courtyard. Duc is with two other little boys about his age, trying to kick a full-sized soccer ball around. He sees her, forgets the ball, runs to the jeep, climbs into her lap, wraps his little arms as far around her as they will go, and pulls himself close. She can smell the sweat on him as she pulls him in tight and kisses him on the head.

After a minute or so, he takes her by the hand and leads her into the orphanage up to the room where he sleeps with four other little boys and says, "Colleen," as he hands her the coloring book. He's almost finished it and is very proud of his work. At the sound of her name coming from Duc's mouth, her eyes mist up and tear over.

~ ~ ~ ~ ~

It's another ten days before Colleen can get back to the orphanage. Duc isn't in the courtyard playing as usual. She parks the jeep and goes in looking for Sister Mary.

"Is Duc in class with the other kids?" she asks hopefully when she finds Sister Mary.

"No. Duc has been claimed by an uncle and taken to Nhon Hoa west of Tan An."

Colleen winces at the news, as if she took a round from a Viet Cong rifle. A cold emptiness rushes in. It fills her body and soul. The world turns gray, like the nun's habit, devoid of color. Disappointment and sadness take over as she all but collapses into a chair in Sister Mary's office. Her lips are pressed tightly together as she lowers her head into her hands and lets out a long, mournful sigh.

After a few minutes, Colleen blows her nose and wipes the tears from her eyes. "I should have foreseen this possibility. I guess now I can concentrate more completely on my discernment of taking the veil," she says in resignation.

~ ~ ~ ~ ~

In the name of the Father, and the Son, and the Holy Spirit, one God. Amen.

Christ, have mercy.

Lord, have mercy. Lord, have mercy.

Lord, bless us.

Amen.

Glory be to the Father, and to the Son, and to the Holy Spirit,
Both now and ever and unto the age of ages.

Amen.

Colleen has added the Sixth Hour Prayer to her daily litany. It's short and can be snuck in at noon without any disruption to her work. She says all her prayers with great fervor, almost as if the sound of them is meant to drown out something else or fill a void.

~ ~ ~ ~ ~

Three days before the end of Colleen's tour, they start receiving casualties from a major battle at Nhon Hoa.

Her sixth patient, a very young Vietnamese child, is brought in and laid on the table. His lower left leg has been hit by a large piece of shrapnel and almost amputated. As she's passing a heavy scalpel to the doctor to cut away the remaining muscle below the knee, she notices a birth mark on the inside of his thigh. It's shaped like a shoe. Colleen looks at the child's face, recognizes Duc, and almost passes out. She reels in her anxiety and continues doing what needs to be done to save him. She refuses to look at Duc's face and buries the instinctive need to hold him tight. She concentrates on the wound and keeping him alive.

Duc's riding a thin line between life and death as she wheels him into the ICU. She doesn't wait until she's in her room to pray for him. She crosses herself and prays, "Dear God, please let this boy live. And help me make the right choice about where my life goes from here."

Leopold J. Kovar • Brainard, NE

A Useless Man

Holy Saturday morning. Farmers in pickups pulling torpedoes of anhydrous ammonia, having heard the weather forecast of 90 percent chance of rain for Easter Monday.

"Wouldn't you know it," one of them said, sparing a few moments for coffee and conversation at Rod and Millie's. "Sunday's going to be the best day of the week and I've got to go to church and then spend the afternoon watching grandchildren hunt for colored eggs."

"That's what we get for listening to women," grumbled one of the men.

Fred Houba sat alone, his usual companions gone off to spend the weekend with their children. Gary's chair at another table was empty.

Bill Merck tapped Fred on the shoulder. "Where's that son-in-law of yours?"

"Working his cows."

"How many calves he got now?"

"Ten. They're coming in slower than he wants."

"Gary's timing has always been off."

Fred marveled that he could talk like he knew what he was saying. He only caught bits and pieces of what Gary said, in between mumbles and bursts of profanity. Finishing his coffee, Fred walked back to the farm which was on the edge of town, two blocks away. He walked out to what had been in his youth the orchard. All the apple and pear trees were dead, replaced by volunteer box elders that bore only tree mushrooms. Only last week he had cut up the last fallen apple tree, marveling at its density. Even in death it seemed substantial whereas the box elders in life spread out and upward and appeared flimsy. Limbs twisted and broken from last year's ice storm still remained caught in the branches, making the trees look as if they were in perpetual mourning. Fred went out almost every day with his triangular saw and his clippers to cut dead wood and unwanted shoots. This was a useless job, never done before on the farm, not asked for or valued. For him, it was something to do.

He felt a kinship to his great grandfather, Jaroslav Houba, whose pride was working in the tulip beds of Castle Starovek. Forced by his wife to join her brothers in America, he never adapted, a gloomy Hussite watching his sons gravitate to the Catholic church because that was where the girls were. Near the end of his life, Jaroslav refused to come out of his bedroom and face the sunlight. The plains of Nebraska had no need of him.

Fred made a mental note of several rosettes of musk thistles that needed a shot of Tordon. Gary hollered for him.

"Dad, stand over there. I want to chase this cow and calf into the lean-to."

Gary rarely asked for any help from him. Fred felt he was usually just in the way. Now he served a function, as a sort of moveable fence.

"How's it going?"

Gary made a sour face. "Every one of these calves is too big. I have to pull every one. I'm sure to lose a couple, at least. As long as I can save the cow."

Gary knew what he was doing. Raised on a farm, he'd already put in fifteen years in the muffler plant. Having five kids to raise, this burly, bearded man kept his factory job and farmed and ranched in the evenings and on the weekends, chewing antacid pills half the time.

Fred never expected to be living in this house. His mother always referred to him as a town kid, smaller and weaker than his brother, Clem. The army doctors who checked him out at the time of his induction thought he looked sickly, but his physical exam showed nothing out of order. He spent his Korean War duty as a supply clerk. Then he came back to Haugers where at first he worked part time as a substitute postmaster before Elda Frichert retired. After the morning rush, he spent most of the time alone. He hadn't the ability to collect and distribute news the way Elda did. His wife, Mary, was called a quiet woman. What bothered him was that they never had much to say to each other. Their prime attraction to each other was availability. She probably would have borne three children regardless of whom she married. She died as she lived, quietly, from an inherited heart condition previously unrecognized in her family.

Fred's mother could see his house from her front window, but she rarely visited. An invisible line had been drawn separating town and country.

"Fred's never going to be a farmer," she said. "Now, Clem, on the other hand, he'll do all right. Not so many fancy ideas. It's good to have one son that amounts to something."

Her last words in the hospital were, "I always been able to depend on Clem."

One day six months after Fred retired after thirty years of federal service, the siren blared. Fred walked out to the corner and saw the ambulance drive into Clem's yard. He heard his phone ring.

"Freddie, Clem's had a heart attack," Ben Moyer said. "He called me to say he wasn't feeling so good."

Fred thought it typical of Clem to call one of his drinking buddies rather than him. Still, he felt this was no time to be ungenerous.

"Do you want to ride with me to the hospital?"

"I'd appreciate it, Fred."

Ben changed shirts since Fred saw him earlier in the morning. As he pulled up, Fred saw Ben hesitate, cracking his last knuckle before he opened the car door. Fred could smell beer on Ben Moyer's breath.

"Old Clem looked just fine yesterday."

"When do you get your license back?"

"They may not want to give it back to me. I haven't killed anybody or anything, but those cops just don't want me on the road." Ben reached for a cigarette loose in his shirt pocket, but then thought better of it. "Man can't drive anywhere these days. Too damned many people in this world."

Fred knew the statistics. The population in the county declined every census since 1900.

"It's cars, Ben. They go too fast and crumple up like tinfoil."

"That must be it. I knew there was a reason."

The parking spaces in front of Burgess County Hospital were full so Fred pulled into the handicapped spot to let Ben out before finding a place halfway down the block. Ben waited for him by the admissions desk.

"A lot of sick people today. I checked the board and I don't know half of them. We got nothin' but strangers around us these days."

The latest magazines filled the magazine rack of the surgery waiting room. The TV seemed to be on permanently. The light blue walls had been painted recently. Nothing made the waiting easier.

"If anybody can do anything for Clem, Dr. Vatz can."

Ben, though he'd been to a doctor only a few times in his life, swore by Dr. Vatz. The Mrzeks remained so tied to the old country that they named their first son, Vaclav. Though now semi-retired with most of his patients grudgingly drifting over to younger, more professional-looking doctors, he still saw the older farmers, emotionally a part of their world. Still holding an interest in his parents' Cuming County farm, Dr. Vaclav Mrzek reminisced about the hoof-and-mouth disease panic almost a half century earlier or an outbreak of hog erysipelas rather than the latest advances in medicine.

Dr. Vatz's office was one of the few places where Clem and Fred happened to meet. They shared their mother's distrust of men in white coats. They preferred to hear bad news from a doctor in a short-sleeved shirt. Clem and Fred never exchanged more than a perfunctory greeting. Fred wondered if Dr. Vatz scheduled the appointments just so they could meet and maybe iron things out.

Ben noticed a priest pass by.

"Oh, Christ, it's got to be serious."

Ben grabbed the arm of a nurse. "Can you tell me anything about Clem Houba?"

"We're doing our best, sir."

A woman in a gray suit stopped at the door. "Is there anyone to sign papers for Mr. Houba?"

Fred hesitated. "Come with me, Ben. There may be some things you know that I don't."

Clem had never been hospitalized before. Fred could answer most of the questions. Date of birth, parents, never married, military service. Clem's phone number stumped him. It was the same as when their mother was still living, but Fred never called. Ben also knew that Clem was covered by Part B Medicare and also carried private insurance. Signing the form, Fred felt like a fraud.

Fred and Ben waited another hour in the waiting room. When they saw Dr. Vatz come in, they stood up. The doctor put his hand on Fred's shoulder and sighed.

"Well, Clem has had his last hi-ball."

They spoke in low voices and nodded, words repeated over the years in thousands of different locations, nothing new. The priest waited in the hallway for Dr. Vatz to leave.

"Hello, I'm Father Holley from St. Agnes Parish. You'll be comforted to know he died in a state of grace."

Fred stood for a moment, reflecting that he had never missed Sunday mass or a Holy Day of Obligation, yet Clem pried his way through a crack in Heaven's door without an inch to spare. Maybe it was true that God protected drunks.

The Legion Auxiliary prepared lunch after the funeral. Matt Durkin pulled Fred to one side.

"I'm going on a three week vacation to England and Germany beginning next Thursday so you may want to come in and start the paperwork before I go." Fred looked blank for a moment. "It shouldn't be complicated. He didn't leave many debts so far as I know. Even his funeral was prepaid. So what's left is yours, but I figure you knew that already."

Fred had not stepped on the farm since his mother's death twelve years before. Fred looked at the pasture. Thank God it was summer when cattle grazed contentedly, requiring little human intervention into their lives. Before going to work Gary turned on the pumps and filled the water tanks. Fred walked all over the farm as if rediscovering a foreign land. I know nothing about farming, Fred told himself. He had always been the little brother who took orders, never having to think on his own. Whenever Clem needed help, he called on hard-drinking, hard-smoking buddies like Ben or Gary, if he was really in a pinch.

Fred drove over to the double trailer in the south part of town where Gary and Maxine lived. Maxine only worked mornings at the Shop-Eaze.

"I've decided I want to move back into the old place," he told her. "I'm wondering if you and Gary want to move into my house. It's too big for me."

Maxine threw her arms around him and began to cry, Oh, Daddy. Fred knew that the cramped trailer had been the source of some of their marital discord. Gary turned down a previous offer because he never wanted to live with relatives.

Even Gary joined in the cleaning of the farmhouse. Maxine stood in the middle of the kitchen and shook her head.

"Uncle Clem was no housekeeper. Didn't he ever have a girlfriend?"

"Not that I know of," Fred said. "There was a whole generation of men that simply never had anything to do with women. They worked, they hunted and they drank. I think women were just too complicated for them. They liked to look at dirty pictures but that's as far as it went."

Fred called his other two daughters. Both understood the unstated rules. The property eventually would go to Maxine and Gary because they stuck around. Janice had a doctor husband who prided himself on his investments. Danielle married a theatrical agent in New York who shuddered at the thought of anything rural.

Now Fred was enjoying an independent life, cooking what he wanted, not having to worry about mowing the lawn. Gary would shred the yards when the weeds got high. Thinking about it, Fred had to conclude he was living a useless life. He looked out into the pasture to see Gary and his oldest son, Trevor, chasing a heifer. Fred stood where the heifer wouldn't see him. Gary closed the corral gate.

"Trevor," Gary barked. "Don't just stand there. We have to chase her into the barn."

Trevor waved his arms and gave an ear-piercing yell to which the heifer reacted wildly.

"Don't scare her, for Chrissake. Stop acting like a town kid."

"That's what I am. That's what I've been all my life."

Fred could see that his slender, scraggly-haired blond grandson started out too late. He hated farm life with every ounce of his body. His little brother was poking the previous heifer's afterbirth with a stick while the Australian Shepherd puppy, Pearl, chewed on another part. The baby was chasing Muscovy drakes in and out of the pen.

Gary stood for a moment with the hip-puller held at arm's length. With its curved top, center pole and heavy chain, it looked like a standard for some ancient primitive religion with Gary as its priest.

Fred went to Rod and Millie's for another cup of coffee. At the back table with a notebook before him, Curtis Mullin sat working on his next project. Regarded as a dummy in school, caught fire with a tape measure and hammer in his hand, earned respect as the town builder. Fred shrugged. Curtis was serving a purpose in life. Fred, in his declining years, saw he was useless. He had nothing to pass on.

Mark M. Peyton • Gothenburg, NE

The Tree

The tree came awake. What was that? Something moved. There was no wind. A quick survey showed no birds in the branches. What moved?

There! It happened again. The roots. It was the roots. The tree's roots were moving. In its long life, nigh on more than one hundred years now, its roots had never moved.

All the senses of the tree took on a heightened awareness. The roots registered a new openness—a freedom never before experienced.

"My roots are open to the air," the tree realized. "The ground is caving away!"

A cold fear rose through the xylem of the tree. A fear only felt once before a long time ago. That was when the fire had swept up and over the ridge. The tree survived the fire . . . but this?

On Black Canyon Ridge, air on the roots meant only one thing. The Dismal River had undercut more of the bank. Her bank. Last season, or was it two seasons ago, the old cottonwood, her best friend, had fallen when the bank below it had given way.

The old cottonwood. As long as the tree could remember that cottonwood had stood there just to the north. In fact, the cottonwood had told the tree of its "birth."

"Let's see. I think it was a blue jay . . . yep, a blue jay. That jay used to sit on my branches and bitch at the world. All day long it would bitch, bitch, bitch. Anyway, it fed on some berries from across the river there . . . yea, you can still see the body of the old tree he fed on. Over there. Do you see it . . ."

The tree had never seen the "body" but she had always said she did and the cottonwood would go on with the story.

"Where was I . . . oh yea. Anyway, that bird flew over to do its daily bitching and of course its daily 'constitutional.' I don't know why that bird liked to do his business from my branches, but he did.

"Sure enough, right where it would go, the next season there was this little cedar growing . . . that was you. Now, beings that your momma was way over there, it only seemed natural for me to help out and take care of you, so I did. Those first few years you would sit in the shade of my branches and cry out in hunger. My roots grew over and met up with yours. After that I could send some food down and across to you and you ate. Boy, did you eat!

"You weren't the only one, you know. There was a bunch of you little saplings over the years, that's why they call me "Mamma Cottonwood." No, you weren't the first, or the last, but you was the toughest."

Mamma Cottonwood. For years the two of them had slowly grown and watched as the cycle of life went by. The warblers in the cedar raising their young year after year as the robins did in the cottonwood. Just a few years ago it was a red-tailed hawk that built a nest in the upper portion of a dead branch of the cottonwood. That spring, before Mamma Cottonwood slipped into the river, a great horned owl arrived in February and took over the nest. Boy, were things lively for a while when the hawks got back, but that owl knew a good nest when she saw it.

The two trees had seen a lot together. They endured cold, drought, and even that fire ten years ago . . . or was it twenty years. Time moves so slowly for trees. Just the telling of the story of her birth could take a couple of months. When was that fire? She could have looked at her rings. There was a perfect record of the years—the dry ones, the wet ones, the cold ones, and the one with the fire.

Then Mamma Cottonwood was gone. There was no warning. It was a windy, rainy night during a particularly rainy spring. It was a hard rain. Had there ever been as hard a rain as that night?

She heard the sound. The cedar felt the scream of Mamma Cottonwood and felt the roots and fungus that connected them tear apart and then, Mamma Cottonwood was gone!

The cedar felt with her roots. She sent out clicks and clacks from the roots. No reply. There was no communication. Then the cedar cried as only trees can. A long, slow, and mournful cry. Campers on the bar across the river, huddling in their tents out of the rain, called it the wind.

As spring turned to summer the tree heard rumors about Mamma Cottonwood. The robins told her she was just below the bank, in the river, but the cedar couldn't talk to her anymore. Their roots, their lines of communication, were severed. The cedar would call out. Nothing.

One day the tree heard the sound of a chain saw. Every tree knows the sound of a chain saw. The warblers told her it was a man in a canoe cutting off the cottonwood's branches that stuck out into the river. She knew then that her old friend was truly gone.

Movement! Again the ground moved. This time it wasn't a sudden jerk. It was a slow slip as the bank under her melted away in the current of the River. She tried to hang onto the bank but with a loud crack one of her major roots broke and she fell screaming through the air.

The tree lay there. Her crown was in the water. She could tell she lay almost across the river with some roots still in the dirt of the bank. She was still alive.

As the sun rose and the day wore on, the tree took stock of her situation. The elation of being alive gave way to the depression of truth. Lying in the river, most of her branches were in the water where the sun couldn't get to them. Without sun she couldn't make food and even if she was in the river, most of her roots were up in the air. She couldn't get water through the needles of the branches, only through the roots. But she tried.

She had plenty of food stored up and she started to use it to grow roots into the bank and new branches up to the sky. She tried. But that wasn't natural for a tree and as the heat of summer came she grew thirstier and thirstier. Her time had come.

The tree thought again on that last day of the cottonwood. The two of them living and talking, making seeds.

The cottonwood would gaily fling its young to the wind. White pieces of "cotton" lazily floating in the canyon air. It had been an enjoyable time.

The tree's young had been the blue berries she made for the birds to eat. The birds would then fly somewhere else and go to the bathroom and her offspring would grow there.

But the cottonwood was gone, and now it was her turn. As she slowly drifted away she heard a sound. It was the sound of a chain saw. Every tree knows the sound of a chain saw. She knew what that meant. She was gone before she could feel the pain of the sharp teeth cutting through her trunk, opening up the channel for this year's crowd of people canoeing the Dismal River.

Nonfiction

Conor Gearin • Providence, RI

Cather in Omaha

"The red of the grass made all the great prairie the color of wine-stains, or of certain seaweeds when they are first washed up." One of Willa Cather's most famous lines, from the 1918 novel *My Ántonia*, mainly refers to the color of little bluestem (*Schizachyrium scoparium*), one of the key grasses of the mixed grass prairie where she grew up in Red Cloud, Nebraska. The species has a bluish color in spring but matures to a copper red in autumn that reflects the fire of a Great Plains sunset.

The first place I connected Cather's words to little bluestem wasn't in farm country but instead at Glacier Creek Preserve on the outskirts of Omaha. Years of restoration transformed terraced crop fields into a glimpse at the flora of mixed grass and tallgrass prairies accessible to city dwellers. In the Midwest, we've lost nearly all of our native grasslands to agriculture, meaning that if you grew up in a city like Omaha or St. Louis—my hometown—your first look at a grassland was probably a restored site down the road like Glacier Creek. This modest-sized preserve offers a glimpse of the most threatened type of ecosystem in the world. As a biology teaching assistant, I would help lead university students at the preserve in collecting soil samples, estimating plant biomass, and identifying bird species.

When Cather was a student at the University of Nebraska–Lincoln in the 1890s, Omaha was a cultural destination, and she wrote incisive theater reviews to help establish herself as a writer.

Her fiction reflects this early view of the big city. Especially in *My Ántonia* and *O Pioneers!*, Omaha looms as an urban hub, reachable by train for a cosmopolitan weekend outing, the place to go for fancy fabric and renowned actors. Cather's careful depictions of small-town Nebraska take their meaning partly from the contrast she draws to these growing cities a few rail stops away.

Later in her career, Cather returned to Omaha on a brief Midwestern speaking tour. At a 1921 gathering of the Nebraska League of Women Voters in the tea room of the stately Brandeis department store in downtown Omaha, Cather advised the audience not to imitate other places. "It seems to me as I travel out through the great middle west, the people are trying to imitate New York," she said, as quoted by the *Omaha World-Herald*. "Red Cloud and Hastings are trying to be like Omaha; Omaha and Chicago are trying to be like New York. One thing I like about New York is that there we wear the kinds of hats we like, we wear the kind of clothes that please us."

The remark feels strikingly contemporary. Reading it, I think of how today's Midwestern communities often converge on a suburban sameness: small towns grasping for big box stores, larger cities sprawling out subdivisions into farm country. The result is a landscape that's hard to distinguish from hundreds of others, their quirks of ecology smoothed over and refashioned with evenly distributed brand names. But I think, too, of the distinguishing features that remain: the grasses and herbs of eastern Nebraska I saw in the field and through the microscope; the improbably steep slopes of the Loess Hills across the Missouri River; all the different kinds of live music wafting out of bars in Omaha's Benson neighborhood on a First Friday. I think of Omaha's cultural legacies—the Indigenous peoples of the Oceti Sakowin; black families that arrived in the Great Migration; generations of immigrants from throughout Europe, Asia, Mexico, Central America, and more recently Sudan, Nigeria, and other African nations—and how those legacies often appeared in the students of my commuter campus. Foregrounding these, it's harder to write off the city as interchangeable with any other in the Corn Belt.

Historically, Omaha has looked to Cather's words for help in establishing a sense of place. When I lived there, my local library was the Willa Cather Branch. There's a Willa Cather elementary school and a Willa Cather playground. Despite living two hundred miles from Red Cloud, many people in Omaha (like their fellow Nebraskans) have felt better represented in her fiction than in contemporary works like *The Great Gatsby*—where the Great Plains are a grim wasteland, a place to escape.

But it would be a mistake to portray Cather as some kind of saint of Midwestern culture. Her legacy is more complex than that. She left Nebraska for New York to make her way in the literary world. She also largely erased Native Americans in her writing and essentially celebrated white settlement on Indigenous lands. Her view of Midwestern uniqueness was hitched to pioneer exploitation.

We're not beholden to that limited view. Instead, I see Cather's work as a starting point that many writers have riffed on throughout the past century. The thread of her legacy that stands out to me now is the awakening of a Midwestern ecological consciousness, distinguishing the particularity of one place from another. That awareness offers another way to envision the future of a place, one away from evenly-spread amenities and toward a unique trajectory linked to local ecology and culture—a celebration of difference.

If I imagine standing at Glacier Creek Preserve now, I can look southeast toward downtown Omaha, north and west toward farmland, and south toward recently built subdivisions. Despite suburban sprawl, I wouldn't mistake the view for St. Louis or Chicago. The sources of Omaha's uniqueness haven't been completely smothered. But the threats to grassland habitats are as dire as ever. Looking around at the little bluestem, switchgrass, and side-oats grama, I think about Cather's hunch that if we could articulate the special character, the this-ness of a landscape, that might tell us something about how best to relate to that place. If writers and naturalists—myself included—could help more people see grasslands as vital, with inhabitants that have names and life histories, I wonder what new shape our communities might take.

Excerpts *from a* Novel

Valerie Lee Vierk • Ravenna, NE

A Troubled Day

Chapter One

July 14, 1935

Old Eliska Benisek looked up from her hoeing just as the sun crept crimson over the horizon. She stood there—transfixed—as the beautiful ball climbed higher. But as she watched, her awe at the beauty of the sunrise faded and was replaced by a frightening uneasiness. She made a low sound in her throat as she tore her eyes away, knowing that even though the sun had no rays shooting out from it, she dared not look at it too long.

She looked over at her black companion lying in the dust two rows away and said, "Ah, Hanci, a red dawn. It bodes ill." Hanci blinked her yellow eyes twice and continued to look at her mistress. "Something terrible will happen today, I fear. I have had this feeling before, this approaching blackness, and never have I been mistaken." Eliska was remembering the most terrible time, the night so long ago, when her life had taken a tragic turn, never to be righted. The morning of the day had dawned like this one.

But Hanci, unaware of Eliska's distress, began to groom herself. Eliska glanced back up at the sun that was now hanging suspended like a glorious red orb in the gray sky, and then she resumed her hoeing, but her mind was troubled . . .

Sammi Hoard • Alma, NE

Bed and Breakfast and Beyond

Chapter One

Alice Jackson sighed heavily and set the cleaning cloth down on a side table in the entryway of her deceased mother's former bed and breakfast. Pushing her thick hair away from her face, she stared at her reflection in the mirror above the umbrella stand. Wrinkles were forming in the corners of her green eyes, one thin line for each of her forty-eight years on this planet. "Mirror, mirror on the wall . . ."

"Hello?" Molly Miller-Brown, a close friend and colleague, called from the front door.

"Come on in," Alice said. She peered into the mirror again and assessed the increasing grey strands popping up in her mahogany hair, shaggy and hitting her at the shoulders. She contemplated getting an appointment for a cut and style. Then remembering that her finances were in that proverbial toilet, she nixed the idea.

"You're still gorgeous, love," Molly said as she plopped her burgundy leather oversized handbag on the secretary on the east wall.

Dressed to the nines in a form-fitting, cream-colored dress with a burgundy and black scarf at her neck and a thin burgundy belt at her waist, Molly's dark brown highlighted hair was swept up into a clip. Molly defied not only gravity with her still-curvy figure but her face, which was wrinkle-free and belied her age of fifty-one.

Alice felt fuddy-duddy in denim overalls and a paint-stained T-shirt she'd found in her mother's closet. She'd sustained this melancholy for the last year, since her divorce was finalized. Feeling attractive wasn't in her mental make-up these days and most likely would never be again.

"What're you up to today?" Molly stood her distance, seemingly afraid to get dust and grime on her dress.

"Cleaning and prepping. I'm going to paint later."

Molly walked to the small credenza along the west wall. She shuffled through paint chips that Alice had picked up from the big-box hardware store earlier that morning. She selected two, a mint green and a teal. "Oh, I like these." She held them up for Alice.

"I like those too. I'm thinking of adding this wheat germ pallet for accents." She handed the third color to Molly.

Molly nodded. "This will really lighten up this space."

"There you go talking like you're a real estate agent," Alice said with a chuckle.

Placing one hand on her hip, Molly smiled. "That's because I am. And so are you, little missy."

"With my divorce, then my mother's battle with cancer and death, I haven't sold any properties for a very long time," Alice said flatly. She swept her arms in a wide arc, indicating the peeling paint on the walls, the scuffed dark walnut woodwork. Feeling overwhelmed with all that needed to be done to sell this monstrosity, she swiped away a tear that escaped and trickled down her cheek. "What was Mom thinking of, leaving this to me? I can't do the repairs this place needs. I don't have the skills. I don't have the money."

"You'll repair what you can, then hire someone else to do what you can't."

"Hello?" More tears slipped down Alice's cheeks. She hurriedly scraped them away. "No money?" She pointed at herself with both index fingers. "Divorcing Jason, what with his impossible demands for what property he thought he should get, wiped me out financially and emotionally."

"I can loan you the money," Molly said softly.

Here we go again. Molly and her oodles of cash from the death of her husband, Paul, in a fire three years ago. His firefighter's life insurance plus accidental death policies helped cushion Molly's future without him. Alice chastised herself for having such negative thoughts. Molly would rather have Paul alive again and be poor than have any of that insurance money. "I can't borrow money from you. It wouldn't be right. I'd break down in tears every time I spent even a penny of it. Paul's death is tied to that money. Besides, the experts say it's lethal to borrow from a friend. Considering you're pretty much my only friend . . ."

"Thank you for the sentiment," Molly said quietly. "But Paul wanted me to be protected in the event of his death." She stopped. Drew in a deep breath. "And I think you have more than me you can count as a friend. That bit about not borrowing from me? Of course you can. I have enough and then some to help you out. Who was there with me when Paul died? You were," she said, her voice cracking. She stopped, tears lingering in her lashes, and waited a couple of beats to compose herself. "There'd be no hurry for you to pay me back either."

Uncomfortable with the conversation and wanting to change it, Alice went into the parlor just off the entryway. She crooked a finger for Molly to follow. Alice cringed at the state the parlor was in. Chunks of plaster were missing. Gaping holes outnumbered the places where the wallpaper was still in contact. That faded, dirty, horrible green wallpaper. Disgust shivered down her spine. "See how this room is falling down into itself?"

"So? Just knock down all the plaster and hang drywall."

"I should sell the place *as is* to someone who can restore it to its former glory."

"Dear Alice," Molly said as she wrapped an arm around Alice's shoulder. "You can't do that. It was your mom's B and B. It was *the* place to go for anniversaries and quick honeymoons in its heyday."

"Well, that was a long time ago."

The doorbell chimed, cutting their conversation short. Alice leaned back and peaked toward the door. "It's Grady Dunlop," she murmured. "He's got on his Kelly green blazer and razor-pressed khakis." Grady was good-looking in his competing realtor's attire, but for some unknown reason, besides making her skin crawl, Alice didn't trust him.

"What does that snake want?" Molly whispered a bit too loud.

With a shrug, Alice said, "Let's have some fun and find out while we mock him." She walked to the door, stood there without opening it. Her dislike of Grady intensified when he stepped in and pushed his way past her. "Well, just come on in."

"Thank you," he said, his lips hooked upward in a crooked smile. "I wanted to visit with you about selling this . . ." He glanced around, his abhorrence at what he was witnessing evident on his too-handsome face with a chiseled chin and a dimple right in the middle of it. Lots of cha-ching had gone into Grady's youthful facial maintenance. ". . .this place," he finally finished.

"It's not for sale," Molly said before Alice could form a coherent thought, let alone voice it.

Alice gazed over her shoulder at Molly and mouthed, "Way to go."

"I'm prepared to pay a fair price," he said and widened his smile ad nauseam.

"Yeah, what she said," Alice replied. "This *place* is not for sale." Not yet anyway. Not to him ever.

"Are you planning to sell it in the near future?" Grady withdrew a business card from his blazer breast pocket.

"Nope," Alice said without hesitation. "Maybe down the road sometime. Not that it's any of your concern. I won't give you the business."

"You've been out of the loop, sweet girl. You'd have to renew your license and whatnot."

Sweet girl? Oh, gag me. Who did this conceited jerk think he was? "My real estate license is still very much alive and well. Are you afraid I'll get the commission you're always skulking around trying to steal from other agents?"

"You go, girl," Molly murmured and not too quietly. "I think you're afraid, Grandy," she said, snickering after she purposely mispronounced his name, knowing he hated the town's nickname for him. "Afraid that Alice will look better in that crazy green blazer than you do? Outselling you? That's a given."

"I just came over to offer my services," he started. Both Alice and Molly broke into all-out belly laughs. "Really? Are you challenging me to a contest? Is that it?"

Both women continued laughing. Nodded as if they shared the same spinal cord.

"You know I'll win," he said loudly over their laughter. The women chortled even more. He looked around the old B and B entryway, shuddering. "I have a property in about the same condition as this one. I challenge you that I can have that place remodeled and looking great, maybe even in Taj Mahal fashion, in six weeks."

"Yeah, right," Alice said. Her sides ached from laughing so hard. "Taj Mahal in Hastings, Nebraska?"

Grady stood rigidly straight, towering over Alice and Molly at his full six-four height, his bright blue eyes practically boring into Alice's soul. He ran a hand through his pale blonde hair that was too long in the back. "What say you? Are you open for this challenge?"

"Yeah," Molly said, not giving Alice a chance to decline. "Six weeks. Easy-peasy."

"Alice?" Grady held out his hand toward her. "Agreed?" When Alice didn't answer right away, he smirked. "Can't handle the pressure."

"Can't handle the pressure?" Alice leaned into him, stretching up on her toes to shove her face close to his. "You're on."

"Yeah, you're on," Molly said from behind her.

"So it's a deal. Shake on it or we can draw up a contract."

Alice took his clammy hand and gave it one giant shake. "You are so on!" She dropped his hand and took a step back. "It's September twenty-second, so this challenge would end . . ." Grabbing her phone, she brought up the calendar.

"November third," Molly said and pumped her phone in the air.

"Log it into your phone, genius," Alice said to Grady as he gawked at her.

Punching the info into his cell, Grady backed away. "May the best man, umm . . . real estate agent win."

"Oh, I will," Alice replied with gusto. "I will."

"What will the winner get for a prize?" Grady stood beside the doorway. His crooked smile was too much to handle as doom settled into Alice's gut. Prize? She had just enough cash to get a couple of gallons of paint and that was it.

"We'll figure it out," Molly said. "Video your progress, Grandy. We'll tape ours. As for the prize, let's keep it simple, like the loser buys the winner gift cards for a dinner and a movie for two."

"I'm good with that. The winner will get their picture in the *Tribune* too," Grady said.

"And the winner will get a guest spot on KSNB Channel 5. So you better film what you're doing over there," Molly said. She stepped around Alice, jabbed a finger at Grady.

Grady leaned back from her extended finger. "I'm all for that too. That will definitely raise KSNB viewership." He chuckled, turned, and left. He continued laughing as he walked to his car. *Arrogant fool,* Alice thought as he climbed into his sleek red convertible.

The balloon of confidence that had been bolstering Alice deflated. Her arms dropped slowly to her sides as if they were made from gelatin. "What have I done? I can't get this remodeled in six weeks."

"Sure you can," Molly said with an exaggerated smile and doing a double thumbs-up.

"I don't have any money to hire anyone to help."

Molly tapped the keypad on her phone and held it to her ear. She raised one finger as she waited for whomever she was calling to answer. "Hey, Randy, this is Mol. Remember that favor you said you owed me?" Pausing, Molly flashed Alice a big smile. "Well, I'm calling in that favor now. And when I say now, I really mean *now*. Can you meet me, say," she said while checking the time on her thin gold diamond-encrusted watch, "in thirty minutes at Blue Moon?" She nodded, then nodded again. "See you in thirty."

"Randy?" Alice stared at Molly in awe.

"Randy Johnstone."

"The contractor that's booked solid for months and months into who knows when?" The one who has a thing for Molly and, if Alice was reading Molly correctly, had the hots for him too.

"Yep, that's him." Molly slung her purse over her shoulder. "He'll get this place in amazing condition."

"Did you miss it when I said that I have no money? I can't pay him."

"I know. I'll take care of his and his crew's wages."

Alice laughed lightly. "I can't pay *you* back either. Not unless you agree to five dollars a month from now until doomsday,"

"Look, Sweetie, I really want to see this bed and breakfast reopen," Molly replied. "It's going to take money. Money that you don't have at the moment. I'll pay for the materials needed for the repairs and the labor."

Another tear slipped down Alice's cheek. She wanted desperately to accept Molly's kind and gracious offer. But her pride, much like her mother's, was preventing her from answering yes. Shaking her head, she bit her bottom lip to hold back more tears. How had she gotten to this position, almost destitute? Yes, she could go back to selling real estate, but her heart just wasn't in it right now. And she wasn't sure it ever would be again; she was still grieving the loss of her mother. Amanda Glade, the elderly owner of Hastings Hometown Realty, where Molly and she both worked, understood the depth of Alice's grief and had given her an open-ended six month leave of absence.

"No?" Molly asked incredulously. "You're saying no to my loaning you the money on a no-end-date and no-interest note?"

More tears pooled in Alice's eyes as she shook her head again. "No," she forced out. "I can't take your money because that's what it would wind up being, knowing I can't pay you back."

"*Okay*," Molly said slowly. Her hands rested on her hips and she stood in what Alice recognized as her stance of not taking no for an answer. This wasn't going to be pretty. "I'll become your partner. You help Randy with the repairs and what-not. I'll put up the cash and we win the bet with Grady. You run the bed and breakfast after the dust settles or you can hire a manager and get back into the real estate game. It's a win-win for us both. For the town, too, because they'll be getting back the best bed and breakfast ever. And having it in both the newspaper and on Channel 5, it will let people know that the B and B is back in business. We need to figure out a catchy name so we can apply for the permits and such."

Molly tapped her chin, deep in thought. "How about Bed and Breakfast and Beyond?"

Molly's enthusiasm was catching. Alice, excited, felt there was hope after all. Then her energy drained completely and left her bereft once again.

Sensing Alice's dive into despair, Molly said, "If you turn down this offer, I'm off of you for good."

Alice gaped at her then laughed. "You can't use that line from that Paul Newman movie on me. 'Off of me for good . . .'"

"It was worth a try," Molly said and laughed.

"That was such a cheesy movie, though."

"Hey, it was not. Anyway, are you in for the partnership? I can get the papers drawn up after I meet with Randy."

Alice hesitated, wanting to say no, that she'd find the money somewhere else. But who was she kidding? She didn't want to remortgage the bed and breakfast because that would include regular monthly payments that she couldn't pay either. She sighed, sucked in a ragged breath. Gave in. "Yeah, we can be partners. Thank you." She turned toward the table where the paint chips were, then looked over her shoulder at Molly. "That's a great name by the way."

~ ~ ~ ~ ~

Molly entered the Blue Moon Coffee Shop on Second Avenue. She loved this place. Several mismatched tables and chairs scattered in the center, along the walls, and nestled in two window nooks, provided great seating for customers to enjoy their coffee, other beverages, and food. The exposed red-glazed brick walls and the low lighting gave the coffee shop an inviting and cozy ambience. She looked around for Randy. Spotting him at the sugar and cream station, loading up his coffee, her heart kicked up a beat. Too bad he was younger, what with his naturally sun-kissed brown hair that came to his broad shoulders. She'd definitely be interested. Instantly she felt so guilty, gazing at another man this way, betraying the love she still carried and always would for Paul.

Randy turned and his gray eyes locked with hers. Her heart rate ratcheted up again. What was she going to do about how she reacted whenever he was around? Randy smiled, waved. She returned both. After ordering her standard Café Mocha, she paid and joined Randy at a table by the door.

"How are you today?" Molly sat down adjacent to him.

"I'm good. Extremely busy these days, which is great. Considering a year ago everything was up in the air."

"Tell me about it. It took several months for the housing market to get back to normal."

"About that favor," Randy began. Molly gave him what she thought was her most charming smile. "What're you asking me to do?"

Very blunt and to the point. That's what she'd always liked about this guy. That and the way he filled out blue jeans. Plus many other things. He'd give you the shirt off of his back. Yet he'd suffer no fools, particularly greedy or narcissistic fools.

"Do you remember Alice Jackson?" Molly waited for Randy to answer. He stared at her blankly. Okay, so try another tack. "Her mother died from colon cancer about four months ago. She owned the bed and breakfast over on the east end of Boyce Street."

"Across from where the mall used to be?"

"Yes. Alice inherited it and it's in disarray."

Randy snapped his fingers. "I know what place you're talking about now. Disarray? More like in shambles."

"Yes, you're correct," Molly said, then paused.

"You aren't wanting me to remodel that property are you? It should be torn down and sell the land."

"Well," Molly replied. How could she answer his question and convince him to sign on for the project?

"I'm busy, Mol. Really crazy busy. I wouldn't have time to even start that massive project."

"You can't rearrange your schedule to work her in? Please?" She clasped her hands in front of her and hoped he'd accept. Prayed she didn't appear as silly as she felt.

Randy stared at the table and said nothing for several long seconds. "That's a big favor, Mol. Way too big."

Had she angered him? She hoped not. "She has a bet with Grady Dunlop that she can finish her bed and breakfast before he can remodel a similar property in six weeks."

"Well, in that case," he said and raised his gaze to hers. "You know full well that I detest Grady. That changes this whole scenario." Steepling his fingers, he rested his chin on them. "My team's ahead of schedule with the place we're working on right now. That would give us about two weeks to work on Alice's."

Molly's hopes for Randy for the full six weeks crumbled. Sadness ebbed that Alice would lose the bet with Grady and it would be her fault because of her big mouth.

"I have four on my crew that are always wanting more hours. We stop at the current job at five each day because they still have children at home. Maybe they could work on the B and B from six to ten. The downside? They'll expect overtime pay. I can work on it in the evenings, too, I guess. I do have two kids in college." He picked up his coffee and sipped. "That's about the best I can do right now."

Molly was so happy that they now had a fighting chance to beat Grady, she was about to jump out of her skin. "That's great,

Randy! And don't worry about the overtime pay, we can cover that. Thank you, thank you so much!" Getting up she wrapped her arms around his shoulders and kissed his cheek.

His hands slid over hers and gently held them to him. Molly realized he had feelings for her, more than just friendship. It was amazing she hadn't known it until now. And she definitely felt the same way about him. Her heart was about to beat right of her chest. *Sorry Paul, you know that I'm always going to love you,* she sent upward silently. A peace settled deep inside of her, understanding that Paul had somehow answered her just then. He didn't want her living the rest of her life alone. Randy was someone she could find happiness with, and love. She was certain of it.

Randy turned his head to gaze at her. Without any hesitation Molly pressed a light kiss on his mouth. Reaching one hand up, he brought her lips back to his for another. Someone close by cleared their throat. Molly rose to her full five-seven height, one hand still on Randy's shoulder. "Finish that later?" she murmured. Randy nodded.

"I should probably go see what condition that old B and B is in," Randy said, then downed the rest of his coffee.

"I'll follow you over." Molly dug out four dollars from her purse and left it on the table. She held out a hand to Randy, he grasped it, and they left Blue Moon holding hands. When they got outside, Molly stopped in the window alcove. Randy's face hovered over hers and he whispered, "Going to finish that conversation now, okay?"

Molly merely nodded, her heart clogging her throat. Their lips met, and time and reason flitted away. They finally parted when a driver traveling down Second Avenue honked their horn.

Resting his forehead against hers, Randy chuckled. "I've been wondering what this would be like."

"Nice," she answered breathlessly. "Should we go over to Alice's now?"

"Yeah. I'm going to call my brother, Royce, to meet us over there."

~ ~ ~ ~ ~

Alice tore a huge strip of wallpaper off in the entryway, no longer caring about the plaster breaking free. With Molly's partnership, this place was going to be restored to what it once was.

"Knock, knock," Molly called from the doorway.

"Come on in," Alice said, noting that Randy Johnstone was with her.

Molly took Randy's hand and led him around the old B and B, leaving Alice standing there. Yep, they're an item now. Alice was happy for Molly that she was finding happiness again. After Paul's death Molly had drawn into herself for the first several months. It had taken gentle guidance to lead Molly back to the land of the living.

The doorbell chiming brought Alice back to the present. Walking over, a tall six-foot-four man in jeans and a flannel shirt stood on the front porch. He looked familiar.

"Hey, Alice," he said. "Remember me? Royce the dork?"

Of course. Royce Johnstone, Randy's older brother. They'd graduated together. And if her memory served her correctly, she hadn't taunted him with that title. She'd sensed his loneliness and isolation so she didn't fall for the peer pressure to bully him.

"Yes, I do." She stuck the scraper in her back pocket. Opening the door, she stepped aside so he could come in. "What are you doing now?"

"I graduated from college and moved to Lincoln, got what I thought was my dream job. Crunching numbers with other people's money. I burned out and quit about a month ago. Randy asked me to become partners with him. And here I am." He ran one hand to push back his sun-streaked dark brown hair, so much like Randy's. With his hair, his grey eyes and thin nose, he looked more like Randy's twin than an older brother. The shyness that she remembered from high school was still apparent.

"I didn't make it back to go to your mom's funeral. I'm sorry that she passed. It's difficult to lose anyone to cancer."

"Yes, it is. Thank you."

"You're selling real estate now?"

"For almost two decades. College really wasn't for me so I got my real estate license instead."

Randy and Molly came into the entryway. They were still holding hands. Envy worked through Alice. *Not jealousy,* she reasoned, because she wanted Molly to be happy. She missed the time when she and Jason were at that stage where they still liked each other. Actually wanted to be close. To hold hands and steal kisses. Tears welled in her eyes and she hurriedly wiped them away. Would she ever stop loving Jason? He'd stopped loving her a long time ago.

"Hey, Royce, want to take the tour with me for this special time-crunch project?" Randy let go of Molly's hand and kissed her forehead. He walked into the parlor.

"Sure. It was nice seeing you again, Alice," he said before joining Randy.

Molly and Alice stood silently, staring at each other. "When did this happen?" Alice waited for Molly to answer.

"Today," Molly said softly. "He's such a good man. Paul gave me his okay."

Alice's brows rose.

"I'll explain later. Randy and Royce are such hunks. And Royce is divorced," Molly whispered as Randy and Royce returned to the entryway.

Alice couldn't argue with Molly's assessment of the Johnstone brothers. She'd definitely noticed that Royce had matured into a well-built middle-aged man, and the awkwardness from his youth was gone.

To be continued . . .

Bill Roberts • Omaha, NE

Snowfire

Chapter Eight: Leverage

After the new year the weather in the Midwest seemed to worsen: longer snows, harsher winds, temperatures that stayed below freezing. Sean Large almost regretted coming back to town during the winter. He stayed in the comfortable home of a retired couple who wintered in Arizona. The place was creamy stucco trimmed with thick dark timbers, and Mr. Large liked the way it conveyed wealth without worry as he explored opportunities. For example, the fact that Loren Wrightfield could write a check for two hundred thousand dollars meant there was more opportunity there than his lifestyle might suggest.

Today Mr. Large had invited over a rough-and-tumble fellow, name of Don Moy, who after a few decades of heavy drinking had sobered up, returned to his hobby of tinkering in the garage, and come up with something interesting. Mr. Large heard the car door outside and looked through his chilly window.

Moy shambled up the walkway like a coat rack on rusty wheels. He was tall, blond, big-shouldered and—Mr. Large had been told—socially awkward. Apparently Moy talked in a mumbled, jumbled rush of words, although the important ones were sometimes understandable. His host asked him to take his snowy boots off in the foyer, directed him to an overstuffed chair away from the knick-knacks, and got him a cup of hot cocoa and three cookies. He said he'd heard Moy had been working on a promising invention.

"Promising? Yeah, rarrha, rarrha, rarrha. Weapon. Rarrha, rarrha, rarrha. That right?"

Mr. Large nodded. Yes, he was interested in the weapon.

Moy nodded, scratched his wrist, glanced around. "Rarrha, rarrha, rarrha, rarrha this weather's bad?"

Once, Mr. Large had seen muddy water pumped out of a flooded basement, and Moy's speech reminded him of that. He frowned and waited for him to repeat himself.

"Rarrha, rarrha ask you this. Rarrha, rarrha think this weather's bad?"

"Do I think this weather is bad? I certainly do. It's one of the coldest and snowiest winters I ever have seen."

Moy nodded, looked around and licked his lips. Outside, frozen snow clung to the windows and the wind faintly whistled. "Rarrha, rarrha, rarrha very bad. Rarrha, rarrha, rarrha. Snowfire rarrha worse."

"Well. Tell me about Snowfire."

Moy smiled. "Snowfire rarrha invention. Rarrha, rarrha, rarrha totally new. Rarrha, rarrha cold, rarrha, rarrha flames, rarrha combined. Rarrha, rarrha bad-ass."

Mr. Large chuckled. "Yes, I think it's appropriate for a weapon to be bad-ass. But how does it work?"

"Rarrha, rarrha? Cold rarrha absence of heat. Rarrha, rarrha, rarrha Freon rarrha, rarrha refrigeration rarrha, rarrha air conditioners. Rarrha, rarrha, rarrha take away heat, and rarrha, rarrha left is cold."

"I know how refrigeration works. You say Snowfire is different?"

He nodded. "Rarrha, rarrha with Snowfire, cold is a presence, rarrha, rarrha, rarrha—not an absence."

"I don't follow."

"Snowfire cold is rarrha, rarrha, dynamic, aggressive. Rarrha, rarrha, rarrha. Point Snowfire at somebody, rarrha, rarrha, rarrha, leverage."

"I see the potential for leverage. But how did you manage all this?"

"Rarrha, rarrha, rarrha, fold over physics, convert the reversion, rarrha, rarrha, rarrha 'til it's right. Rarrha, rarrha, rarrha all the details."

"I understand. What's it look like?"

"Like a flamethrower, rarrha, rarrha, rarrha, cold."

Moy shambled over to his coat, which he had tossed on a sofa, and dug out a digital camera. Bending down so Mr. Large could see, he held the camera and clicked through several photos of the Snowfire invention. It looked like a combination of wheelchair, oversize blow dryer, espresso maker, and loom.

Mr. Large pointed. "So you stand back here and direct the flame of cold toward the target?"

"Rarrha, rarrha, rarrha."

"Impressive. Malevolent. Let me ask you this: Is it safe to use?"

Don Moy shrugged and did a sideways motion with his hand. "Rarrha, rarrha, rarrha, prototype."

Mr. Large supposed it would be hard to engineer a tight seal for a flame of cold. "With financing, maybe you can make a prototype that doesn't leak."

Moy shrugged again. "Rarrha, rarrha, rarrha, everything leaks."

Mr. Large liked this guy's thinking. "So at this stage it's probably best to let someone else actually use it?"

"Rarrha, rarrha," Moy agreed.

Mr. Large nodded. "Tell you what. I'd like to arrange a demonstration. If it all checks out, then we can move right toward using Snowfire to gain leverage in some projects I have in mind."

He gave Moy more cookies, started a pot of coffee, and got out his checkbook. Moy tried to avert his eyes from the checkbook and became fidgety. He asked if he could smoke a cigarette in the house and Mr. Large said, "Well, all right, this once."

Chapter Nine: Waterfall

There was a low-lying area on an ugly edge of town that had been set aside for warehouses and light manufacturing. Over the years it had become encircled by the town's suburbs as they spread to higher ground, and that low commercial swale had been taken over by retail establishments catering to the suburbanites. One such place was Cascading Countertops, a designer showroom where consumers could select the counter surface—imitation stone, cultured stone, or authentic stone—they'd like their contractors to use in their remodeled kitchens. Cascading Countertops had an actual waterfall, three stories high, in an indoor, glass-domed courtyard. Every day during store hours water was piped in, pumped up, and allowed to fall back down. Customers loved the waterfall. On a cold day, nearby suburbanites might look down on the swale from their living rooms and see the steamy glass dome. Any time of year a person could sit in the courtyard—in the mist and din of the waterfall, with daylight streaming through the dome making little rainbows—and discuss their countertop needs with a trained sales assistant. Maggie Forehead happened to be walking through that very courtyard at eleven o'clock one Thursday morning—she was consulting on the software for the waterfall pumps—when she looked across the cataract and noticed Loren Wrightfield standing next to his wife, Ruth, as she conversed with a salesperson.

Yikes.

Maggie clamped down on her gastrointestinal processes (this was no time for a wet accident) and found a place to stand behind some fake spray-coated ferns where Loren wouldn't see her. She hoped. Loren was holding a cup of coffee (provided free), and after a couple of minutes he placed it on a Parisian-style table and took a seat there. Another man also sat at the table. Ruth wandered off with the sales assistant, leaving Loren to gaze blankly in Maggie's general direction. He didn't seem to see her, but Maggie felt she'd better stay put until he gazed elsewhere. So while others browsed the countertop samples, Maggie stood motionless by the damp fern.

The other man at Loren's table was Sean Large. He wasn't "with" Loren, but he gave Loren the kind of friendly nod exchanged between men whose wives are spending thousands on countertops. After a decent pause, Sean spoke.

"Of course all of this"—Mr. Large waved his hand vaguely to indicate the surroundings—"can be protected by insurance or the like. If a countertop gets chipped, if the waterfall runs dry, well, you get it fixed or replaced. All it takes is money. But when you have genuine assets that cannot be replaced, assets that matter deeply—how do you protect them? That's beyond insuring. That's when you need to align with the underpinnings."

Mr. Large had said this as if musing, as if Loren were not there, or his presence were only coincidental. Loren responded: "Underpinnings?"

"That's right. Underpinnings. Come on. You know. The things that never get disturbed. The fix that's always in. Legal, illegal, meh. The assurance that what's important will stay safe. Be it things, people, relationships—any item of true importance. It's violence, if you go back far enough, holding the underpinnings in place. Come on. Everybody knows that. I'm not giving any news report here."

"So certain things, important things, won't be harmed?"

"Exactly. That's all I mean. My point is, you yourself won't have to make that fix, have that money, or do that violence. But you've got to be in sync with those who do. Got to be in sync with the underpinnings."

Mr. Large paused. Loren nodded, mulled it over, and said, "I take it you are in sync with those underpinnings?"

And so they conversed. Loren felt his body hairs bristle and skin chill as Sean got him thinking about the dangers of the world, which naturally led him to consider his newly discovered daughter, Jennifer Forehead. He hadn't even realized how excited he had become to get to know her better, like her more, have her over on a regular basis. And now he worried about her. Damn. Loren used to figure the best thing about having money was that he didn't have to worry about having money. But now that his life had Jenn, he'd discovered how close he was to becoming poor.

Now he'd stumbled over a man who seemed to understand this paradox. They continued talking.

"I congratulate you. Many men never acquire genuine assets," Mr. Large told him, sincerely, at one point, and withdrew a business card from a small metal case. "Now if you're a man who—and I think you are—a man who wants to protect his genuine assets in a world he knows to be dangerous and cold, well, you can reach me here." The card read "Sean Large / Asset Protection and Enhancement Services."

~ ~ ~ ~ ~

Maggie had been hiding behind the fern this whole time. It wasn't so bad. The waterfall entranced her with its beauty and anonymity. The recycled water, pumped up and falling, pumped up and falling, put her in mind of digitized data, flowing back and forth between servers. It was like a lot of human enterprises, come to think of it: the excited pumping up, the brief and beautiful fall, the diligent resumption. Sex was like that. So was a fancy restaurant meal. A vacation. A concert. Eventually Maggie noticed the other guy giving something to Loren, and she took advantage of the distraction to exit, slick as ice, through a small door marked Employee Smoking Area.

Holy crap it was cold! That waterfall had really moistened her! She shuddered, pulled her coat tight and hunched her shoulders.

Outside, the smokers had been granted a small space along the back wall of the building. There was a picnic table, half in a snowbank, and wood privacy fencing that seemed to channel the wind more than screen it. Smoking employees could stand there shivering and look out on an acre of frozen weeds, sloping up toward suburban houses. There was a Smokers' Outpost ashtray tower, about three feet tall, as well as a squat iron bucket that held sand (solid in winter) for cigarette butts. Nobody else was around, but Maggie smelled the residue of smoke.

Then the door opened and out stepped Eugene, the pump maintenance engineer she had met with earlier. He nodded, turned against the wind to light a cigarette, then turned back and took a deep pull. Recognizing her from company meetings, he smiled and spoke.

"Fancy meeting you here, Maggie."

"Hi, Eugene, good to see you again. Pretty cold out here."

"Damn cold. Need a cigarette?"

"Oh, no, no, thanks. I just—well, I came out because I wanted to see what the smoking area looked like."

He snorted. "Looks ugly. No business will ever make a nice place for us to indulge our dirty, nasty habit."

She laughed. "I guess it's not something companies typically invest in."

"Like the pumps for the waterfall. Buy the cheapest crap they can find, then hire a guy like me to keep it running. Plus consultants like you."

"When you put it that way, I guess we shouldn't complain."

"Wouldn't do either of us any good. Here, you want to go back in?" He put his hand on the door handle, offering her an escape to warmth.

"Um, no, actually, I'm going to walk around the front. Give me a sense of the place. Thanks though. Bye."

Maggie was thoroughly chilled by the time she walked through the frozen weeds, across the icy employee parking lot, and finally around to the front of the store. She got inside, stamped her feet back to warm and positioned herself where she could see the customer service counter. After a wait of about ten minutes, Loren and Ruth Wrightfield sauntered through the front doors, chatting and happy, carrying three bulky samples of countertop out of the store.

When they got in their car and drove away, Maggie let out heartfelt gusts of relief, one from each end.

Chapter Ten: Street Theatre

Late one winter morning at Indoor Pastures Coffeehouse, Paul Beene, ex-King of thespians, was in a particularly theatrical mood as he shared lattes with Sam Chrysler, ex-King of believers.

"It's preposterous, you know, that we have to give up our kingships. And just as we realize that we are Kings!" Paul stood, flinging his arms out as if crucified.

Sam, seated like a normal person, felt the eyes of the other patrons. He chuckled and squirmed. "But you have to admit—it's a lighter way to live."

"Lighter? How so? Explain, please."

Sam took a breath and launched into it. "Lighter in the sense of having set down a burden. Of having given up a set of expectations that weren't realistic. Of letting go of the false. And if it's difficult to distinguish the false from the real, well, you admit that difficulty and face it and do the best you can—nevertheless."

"I do love that 'nevertheless.' Always have. Always will."

Sam sighed, shook his head, sipped his cup. "It was tough being King of the believers, Paul. Trust me. Half the time I was trying to fool everybody; the other half I was like, aw, the hell with it—why do I need to impress these people? What's the point? After all, they're commoners!"

Even seated, Paul was still prominent, still the one guy in the coffeehouse everybody looked at. "Commoners. Yes, I am totally with you. That's when you realize: I'm not King anymore. I've lost that royalty, it's not coming back, and I've got to carry on"—here he gestured to Sam to say it with him—"nevertheless."

They laughed, back-slapped, and thanked goodness for the Neverthelessers. The other patrons of Indoor Pastures turned back to their own coffees. A few minutes later Paul tapped his wristwatch and said he had a deal to get to. He explained he was going to a rehearsal followed immediately by a performance of a piece of street theatre. He assured Sam that no, he was not "getting all kingly" about this thespian assignment—the gig was just too easy, too profitable. He'd be crazy to turn it down.

~ ~ ~ ~ ~

Several blocks away, in a staff office at the Upsy Daisy, one of Bisonton's biggest nonprofits, Brooke Nottingham was explaining details of accounting, filing, and recordkeeping to Jennifer Forehead. The usual Thursday bustle swirled around them: classes, intake interviews, counseling sessions, volunteers sorting through donated materials. Jenn licked her lips and tried to get into robot mode to absorb the information more efficiently. Brooke thought Jenn didn't take it seriously enough.

"I understand, derstand, derstand," Jenn said, robot-style. "I will file. I will make triplicate copies. Quadruplicate when the client is covered by a grant. Robot Jenn will copy and file and file some more."

"Yeah, well, make sure you do, because the way you lose those grants is not having records when they do a visit."

"What we need is a robot filer. A robot filer never makes a mistake."

Brooke tried to smile politely, but this wasn't her favorite style of humor.

"I mean it, Brooke. You should hire somebody who's, like, way organized, file-oriented, very good at recordkeeping and number crunching. And then let them take care of it! I want to be out there helping people, not in here filing forms."

"You do that, you end up spending too much on administration. It's something you've got to learn. Believe me, Jenn, nobody signs up at the Upsy Daisy to do filing. We're all here to help people! But filing and records are facts of life."

When she couldn't think of an argument, Jenn liked to repeat the other person's statements, robot style. "Facts of life. Facts of life. Facts of life." Again, Brooke tried to smile politely. Then she saw a wall clock and remembered.

"Oh, hey, Jenn. I've got a deal to get to. Supposed to do some street theatre with a guy I know. I'll be back in a couple of hours."

"Street theatre? Cool! Need some help? Can I come?"

Brooke, who'd never explained the street theatre aspect of the day she had met Jenn, shook her head. "No, it's all set up. It's me and a guy; we're experienced; we'll do it quick, collect a couple hundred bucks each, and be back well before the end of the day. Don't you worry your head about it." Off she went, and Jenn put her robot skills to the task of setting up for lunch at the Upsy Daisy.

~ ~ ~ ~ ~

Paul and Brooke drove separately to Cascading Countertops. Mr. Large met them inside by the waterfall, escorted them through the Employee Smoking door and locked it behind them. No one else was around. They saw a big contraption like a blow dryer (but as big as a wheelchair) positioned just behind the privacy fence. They figured it must be a snow machine for clearing the parking lot.

"Paul, you'll be sitting at the picnic table when Hugo, the fellow we want to help quit smoking, will come out and sit here next to you," Mr. Large said, guiding Paul to the picnic table. "He'll light his cigarette and sit next to you, smoking. Then you stand up, light your cigarette, take a big long drag and walk over this way. You can smoke, right?"

"Oh, sure. Now, this Hugo—what's his story? What kind of guy is he? What's his age? Fat, thin, short, tall?"

"Hugo always has fancied himself a cowboy," the organizer said. "But it's all for show. He's about forty, a little overweight, a lot out of shape. Still, cowboy is how he sees himself, and he's good natured about the ribbing he gets from folks about it. You play him up as a cowboy, he'll see himself in you. That's for sure."

"Cool. After rehearsal, I'm going to dash home and get a cowboy hat."

"Fine, fine, good idea. Now Brooke, you're stationed here with the snow machine, where Hugo can't see you. When Paul walks to the edge of the fence, you blast him, OK? He'll get a harmless coating of snow, his cigarette will go out, and then you step out and say, 'Hugo, you need to stop your smoking cold!' Paul, you look kind of dazed and say, 'You think?' Trust me, it'll make a big impression on him."

"Cute," Brooke said. "Heck, this is an intervention!"

"Exactly! An intervention! I think it'll be very effective. Hugo will come out for his smoke break in less than an hour, so right now let's do a rehearsal."

They took their places, Sean off at a little distance to observe. Paul stood up from the picnic bench, lit up, walked in a small circle with greatly bowed legs and a loud Western twang, then stepped past the fence. Brooke flipped the Snowfire switch.

With a deep *womp* the Snowfire machine produced a brief, bright white cloud that enveloped Paul and Brooke. In a quick moment there was a sound like glass breaking. When the cloud dissipated, both of them were frosty corpses that had fallen to the ground. Their skin was dark and cracked like burnt leather. Their clothing was frozen hard. Little chipped-off pieces of fingertip, nose, and ear lay nearby.

Mr. Large muttered, "Definitely best to let someone else use it." Then he drove his Navigator around to the smoking area. He and his old bent father, Harvey Large, who had been sitting in the Navvie reading a woodworking magazine, loaded the bodies of Brooke and Paul and the Snowfire machine in the back of the vehicle. After looking around to make sure they'd swept up and collected all the loose evidence, Mr. Large unlocked the Employee Smoking door and drove across the frozen weeds back to the parking lot. Harvey Large used Brooke's key to get in her Nissan and follow his son, who drove to the banks of a small deep creek outside Bisonton. Later they went back and did the same thing with Paul's Volkswagen, in which they left a note. The two cars would be found creekside, the two bodies would be pulled out frozen, and authorities would conclude it was a lovers' suicide pact.

Sean felt good about the whole deal. He'd eliminated the only witnesses to the street theatre that had brought Jennifer Forehead to the Upsy Daisy. Once the tragedy of Brooke's death was discovered, Loren Wrightfield would have good reason to fear for Jennifer's safety—good reason to align his assets in sync with the underpinnings.

Kathy Jewell Raabe • Gretna, NE

The Freeing of Katie Fitzgibbons

Chapter One: Katie Marries John

September 1970

Can a person change in their life? Does their personality change? Could it remain the same forever? I mean, if you're an introvert, which I am, you are always an introvert, right? I'm so shy, I can barely stand it if anyone speaks to me. I shake sometimes answering a question in school. Well, I need not worry anymore; I graduated four months ago. All done! The only one of my friends not going to college. Don't care; I'm getting married!

Little did I know, a short twelve years later, I'd be the black sheep in the family. I would unleash the wrath of my mother in ways I couldn't believe. Me. The quiet one. A rule follower. The compliant one.

~ ~ ~ ~ ~

Mom finished pinning the headpiece that held my mantilla veil and train. She fluffed it and stepped back.

"Now make sure you carry this over your arm. I don't want to see you dragging it on the concrete sidewalk."

I rolled my eyes, thinking, I'm not stupid.

Mom turned and pursed her lips. "What next?" she said to herself.

She directed my bridesmaids to the little room at the school.

"Girls, you need to set the pace for the processional. The boys will try to walk too fast. You need to slow them down."

"Yes, Mrs. Fitzgibbons."

"And I don't want any of you drinking at the reception. You are all underage, and we don't want any problems."

"Yes, Mrs. Fitzgibbons. We know."

"You all look so nice. Let's have a fun day."

Mom turned. "Katie, make sure you and John take your marriage license with you on your honeymoon. You are so young, they may not want to rent you two a room. You need that proof that you're married, not just out fooling around."

I turned red. "Yes, Mom. Whatever you say, Mom."

~ ~ ~ ~ ~

My dad held out his arm and smiled at me. I returned his smile. I threw the many yards of tulle over my arm and took his arm. We began our walk.

"Katie. You're sure about this?"

"Yes, Dad. I am."

"Well then, let's go."

We leave the school building and walk half of a block to the church. It is a beautiful day. My wedding day. I will miss Dad. And Edward. And Mikey.

My older brothers, Patrick and Edward, finished their ushering duties. Edward flirted with all the ladies. Patrick did, but not much. He's married. Edward blew me a kiss, then winked at me.

"Knock 'em dead, Katie." He has such a pleasant smile. He always encourages me.

Dad and I walked down the aisle. People stood, turned to see us. My tulle-mantilla veil caught on the carpeting. Dad stopped a second and let Aunt Carolyn straighten me up. I'm dying. John, at the end of the aisle, catches my eye. He was with the parish priest, the groomsmen. My cousins were serving Mass. My heart fluttered. I love him so very much. I cannot wait to start our life together.

Dad squeezed my hand. We stopped at the foot of the steps leading to the sanctuary. Dad kissed me on the cheek and shook John's hand. John took my hand in his. The priest talked. Mary Clare swayed.

She came from Colorado to be my maid of honor, and her entire family came. They stayed with family, and she stayed with me. She told me she's pregnant; she had morning sickness. Her parents did not know. My mom guessed. It shocked me when Mom asked about her. How could she tell?

Mary Clare regained her composure. We get to sit. Catholics sit and stand frequently during a service. We completed the service; we are legal. Can't drink. We are man and wife. The vows and Mass concluded. The priest introduced us, "Mr. and Mrs. John Sutter." I smiled so hard, my face hurt. All I ever wanted, now. How lucky I am. I had no way of knowing how my luck would change.

~ ~ ~ ~ ~

I stood with John and our parents in a receiving line, thanking everyone for coming to our wedding. Many gave regrets for not attending the afternoon reception. It was weird seeing people who were friends of our parents. Many we invited, and all wished us well. John defied my mother. He wore his cowboy boots with his tux. She is mad. Everything riles her up, so it should not have been surprising. I loved John for speaking his mind. I wish I could. How does a person learn that?

All the attendants drove in a procession of cool cars with crepe paper decorations, white shoe polish graffiti sayings as "Hot

Springs Tonight!!" Mom made John park his car in Dad's locked garage to prevent anyone from tampering with it. We entered the reception, all sat in our appointed seats. My aunts made the food with Mom, it was delicious. A dance added to the expenses, so Mom nixed that idea. She made it clear she would not spend a fortune; it was her way or it wouldn't happen.

The wedding party ate, and we greeted people more. My brother Edward, with a groomsman, Dennis, approached me. Edward leaned down. He whispered in my ear, "We are stealing the bride. Come with us, my sweet sister." I shot a glance at John. He was laughing. I dawdled, hoping John would come get me. I did not want to ride around anymore today. John waved us away. He was no help.

We stopped at a few bars Edward frequented. Edward and Dennis drank shots. Some people gave me a ten dollar bill or a twenty if they were feeling generous.

I wasn't old enough to drink. I wanted to die.

I always followed the rules, so I had ice water.

I wanted to die.

Edward had a brand new 1970 Chevelle SS 454 L6S, and he made it look good. He drove it as one should drive it—fast. He told me I deserved a ride in this car, since it was the envy of everyone. The Mediterranean Sea paint job complemented his sky-blue eyes and strawberry blonde hair. An Irishman overcome by some German genes. He was a handsome man and talented electrician. All the girls wanted him. All the boys wanted to be him. I loved him for being unconventional, spontaneous, and fun. And my best older brother.

We walked into the reception hall. Mom was furious.

"What in the hell is wrong with you, leaving like that?" She wasn't addressing Edward or Dennis. She was yelling at me. In front of the guests that remained. My face burned.

"Mom, I didn't know what they were doing." Tears filled my eyes. I turned to talk to my little brother, Mikey. Mikey hugged me. I held on to that little boy. I missed him already.

My John came up to me. "Why were you gone so long?"

"I thought you would stop them."

John said, "Well, from now on, you're mine. No one else's."

I had a tightness in my chest. "Sure. Wouldn't want it any other way."

John turned my head towards him and forced a kiss on me. "Good."

Embarrassed, I pulled away. I perspired heavily. I turned away and walked over to my dad.

"Are you ok?"

"Yes, I'm getting tired. Didn't sleep too well last night."

"I'm sorry. You will always be my girl. Remember that."

"Oh, Dad, I remember." I put my arms around him and hugged. He can hug me and make the broken pieces as if they fit together again. "Oh, how I remember. Thank you."

I turned and saw Mom talking to my John. "Oh, no. What is she doing now?"

"Yeah, Evelyn, I'm a grown man and I can wear what I want." The cowboy boots.

Mom was so strict on things she considers appropriate. Cowboy boots at a wedding. A no-no. It doesn't even matter anyway, it's over.

"You're not too big to get a spanking!" Mom threw over her shoulder as she walked away from John. He laughed at her. Everyone laughed. But they don't know she meant what she said. She tells me that all the time. Crazy.

~ ~ ~ ~ ~

Mom's sister, Carolyn, approached me and gave me a hug.

"Aunt Carolyn, I've missed you so much."

"We all know how your mom carries grudges. All I did was get a divorce. And marry someone she didn't approve of." She laughed.

"I just did about the same thing!"

We laugh more. Mom carried grudges a long way.

"You look beautiful, Katie. Always remember, your mom has always been how she is. Make your own home now. You're very capable. Life will be better."

"Thank you, I'll remember. Have you talked to Mom yet?"

"I haven't had enough Southern Comfort yet! Today is about you and your man. He's a doll. He acted like I caught him off guard when I hugged him."

"They're not huggers, Aunt Carolyn."

"Well, that's what he's getting from me. Where did he go? I will hug him until he looks forward to it."

She hugged me then walked towards John, across the room.

Edward and Patrick were sitting together, smoking and drinking beer. John joined them with a glass of ice water.

"Too bad Mom is acting as if none of us drink, right?" Edward shifted in his chair.

"I know," said Patrick. "She puts on a good front. I've seen her out with Aunt Mae when Dad's at work."

"What?" The statement flabbergasted John. "Wow, do you think your dad knows?"

"No," said Patrick. "And I won't be the son who tells him."

He approaches me.

"So when's the baby due?" Patrick asked.

"What are you talking about?"

"Well, you're pregnant, aren't you?"

"Absolutely NOT, Patrick." I stomped my foot. "Why would you think I'm pregnant?"

"Sometimes I get home after you do. You were always out too late to be behaving yourself. I'd see John's car on my way home from the bar."

"No, I'm not pregnant. There is one pregnant girl here, and it's not ME. It's Mary Clare, but her parents don't know yet, so don't tell them."

Patrick held out his hands, palms up, grinning like a Cheshire Cat. "What?"

"You're an asshole."

~ ~ ~ ~ ~

Edward stood talking to some of my girlfriends from high school. I joined the group as the girls all laughed with him. He had a way with the ladies. Edward takes the cigar from his mouth and sipped his beer. "Katie, you didn't tell me you had such beautiful friends."

"Only believe about half of what Edward says, girls. I don't want to lose all my friends."

Edward sipped his beer. "Katie, you know I'm your favorite brother. Why do you say that?" The girls giggled more. He puffed on his cigar.

"Edward, it's because you're my favorite. I don't want to share you with anyone."

"Sweet Katie, you're about as full of the devil as I am." The girls laughed out loud. Everyone turned and saw Edward bend me backwards a bit and give me a kiss. He stood me back up and whispered, "Katie, if you ever need anything, ask. Whatever you need, Princess, it's yours."

"Thank you, Edward. You are a dear, sweet man."

Mary Jo and Janet are swooning.

Immediately, my John was at my elbow. "What was he doing with you?"

"Edward? John, he's my brother. He's being silly."

"Well, he needs to keep his hands off of you."

"What? How much have you had to drink?"

"Not nearly enough. Your mom keeps meeting me at the keg, telling me I'm not old enough."

"Oh, I'm sorry. She won't let me have any either. That's why we had water in our glasses for our toast. Lame, isn't it? I don't like beer anyway, it's ok."

~ ~ ~ ~ ~

The rest of the guests were leaving. Mom made me stand by her and thank everyone as they left.

"Mom, they only steal the bride once per reception."

"I don't care. You know, there are brides killed in car crashes on their wedding days; do you want that to happen?"

"No, Mom." I roll my eyes. She gives me the look. The one that makes chills run up and down my spine. I blush.

John comes over and asks when we can leave the reception.

Mom said, "Now. Go change your clothes at my house, and you can leave for your honeymoon."

"We'll go to Mass first, and that fulfills tomorrow's obligation. We'll drive to Lincoln and stay the night." John is always thinking.

~ ~ ~ ~ ~

We took our two small suitcases to the old Rambler station wagon. It was really a heap. It cost less than John's motorcycle did. I loved riding the bike with him, but it wasn't a choice for the honeymoon.

We had a nice steak dinner. We checked in at the motel with no problem.

We stopped at the threshold.

He scooped me up in his arms and entered the room.

He set me on the bed.

"Well, here we are."

"Yes, here we are, Mr. Sutter." I tried to be sexy and desirable.

He stood up. And walked to the TV. Turned it on. "Oh well, we can still watch Carol Burnett tonight."

"Are you serious?"

"Sure. We can have sex anytime, now that we're married."

"Oh." I could not believe what I was hearing. One of the reasons we got married was we were having sex. We thought it made it less wrong. And now he doesn't want to? TV trumps me on our wedding night? Wow. I am foolish for even hoping I would have sex with my husband on my wedding night. Oh well. There's always tomorrow. No, not really. Would this become normal for us?

I retreated to the bathroom, put on my pink and white peignoir, and cried as I washed my face and brushed my teeth.

This can't be happening. Is this what my life will be?

Johnnye Gerhardt • Omaha, NE

Sunsets with Walter

In his no-longer-white tee-shirt and bib overalls held up by one strap attached with a roofing nail, Clovis Hartman shuffled from the barn to the house across the packed-dirt farmyard. The ringing phone called him away from nothing in particular. His graying German shepherd, Adolf, strolled beside him. Holding the front door for the dog as they entered the dilapidated, Sears Catalogue, Victorian-style farmhouse, neither seemed enthused about finding out who was calling. Clovis yanked the phone out of its cradle on the wall just in time.

"Hullo."

"It's me. Denise." He recognized the young woman's voice but couldn't help taking a dig. It had been six years, after all.

"Denise who?"

Clovis waited for a sharp-tongued response. He didn't know how to talk to his daughter anymore.

"I'm coming home." The declaration of her arrival came in an exhale. He could tell she had been holding her breath before she spoke. There was probably a glass of wine involved as well.

"Why?" He prepared himself for a rant about Denise's mother, Addy, and her death. Denise held her breath again, then words came in an unexpected torrent.

"I'm engaged. His family wants to see the farm. They've never been to a farm." Denise rattled it off without stopping. "They're from the East. Old money. They want to meet my family." Denise took a breath. "What's left of it. In two weeks. I want everything to be perfect. You understand?"

"I don't think I do."

"I want it to look like it did when Mom was alive, especially her garden. You have been keeping that up?"

Clovis checked with Adolf, who sat at his feet and lifted each eyebrow in turn. "What," Clovis said in response to the dog's expression.

Denise spit, "I said I want—"

"I wasn't talkin' to you."

"Who's there?"

"Adolf."

"Can Walter take him until they leave?"

"Take who?"

"Your dog."

"Why would Walter want to take Adolf?"

Clovis listened to Denise breathe. He knew by the deep slow breaths she was on the verge of yelling at him. He held the phone away from his ear and waited. But the yelling never came. Instead, her voice softened like when she was a little girl and wanted him to take her into town. He missed that.

"Could you at least change his name?"

"What for?"

"They're Jewish."

"Adolf was my father's name. Want me to change his name too?"

Denise slammed something shut or down. Clovis cringed. She exhaled like a disarmed soldier. He pictured her phone in a death grip.

"I need your help."

"Say again."

"Clovis . . . Dad, please. I want this more than anything."

Clovis eyed the back of his dead wife's picture. The framed photo sat on the windowsill above the sink and looked out. He put it there so he could see her at the window just like he used to when he came in from the barn.

The picture was of a young woman in a housedress and apron standing in the middle of a flower garden that used to be the front yard. He turned it around and wondered if Denise would think putting it in the window was okay, then decided he didn't care.

"Let me think on it. Call tomorrow afternoon before Walter gets here."

The frosty edge around every word that was this Denise returned. Her words hissed in his ear. "You owe me."

The phone went dead. Clovis Hartman unemotionally set it in its cradle.

Clovis looked at Adolf who sprawled in a square of sunshine on the floor. "First time she calls in six years and she wants somethin'. Ain't that just like a woman?"

He glanced at his wife's photo. "Not you, Addy. You never asked for nothin'."

Crouching next to Adolf, he stroked the dog's side. "You and Walter get me all right and that's good enough. We're gettin' old and don't give a puppy's turd about nothin' anymore."

~ ~ ~ ~ ~

Dishes, utensils, pots, and pans filled one side of the chipped and stained kitchen sink. An Amana refrigerator, once white, had yellowed with age. The 1950s kitchen dining set still looked pretty good except for the faded color and grunge packed in the gaps between chrome and Formica. Clovis couldn't remember exactly what color the floor used to be. Mud, grease, and everything else Adolf and he either spilled or brought in had turned the linoleum a dull gray.

He tried to keep things the same at first. During the year after his wife died, her voice told him what to do. "Wipe your feet. Wash your hands. Take the tools out of your pocket before you sit down." But like the colors, her voice faded. He made sure, though, that her image stayed crisp.

He used to lay her picture on the pillow next to him, but it fell off one night. The glass broke so he took it into town when he went to get his monthly haircut. Rumor had it that he intentionally broke it because she left her savings to Denise. That was the way of small towns. When the church ladies got tired of television soap operas, they created their own.

~ ~ ~ ~ ~

Later that afternoon with chores done and only the important bits of Denise's call lingering, Clovis filled a pot with water and placed it in front of Adolf who lapped enthusiastically, splashing as much as he drank. The sun's rays having abandoned the kitchen stretched through the trees and onto the living room floor. Sniffing a carton of milk before he took a sip, then poured it into the cleanest glass in the sink. At the kitchen table a TV dinner with what was supposed to be Swiss steak but resembled a patty of undetermined origin the same color as the floor lay before him. Tiny portions of peas and potatoes that didn't look anything like the picture on the box reminded him he'd lost the best cook in the county. Addy's picture sat at her usual place across the table. As he lowered his backside onto the chair, a screwdriver protruding from a hole in his back pocket ripped through the vinyl.

Clovis jumped off the seat, knocking over the chair. Adolf darted for cover. "Jesus!" He glanced at Addy's picture. "Mary and Joseph, pray for us sinners now and at the hour of our death." Clovis picked up the photograph. "Sorry, Addy." Adolf came out of hiding and sat at Clovis's feet as he righted the damaged chair.

If a stout, old German farmer could look defeated, Clovis knew he did. He took the screwdriver out of his pocket and threw it in the sink. Adolf started at the clatter and trotted as fast as his old legs would allow into the living room. Clovis set the picture on the table facing away from him and his guilt. He righted the chair. Staring at the tear, he covered his mouth and wept.

"I'm sorry. I'm sorry. I'm sorry."

Drained, he pulled a hanky out of his other back pocket, blew his nose, and wiped his eyes. He moved to another chair and, mixing the peas with the mashed potatoes then smearing them onto the patty, he finished his meal. Adolf returned and lay close to the table in case something dropped. Clovis always made sure something did.

Most of the food eaten and the tray set on the floor for Adolf to clean, Clovis eyed the rip. He gave the back of Addy's picture a glance. "Better do something about that before the city folk get here. As a matter of fact, we better fix it afore Walter gets here and tells me how to do it." Adolf ignored him.

~ ~ ~ ~ ~

With Super Glue in hand, Clovis ran a good-sized bead of the adhesive down the middle of the tear. Tossing the glue onto the table, he placed his hands on either side of the rip and pressed the vinyl together. And waited. Adolf lay a short distance away on a tattered, braided rug. Satisfied the glue had taken hold, Clovis pulled his hands away. The chair came with them.

Twisting his hands this way and that, he struggled to free them. The tear lengthened. Adolf sat up and ogled him.

"What're you looking at?"

The dog tilted his head to one side as if to say, "I'm not sure."

"Go on. Git." Clovis shook the chair at him. Adolf nonchalantly turned away and stared at nothing in the hallway to the bedrooms.

The phone rang. Clovis moved to answer it then realized he couldn't. It rang again. He glared at it then turned an icy gaze on the dog.

"Probably the Widow Barnes wantin' to feed me, cure me, or put me in the arms of Jesus." Clovis kept his eye on the Shepherd. "Why don't you help me out and take a chunk outta that rodent-on-a-leash she calls a dog?"

Adolf stretched then went over to the pot and drank. The phone's ringing and Adolf's lapping reminded the farmer he needed, really needed, to go to the bathroom.

"Hope that wasn't Walter callin' to tell me he died or somethin'."

He headed for the bathroom. Dribbling water along the way, Adolf followed close behind. As he walked, Clovis raised the chair above his head and used one of the legs to pry his over-all's strap free of the nail. At his frantic struggling, the nail shot through the archway separating the kitchen and living room, ricocheted off a wall, and punctured a lampshade. Released, the overalls made their way down around his ankles. Clovis tried shaking them off but the leg openings weren't large enough to slide off his work boots. The phone ceased its nagging but the look Adolf gave him made up for it.

In the bathroom, his underwear presented another problem. He looked at his fly. Deciding there wasn't any way to work that he used the same technique on his skivvies he used on the strap. With exaggerated contortions, Clovis managed to get his underwear down around his knees. He pressed the chair against the wall above the tank and leaned over the toilet, thankful that Addy's voice no longer reminded him to put the lid down.

Relieved, Clovis lowered a chair leg onto the toilet handle and flushed. Shuffling sideways, he headed for the sink to wash his hands. One of Addy's instructions still resonated in his head on occasion. Clovis stared at his reflection and gestured with the chair.

"Didn't use 'em anyhow."

Standing sideways and using his teeth to grab the medicine cabinet handle, he opened it. Addy's nail polish remover stood tucked behind her sleeping pills. Backing up, he used a chair leg to knock the pill bottle out of the way. It rolled out of the bathroom and into the hall. But Clovis didn't know what to do about the remover. He stared at it for some time before deciding to give it up and wait for Walter.

Taking strides as long as his overalls and underwear would allow, he made it back into the kitchen. Adolf trotted ahead of him, kicking the TV dinner into his path. Clovis stepped onto the frozen dinner tray, which slid on Adolf's dribble. He fell flat on his back by the front door. The chair came to rest straddling his hips. He lay stunned for several seconds. Pressing on the seat, he attempted to raise himself into a sitting position, but the chair scooted toward his ankles. Pulling it closer, he squeezed it with his forearms and pressed on the seat. This time he was successful. Adolf escaped through the kitchen side door's torn screen, turned, and gave Clovis a look that he read as embarrassment.

"Keep movin'." Adolf's tags jingled as he trotted down the steps and around the house to the front porch.

Hours passed while Clovis tried to maneuver from under the chair. At the screen door leading to the porch, Adolf peered at him off and on, but all Clovis saw was Adolf's ears and eyes. The bottom half of that door was paneled and Adolf did not seem inclined to jump up for a better view. Clovis accused him of desertion. Exhausted, he lay his head between his hands on the seat and waited.

The sound of Walter Perdy's shiny new Magma Red Ford pickup pulling into the farmyard and scattering chickens brought Clovis around. Lying outside in front of the door, Adolf barked. With the sun near setting, Clovis knew Walter would wonder why he wasn't sitting on the porch with the usual pitcher of iced tea. Torn between yelling for help and letting Walter discover him, he remained silent and watched Walter scan the yard.

"Clovis!"

Slamming his forehead against the seat in frustration, Clovis knew what had to be done.

"In here."

Looking more like a country gentleman than a farmer, Walter approached. He paused to scratch Adolf behind the ears.

"What are you doing in there? The sun isn't going to wait, you know."

Walter peered inside. Clovis mustered as much masculine poise as he could.

"You tell anybody 'bout this, you won't live to see another sunset."

Walter remained by the door as he studied the situation. "Hell, I might never speak again."

"That would be a treat." Clovis eyed him as he opened the door.

Walter entered carefully, stepping over Clovis's legs. Adolf wiggled past him. Walter took his collar and ushered him outside.

"I don't think you should witness this."

Clovis let out a deep sigh. "Don't."

"Don't what?"

"Say what you're thinking."

"You mean I can't ask how this—"

"No."

Walter ogled the torn seat. "First, let's get rid of this chair."

Walter grabbed the chair by the seat and lifted. Clovis's hands held fast. He yanked the chair out of Walter's grip.

"They're stuck."

"What do you mean stuck?"

"Stuck!" Clovis lifted his hands. The rip extended all the way now from back to front. "For a college grad-u-ate, you sure are slow."

Perdy gave one of Clovis's hands a tug. "How in the world?"

Hartman gave him a look that said no explanation would be forthcoming. "Addy's nail polish remover is in the medicine cabinet."

The corner of Walter's mouth curled up ever so slightly. "Too bad she isn't here to see this. I think she'd realize the mistake she made in turning me down and marrying you."

Walter headed toward the hall. He stopped. Clovis twisted his neck trying to see why. "I ain't got all night." He noticed Walter reading the pill bottle label.

"It fell. Musta rolled out the bathroom."

Walter didn't seem convinced. "This isn't worth killing yourself. It's only a chair for Christ's sake. It can be fixed." Walter indicated Clovis's situation. "And I'm not telling a soul."

Clovis rested his head on the seat. "Get the nail polish remover." Walter headed into the bathroom.

Adolf whined and scratched at the door, then he, too, left. By the time Walter returned with the remover, Adolf had made his way through the side door. He sat at a distance and gazed at his owner who figured the dog would never obey him again.

Minutes later, Walter had Clovis's hands free. He picked up the chair and moved it aside. Walter glanced at the rip. "Maybe it's a good thing Addy's gone. She would have killed you." With that, he emptied the pills into the kitchen sink.

From under his shaggy brow, Clovis glared at Walter. "Shut up and make yourself useful."

Walter looked around as if not knowing what to do. After being in the same position on a hard linoleum floor for so long, Clovis found it difficult to move. "Give me a hand up, will ya?"

From behind, Walter wrapped his arms around Clovis's chest and lifted. Hartman grabbed onto the table and managed to get onto his knees. Perdy rested a minute then grabbed Clovis from behind again, raising him slightly off the floor. A squeak just outside the door caught their attention.

Miss Hattie Pearl Barnes stood with a gloved hand pressed against her chest and the other holding a plate of cookies and her dog's leash. In a high-pitched little voice that suited her pill box hat and prim ensemble, she finally managed, "Oh my."

Walter dropped Clovis. "Miss Barnes."

At the sound of her name, the woman turned and scurried toward her car, nearly dragging her Chihuahua, Itsy. Walter chased after her. Adolf trotted after Itsy with little enthusiasm.

"Clovis had an accident!"

Holding his bib overalls up with one hand, Clovis caught up to Walter and punched him in the arm. "Don't tell her that. She'll think I messed my pants."

Tossing Itsy onto the backseat and the cookies on the front, Miss Barnes climbed into her older model, but like-new, sedan and, probably for the first time in her life, spun out. Adolf turned away from the dirt and gravel that curtained her escape. Somewhat impressed by the woman's departure, Clovis stared after her a bit, then shuffled back toward the house.

"If I'd known bein' half naked would of scared her away, I'd of taken my clothes off a long time ago."

Walter ran a hand down his face as though wiping something off. "I don't think it was your state of undress."

"No matter. Wish she'd left the cookies."

"It matters. It will be all over town by the time the sun sets."

Clovis picked up a nail lying in the yard. He skewered it through a shoulder strap and virgin spot of fabric.

"What's there to talk about?"

"What do you think?"

"Ain't nobody gonna think nothin' of it, Walter. Remember when we got caught swimmin' naked in the fountain?"

Walter stepped in front of Clovis. "We were ten years old."

Clovis swept Walter out of his way, and they walked back toward the house in silence. Walter took his place in one of three rockers on the porch. In passing, he touched the armrest of the smallest, setting it in motion. Clovis gazed at it for a moment then went inside.

He refilled Adolf's pot of water and grabbed a pitcher of iced tea from the refrigerator. Pinching the rims of two glasses together, he carried them and the pitcher outside. Addy's picture nested under an arm. He set the tea and glasses on a handmade and somewhat wobbly table situated between the two larger rockers. Addy's picture occupied the small rocker which continued its motion for some time. Clovis filled the glasses. The two men settled into their seats and sipped the iced tea. Clovis started the conversation. "Crops lookin' good this year."

The sun dipped below a broken band of clouds. Its rays spotlighted portions of an immaculate cornfield and the soybean field next to it.

Walter waited the appropriate amount of time before speaking. "That's good Loess soil. Thanks for leasing it to me."

"Hell, I wasn't going to do nothin' with it."

"About Miss Barnes and the townspeople. I've never brought this up because I knew you wouldn't want to hear it, but there's been talk about us for a long time."

Clovis stopped rocking and set his tea down.

"They talk about ever'body, Walter. You know that."

"Not like this, they don't. I heard that some of the church ladies find our relationship unusual."

"The ladies are mighty peculiar themselves. You ever ask yourself why they get all gussied up to go to church. Hell, God don't miss nothin'. He sees them naked ever'day in the bath." Clovis shivered. "Let's talk about somethin' else. I don't want that picture in my head when I close my eyes tonight."

"Okay, let's discuss Miss Barnes and town gossip. Think about it, Clovis. I've never married."

"That's 'cause I stole the only decent girl right out from under you."

"She was never under me. We kissed once but that was all." Walter avoided Clovis's glare.

"You're one nasty-minded son of a bitch, you know that, Walter? You need a woman and I just happen to know one what's available." Clovis eyed the skid marks left by Miss Barnes' car.

Walter grinned, then stared at the road that ran by the Hartman farm. His face showed no signs of humor when he looked at Clovis again.

"The town thinks my coming out here every night is abnormal." Walter made air quotation marks at "abnormal."

Clovis rocked a little faster. "Ever since you come back from college, you ain't been normal, so it ain't no surprise to nobody."

"Be serious. We have to do some damage control."

"Speakin' a which, Denise called."

Walter and his rocker froze. He stared at Clovis as though the man had announced there would be no sunset that evening. "What did she want?"

"She's gettin' married and wants the in-laws to see the place."

Walter looked around. "She thinks it still looks like it did when Addy was alive."

"I don't know what she thinks no more. 'Sides, she don't trust me since the accident."

No more conversation forthcoming, the men sat in silence and watched the sun disappear behind the distant hills. Clovis occasionally looked askance at Walter, knowing he was keeping his opinion on the Denise situation to himself. Adolf lay beside Walter's rocker. Clovis wondered if he'd ever get over seeing him naked and glued to a chair. At least he wouldn't be telling anybody about it.

~ ~ ~ ~ ~

Chartreuse, Nebraska, sat like a cowpat in the middle of a grassy patchwork quilt. All its buildings sported brown or tan bricks, not a red one among them. And what wasn't brick was weather-beaten wood. A person could walk from one end of the business district to the other in five minutes and pass the two taverns, one grocery store, a diner, barbershop, beauty salon, and a single-screen movie house. Once Clovis found out from Addy what "chartreuse" was, he couldn't make the connection between the town and its name. For a very brief time it was the topic of conversation at the barbershop, his favorite hangout. No women ever ventured across its threshold. Miss Barnes, however, made a point of walking in front of the picture window several times when Clovis came to get a haircut. But not on this day.

On this day, Marcus Stewart, the barber, had just fastened the protective drape around Clovis's neck when Miss Barnes made her appearance. Bean McAllister, owner of the only tavern, and Charlie Morris, grocery owner, both barbershop regulars and occasional customers, looked out the window. Their eyes followed Miss Barnes as she stepped in front of the window, caught sight of Clovis, and scurried into the street. Charlie stepped outside. When he came back in, he reported that the widow had come back onto the sidewalk several doors down.

"What you do to her, Clovis? She looked like she'd seen a zombie or somethin'."

Charlie sat in one of the chairs lining the barbershop wall. Bean grinned too broadly. He squinted at Clovis. "You ever going to make an honest woman of her?"

Charlie elbowed Bean. "I do believe she's the only virgin in town." The men laughed until Clovis's glare iced the situation.

"I don't want nothin' to do with her."

Bean and Charlie exchanged glances. "Why not?"

"She don't like my dog."

The two men nodded. Bean removed his seed corn hat and scratched his head. Charlie raised his eyebrows at Clovis like a doctor announcing his diagnosis.

"Any woman that don't like your dog is going to be hard to live with."

Bean stretched his legs. "Eeyup."

Clovis caught Marcus eyeing Bean and Charlie who lowered their gaze to the floor. Marcus cleared his throat.

"There's a story going around about you. Is it true?"

As Marcus retrieved scissors and a comb, Clovis leaned back in the chair. "Depends on the story."

Marcus clipped the few hairs still left on top of Clovis's head. He used an electric razor on the thinning hair circling his scalp. "It's about you and Walter . . . together."

"What about me and Walter? Together."

Clovis caught Marcus in the mirror looking very uncomfortable. An alien silence fell. Charlie finally cleared his throat and said, "Well, hell, we just wanted you to know that we don't care. You ain't never bothered us. What goes on in a man's home is nobody's business, I say."

Bean nodded once. "Eeyup."

In the unspoken language of men in a barbershop, that was the end of it. With the exception of Bean, the men went on to discuss crop prices, rainfall, and a new vaccine for cattle. Bean chimed in with a single syllable response now and then. A ruckus across the street scattered their comfortably familiar conversation. His hair neatly trimmed, Clovis joined Marcus, Bean, and Charlie at the window.

Walter Perdy had Miss Hattie Pearl Barnes cornered in the recessed entrance of Charlie McCallister's Grocery. From inside the barbershop, the only audible sound was Miss Barnes's high-pitched squeal in her attempt to form words between sobs. Walter had his back to the street. He stood perfectly still with one foot on the stoop to the door. The woman couldn't escape.

Clovis just knew it wasn't going to end well. The barber's drape flapping at his sides, he burst out the door and walked with purpose across the street. Charlie followed close behind since it was his store and he'd just replaced the glass in the display window after Miss Barnes hit the accelerator instead of the brake on her car. She was all flustered over something she had witnessed. It took hours for her to share it with the Lutheran Women's Auxiliary.

As Clovis approached Walter, Miss Barnes caught sight of him and pressed both hands against her chest. She looked as though she would faint at the slightest provocation. Walter was in the middle of pleading with her to be reasonable when Clovis arrived.

"Miss Barnes, I don't know what you think you saw." Walter looked around. "Clovis got himself into a predicament and that was the only way to help him out. If you'll just give me a minute, I can explain everything."

Her hands went to her throat. "I know what I saw."

The two taverns and diner spewed people who gathered on the sidewalk and into the street. Children were ushered back inside or into trucks and told to roll up the windows. Clovis extended a hand to Miss Barnes. She pressed further back, made the sign of the cross, and folded her hands against her chest. With eyes closed, she prayed. Several of the onlookers made the sign of the cross and clasped their hands in prayer. Clovis took note that all of them were members of the Lutheran Women's Auxiliary. He and Walter weren't going to win this one. He grabbed Walter's arm and urged him away.

"C'mon, Walter, I'll buy you a beer."

Walter jerked free. "We have to straighten this out."

The Johnson twins snickered. A few other wrong-side-of-the-tracks citizens of Chartreuse covered their mouths, but the creases at the corners of their eyes told Clovis they, too, thought it was funny. He saw something else in the crowd. Something that he knew could turn very unpleasant.

Clovis grabbed the collar of Walter's stiffly pressed shirt and yanked. He glared at the people as he pushed through them. Behind them Charlie told the crowd to move along. "If you ain't going to buy nothin', then stop blocking the door for those what are."

Bean offered sanctuary at his tavern. On his way back to his barbershop, Marcus shouted after the three men. "I'd join you, but I can't close up. Not on a Saturday."

A member of the Lutheran Women's Auxiliary walking alongside said, "My God in Heaven. They're a gang."

Another member corrected her. "Homosexuals don't have gangs, dear."

"They wear leather, don't they?"

The other woman took her off in a different direction.

Walter stopped in the middle of the street. He faced Clovis. "See what I mean? We can't let this go. It will get worse."

A couple of teenage boys passed them. "Which one's the girlfriend?"

Walter cocked his fist and stepped toward them. Clovis pushed him toward Bean's tavern. The boys' voices cracked when they laughed. Bean wouldn't put up with any shenanigans in his place. He may have been a man of few words, but no one could match his lightning quick punch. Legend had it that he knocked out three men with one punch before they knew what hit them. His tavern was the most civilized place in town and that included the Lutheran Church on the edge of town.

Tasha Hackett • Stromsburg, NE

Bluebird on the Prairie

Prologue

Ockelbo, Nebraska
April 1879

The thick darkness of her bedroom pressed in until she cried out. She was suddenly awake. And alone.

With a gasp, she sat up in bed. Drenched in sweat with her legs tangled in the sheet, Eloise threw her pillow against the wall. Nausea rolled in her stomach. Scrambling out of bed, she leaned over the washbasin and retched.

At only twenty years old, she felt ancient. She had lived a lifetime already. Eloise Davidson, the widow, had woken up alone for the past fourteen months—months filled with weeks that felt like years. The horrid nightmares had returned.

Gruesome though the dreams were, it was his warm arms, to have him hold her again, his kiss still burning her lips, that brought a new flood of tears. She woke to grief as strong as the day he was taken, yet knowing he was gone forever. Crossing her arms around her middle, she sank to the floor and let the tears run unchecked. She succumbed to the sobs that overwhelmed her. *Oh, Philip.*

Her mind clung to the beauty of what was, yet Death tainted the corners of every memory.

A door creaked, a warning preceding the footsteps coming down the hall. They stopped outside her door.

"El?" The soft voice of her brother called to her.

Chapter One

Zeke fought to keep his eyes open, though he moved his head in rhythm to the song he whistled. He had memorized all five verses to the new folk song "My Western Home" and annoyed his adopted family with it repeatedly.

The tune did little to pass the time today. Nebraska was endless. Grassland for all eternity. Mile after mile, forever and ever and always. Three weeks had taken him only halfway across the state. He'd been advised to take the train. Three weeks ago, traveling by horse had appealed to him as the adventure of a lifetime. But now the expanse of the endless sky only mocked him.

There was a fascinating beauty in its emptiness, to be sure. Moving to the edge of Iowa with the Donnely family last year had introduced him to western life—it had also sparked his desire to keep moving west. As far as he could go. He wouldn't stop until he fell into the ocean.

Another yawn stretched his sun-browned and dust-covered face. It was embarrassing how tired a man could be from doing nothing all day. Well, not embarrassing exactly since there was nobody else around. He wondered where Suzy Girl would take him if he fell asleep.

Probably nowhere. She was a lazy horse he'd bought from a farmer in Iowa only four weeks ago. Given the chance, she would find a shaded patch of new grass near a creek and live happily ever after. In hindsight, he should have asked a bit more why she went for the low price.

"Sing, Hooooo!" He called out to the prairie.

The prairie didn't answer. He continued singing unchecked.

Oh, give me a home,
Where the buffalo roam,
And the deer and antelope play.
Where seldom is heard a discouraging word,
And the skies are not clouded all day.

He drawled out each word and switched to a whistle for the chorus until he lost interest halfway.

When he'd imagined his life out west, he hadn't considered the isolation of traveling alone. For three weeks, he'd followed streams, railroads, and bumpy paths from town to town. The next town should be beyond the next rise, or the next one. Three days ago, he'd looked at a map that someone had nailed to the wall of the diner and discovered he could trim five miles if he left the main road and cut straight to Ockelbo, a Swedish settlement with a population near a thousand. A town that size would have employment opportunities. Which he needed since his money and food supplies had dwindled. Again.

There was evidence of smoke some distance beyond the creek where it curved ahead. He would keep heading toward it and hope for the best. This prairie, though, the empty loneliness was enough to drive him out of his mind.

Suzy Girl slowed to a plodding pace, but Zeke hardly minded. Grass, grass, and more grass was all he could see.

"Hey, horse. Can you imagine living without eyelids?" Anyone's voice, even his own, was a pleasant sound these days. A few weeks of travel and he was ready to rethink his whole life plan. "Fish don't even have 'em. I think. Maybe. Do fish have eyelids? If they do, I've never seen 'em. Frogs have extra." He'd handled enough of those for close inspection.

Suzy Girl dipped her head to snag a bite and slowed again. Zeke popped open his eyes. "Hey! What do you take me for? I didn't say it was snack time. Keep on, girl. Let's go." She turned her head to look back at him with one large brown eye. She blinked and snorted before picking up her walk. "See, if you didn't have eyelids, how would you so expertly express yourself?"

She ignored him.

"I know you can hear me." He clicked his tongue and slapped the reins, but his heart wasn't in it.

And she seemed to know it.

After another half-mile of silence, Zeke filled his lungs and was about to burst into an encore when he heard it.

Splashing. And . . . giggling?

The noise grabbed his attention, though he wasn't near enough to see the water through the scraggly line of trees. Zeke did not see a settlement nor a homestead, but the sloping hills could hide a town a quarter-mile away if a man didn't know where to look. Which he didn't.

"We're not alone, Suzy Girl. Think we should check it out?" She didn't respond.

"Good plan. Me too."

As he came into the brush where the prairie met the creek, he flipped the reins over a branch of the nearest cottonwood. The splashing continued, and he heard a woman's voice.

"Ope! Was it cold? Here goes. Weeee!" She laughed again and Zeke wondered if this woman was deranged.

"Suzy Girl, guard my back, will ya?" The horse snorted and picked at the lush green grass. "Wonderful. I knew I could count on you." With a pat against her neck, he left her there.

He was pushing aside the low hanging branches when a scream froze him mid-step. Instantly reaching for his gun and searching for danger, he scanned the creek. A steep bank separated him from the sandy creek bed. Other bushes and shrubs grew around the water's edge. Looking below, he took in everything quickly. He was confused by the blue cloth hanging from a tree root waving in the breeze.

A woman stood knee-high in the water and held a naked baby as if to use him as a shield. Her arms were wrapped around his middle, hugging him close to her chest. Baby arms and baby legs wiggled, trying to get back into the water to play. Her eyes, on the other hand, large and serious, did not waver. Staring at him, she froze. Her brown hair hung loose down her back, and her pale arms were bare. The skin of her shoulders was visible through her wet underclothes. The child cried out; he begged to be released from the iron case of her arms. The thin muslin of her shift and pantaloons was plastered tightly to her legs, leaving little hidden. The woman's face was quickly turning bright red.

Ah, I'm the reason for the scream.

Apparently, she was not expecting company. She shivered in the Nebraska wind. The sun shone brightly, but spring was still new. The baby was unafraid and continued to windmill his arms and legs all around. One chubby hand flapped up and down at him. Both she and Zeke stood still, staring at each other for a few more seconds. He scratched his scalp under the side of his Stetson. He guessed he did look a little gruff these days. A bath would have been a good idea before entering a town.

"Stay back!" She dropped into the water, scrambling away as best she could with the boy in her arms.

Zeke paused and cocked his head at the sight. *Good grief.* He hadn't meant to frighten her. Here he was, yearning for company, for some other human voice, and the first one he sees screams at him. He holstered the gun. Raising both hands as a sign of peace, he planted his feet. A squall from the child sliced through the air.

"It's okay!" Zeke said. "I'm terrible sorry to come across you this way, if you wouldn't mind just—"

"Go away!"

He'd seen that look in her eyes in wild animals before. In startled chipmunks. And rabbits. He had once seen a chipmunk turn so quickly it bounced right off the nearest tree. His laughter rang out when he pictured a half-dressed wet chipmunk holding a naked baby.

She was furious.

"No! I'm sorry," he said. "Please don't be frightened. I'll stay over here, promise."

She grabbed a handful of wet pebbles and threw them in his direction. They showered the ground near his feet. Her chin jutted out in defiance. *Braver than a chipmunk.*

"You should not be here," she said.

She was right. What was he thinking? Suddenly he felt like the greatest cad this side of the Mississippi. He spun around and turned his back to her. "How's this?" he asked. Another shower of pebbles bounced off his boots. Dutifully, he covered his eyes with his hands and turned slowly back to her. "See? I'm not looking. I can't see a thing. Ma'am? Miss? I'm not intruding, but I heard a noise. Just passing through. Funny thing happened, actually, maybe if you'd just like to point me to the nearest town."

"What's the matter with you!" she said. "Leave me alone!" A fist of pebbles rained on his chest and neck, a few settled on the top of his wide-brimmed hat.

Her aim was improving.

He kept his eyes covered and ducked. "Okay! Okay! I'm going." He turned his back to her again, hands on his face, when more pelted him. "Would you stop that? Don't you listen? I said I was leaving."

His foot slipped off the edge of the bank. Caught off guard and distracted by flying pebbles, Zeke tumbled onto the gravel by the water's edge. The girl screamed again as he fell. His arms and legs flailed about and he landed in a heap, headfirst. Cold gravel pressed into his cheek.

He didn't move. *Ow! That's one way to get her attention.* If he stood and climbed the bank without speaking, maybe he could forget this whole miserable encounter had ever happened. Slowly, he uncrumpled himself and lay on his back with one forearm tossed over his face. His heart pounded in his forehead. He would get up. Soon. He just needed another minute to catch his breath.

Great. Now I've bashed in my head. You really know how to impress the ladies, Zeke. I don't know how you've remained unmarried this long . . . it's probably the horse. No woman wants a man with a lazy horse.

More splashing signaled her return across the water. She was no longer running away or throwing rocks.

He groaned. She probably felt sorry for him now that he was wounded, blind, and ridiculous. He didn't need her help. He'd be on his way. Just as soon as he could get up. He attempted to stand.

"Please," she said, "sit and rest a moment. You're bleeding."

"Yup." Zeke slumped back against the bank in a more refined position. Keeping his face downcast from her, he gathered his wits. His head throbbed. And he wasn't sure where the blood came from, but it was on his hands.

Fell off the stupid bank.

Nothing's broken.

Mostly naked girl standing nearby.

Her bare feet sank into the pebbles, and the water caressed her ankles. Not that he noticed. He didn't know where to look now that she stood right next to him. Suddenly, her face appeared in front of his, and she looked directly into his eyes. She still held the baby close to her chest.

"You okay?" she said. "You have blood all over your face."

Zeke stared at his hands. They were covered in mud, bits of grass, and some blood. "I'm sorry." He looked at her, then turned his eyes toward the creek, the trees, the bank, the clouds, and anywhere else but her. And then he started talking.

"I'm Ezekiel. Zeke. People call me Zeke. Ezekiel James. Whatever you want. My mother used to call me Zekey James, which is just kinda weird if you ask me. Which you didn't, I mean, you asked me to leave. Earlier. Which I didn't. But I was—I would have—I was. Leaving. I was leaving. I didn't mean to, I tried not to, I wasn't even looking. I mean, I looked some, just because I came across you so suddenly on accident." *Shut up, Zeke. Stop. Talking.* He squeezed his eyes shut.

"Why don't you stay here for a minute. I'll be right back." She adjusted her shift, pulling at it so it flowed over her backside. She put the baby in the sand a few feet away from the water.

Finding the end of a rope, she tied it securely around his waist. The other end was already tied to the nearest tree.

The baby scrunched up his face and stuck out a lip, then noticed a bag near him and began pulling all the things out of it. "Naa? Naa?" "Yes," she answered. "It's in there." By the time she snatched the bag from him, he had dumped half of the contents out. A brush and hairpins lay scattered at the boy's feet. "Here." She handed him a large muffin, and he sat down to eat it.

Reaching for her dress and stealing a glance back at Zeke, she hid behind some shrubs. Zeke felt his face warm and pretended to be interested in looking downstream.

"Hi!" the baby called to him.

Zeke smiled and waved his hand. "Hi." It was the best he could do while keeping his other hand pressed against the cut on his forehead.

The girl returned, damp but dressed, and leveled her eyes at him with her chin held high. She didn't trust him. He found that ironic, given that he was the one who fell on his face trying to get away from her. He turned his head. How much more could he humble himself in this situation? She swished something in the water and came toward him, stopping a yard away.

"I don't understand you," she said.

"Well," he said slowly, "I was just as surprised as you. I need to ask; like I said, I'm lost, and you're the first person I'd seen in a while. When I set off, I was told Ockel-something was only a day's long ride." He waved his hand toward the west. "That way. And then you and your baby threw rocks at me and pushed me off the bank." He flashed a cheeky grin at her.

She didn't find humor in it. Instead of smiling, she shoved a wet rag at him. "Here. Let's see how badly you hit your head. And you look terrible."

"Thank you. The bleeding has stopped, I think. I'll mend." He patted his face gingerly and then washed the dirt and mess from the rest of his face, neck, and hands. The rag turned brown.

"There is a town," she said in a measured tone, holding his gaze, "downstream a few miles. Keep following the creek, and you'll find a bridge. You can't miss it. Don't mind the rag; I'll wash it. You can be on your way." She took the stained rag from his outstretched hand. "I'm glad you weren't seriously injured when you . . . fell."

He stood, testing his legs. Everything was functioning again. He tipped his hat. "Ma'am." Without looking at her again, he climbed the bank with as much dignity as the situation allowed. He grappled for roots, and sand gave way beneath his feet. His ears burned, knowing she was standing there watching his backside. Reaching the top, he strode through the dry grass to his horse. She waited patiently where he'd left her. She snorted a greeting as she munched the grass around the bit.

"Hey, Suzy Girl, you'll never believe what just happened to me." She ducked her head and then knocked his hat off with her nose. "Real smart. Clever. Just because you had to stay up here and eat the best grass you've had all day doesn't mean you can mistreat me." With a grunt, he swung into the saddle.

"Come on, girl. We're on the right trail." He nudged with his heel, and she walked through the brush into the open prairie again. "When you have time later, I'll tell you all about the chipmunk I met playing in the creek today."

Suzy Girl dipped her head again.

The sky was empty and blue. The sun was shining with the freshness of spring. The day was looking up. Despite his humiliating meeting.

He smiled, thinking of the woman's concern when she'd knelt in front of him. It was sweet. Unnecessary. But sweet. It had been a while since anyone cared whether or not he had blood on his face. Her deep blue eyes showed strength. Her soft round cheeks held a blush of color on each side. He pictured her mess of brown hair, wet and dripping onto her dress.

He shook his head to clear his thoughts, pushing aside images of the girl. He reminded himself how glad he was to be free, strong, and independent, while shoving aside all other thoughts of her. Especially how her legs appeared through her wet underclothes or the water swirling around her ankles. He thought instead of the ocean and how the waves would look cresting and falling. He'd read before the waves could be taller than a man.

With the wind pushing at his back and the promise of a bed and real food for dinner, he couldn't help but laugh at the sky for his good fortune. "Hy-aw!" he said to Suzy Girl, kicking in his heels.

She seemed to feel his shift in attitude more than his verbal command, and when he urged her again, she leaped forward and they sped across the prairie.

Chapter Two

The wind increased, bringing with it the chill of the evening as dusk settled on the prairie. Zeke shivered and pulled his overcoat tighter. Faint outlines of the homes came into view. The sun eased into the west and made quaint silhouettes of each building. He followed a narrow walking path leading into the edge of town.

Squinting in the fading light, he looked for a Main Street. The path from the creek was not the main road. Or a road at all. He trudged through the outskirts of town, leading his horse. He yearned for a real bed, but he needed a livery—hopefully adjoined to a smithy and farrier. And ideally, all of this would be near a warm supper.

He complained aloud in a high falsetto. "'A few miles downstream,' she said. 'You'll find the bridge,' she said. 'Can't miss it,' she said." *Heavens and stars and all things holy, if I don't find a warm dinner tonight, I'll know who to blame.*

He looked up. "Sorry, God, you know I don't mean it." Except maybe he did this time. The events of the past few hours had put him in a sour mood. *Blasted chipmunk.*

That afternoon, Suzy Girl had joyfully galloped through the grass for near three miles before she ran out of steam. The haze of smoke he'd been riding toward was now behind him. There was no way the girl had toted the toddler this far. Though her family likely lived on a homestead.

He must have missed the bridge already. After a quick turn, he headed back the way he'd come. That's when he noticed something wrong with Suzy Girl's gait. An examination revealed a missing shoe.

"I'm sorry, Girl." He rubbed her shoulder and leaned into her. "We'll get you fixed up." Taking the reins, he led her back along the creek, pushing through the undergrowth and searching carefully for anything that could be considered a bridge. They traveled back two miles at this slow pace when he saw a string of large rocks crossing the creek. *Certainly, this isn't a bridge.* But it was the most obvious crossing that included a lower bank on each side to accommodate an easy descent to the creek bed.

"This is spiteful. If a man asked you to point the way, would you tell him this is a bridge? No. You would not. You would never set out to intentionally misdirect a starving, lonely, incredibly handsome, courteous, witty . . ." He ran out of adjectives. "You wouldn't, would you?"

Suzy nuzzled his shoulder and snorted.

"I don't need your sympathy. In fact, I'm the one feeling sorry for you. You hear?" Zeke's stomach answered this time. He groaned at the thought of eating beans and hardtack again. The afternoon sprint had been fueled by his visions of dinner.

He now stared at the line of rocks and pictured himself seated at a table with a full plate of fried chicken. Freshly baked biscuits on the side. The kind with the crust that flaked all over the plate. Still warm from the oven, with butter melting off the edge. There'd be a heap of green beans and mashed potatoes. After scraping his plate clean, he would order a slice or two of apple pie. Or raspberry or cherry. Any kind would do.

At twenty years old, he knew better than to lick the plate. Only little boys who knew their mothers weren't looking would lick the plate. Very little boys.

Unless the pie was warmed with the gooey insides that spread across the plate, and if there just happened to be ice cream to melt on top of it, and if perhaps he wasn't in a very fancy establishment and there weren't too many people about.

Without waiting for his lead, Suzy Girl pushed past him, yanking the reins from his hand and waded into the water, stopping midway to drink her fill.

He picked up the line where it lay on the water and yanked her back. "You think you outrank me? I'm the brains for this outfit. If I say it's not a bridge, it's not a bridge. I didn't say for sure it wasn't a bridge." *But it's not a bridge.* But it was a crossing. If there was a path on the other side, he would take it. He tugged off his boots and socks and shoved them into the saddlebag. As an afterthought, he unbuckled his gun belt and strapped it to the saddle. Just to be safe. Carefully, he made his way across the rocks with Suzy Girl splashing along beside him.

"Fried chicken," he told her, "the kind you can sink your teeth into and come away with a bite that melts in your mouth. Crispy. Fresh. Juicy. You can peel the skin off if you want. Eat it first. Breaded and browned to perfection. The inside will be white and tender." He groaned. "What I would do for some fried chicken right now." His mouth watered.

Halfway across the creek, an owl hooted directly overhead, startling him out of his dinner dreams. He shot his gaze over his shoulder, searching for the bird that must only be a few feet away. The rock he stood on wobbled, and the movement of the water did nothing to help his balance. His arms flapped at the air, trying to stay on the precarious rock, which wasn't nearly as sturdy as a bridge. He teetered on the ball of his foot with one heel hanging off and the other leg wild and unsteady.

The horse decided it was a good time to jerk the other way toward the bank. There was no helping it. With a yelp, Zeke jumped. Landing on his feet in knee-high water, he gasped at the cold. Zeke's leg tangled in the reins, and they pulled tight when Suzy Girl clambered to the side of the creek. All at once, he found himself swept off his feet, submerged in frigid water that stole his breath. Splashing like a wild man, he was unable to keep any part of himself dry. The water rushed over his head and muffled his curse.

Suzy Girl stopped on the high bank and turned to look at him as he floundered.

He sucked in air when he came up before sending all of his frustration at his horse. "Dad-blame it, Suze! You tryna drown me? Sakes alive!" A shiver coursed through him involuntarily from his core to fingers. Irritation welled up, and he hollered accordingly, hitting the water with both hands. He trudged out and stood at the edge. The sand and pebbles pushed between his toes, and water streamed from his hair down his face. Wiping his sleeve across his eyes, then shaking his arms and hands of the extra drops, he tried to cool his anger. Blowing and spitting the water from his face, he shook his head and flung drops in all directions like a shaggy dog. A tired, hungry, and wet dog.

He yelled at the string of rocks. "My boots are dry!" Heavens, but that water was cold. April was not the season to go swimming, in his opinion, and the afternoon heat had long passed. His trousers clung uncomfortably to his legs. Zeke didn't relish the idea of swimming fully dressed no matter the season.

He shrugged out of his vest and suspenders and began unbuttoning his shirt. Midway, he paused to wipe the water that continued to drip from his hair and into his eyes. *Where's my hat? Please, don't let it be gone.* A man needed a hat. Scanning along the shore downstream, he spied it in a tangle of branches.

"Suzy Girl," he began in all seriousness, "you will stay." After looking her in the eye, he shook his head and tied her to the closest tree. If she decided to wander off in the wrong direction, he was in no mood to go after her. A man needed a horse, and a horse that didn't mind was better than no horse at all.

Sucking in a breath, he waded back into the cold for his hat. A few minutes later, after drip-drying and changing what he could, he picked out a path through the trees and followed it over a rise in the prairie. From the top, he could view the whole town. Relief flooded him. *Thank you, Lord.* It was larger than he'd expected. He was arriving from the east. The main road, he could make out, led from south to north.

His hopes of a hot dinner were rapidly fading. He saw no people in the dim light and heard no sounds of village life. The shops were long closed, and folks were retired for the evening.

His head ached from the earlier tumble, and he was wet and muddy. He looked a mess. He was a mess! Days of patchy stubble protruded from his face. It was looking more like a beard every day; if only he could fill it in.

When he found his way to the livery, he was greeted by Frank—a balding man whose white beard made up for any hair that was missing from his head. He refused to negotiate a lower boarding fee.

"I'll take no less than three dollars," the man repeated. Zeke scratched the back of his neck. "For one night? A week maybe would be fair for that amount. But I'll not pay it for a night. That's downright robbery." Not to mention he didn't have it. And even if he did, he wouldn't spend it boarding a horse and starve himself.

The man's stringy whiskers twitched out of the way as he shot a stream of tobacco juice onto the barn floor.

As was Zeke's habit, he'd saved just enough from the last stop to board them both and buy a few meals on the side with plans to find immediate work before starting west again. He'd begun the journey with limited funds and, for the most part, had enjoyed the eclectic jobs and people he'd met. He knew it would take an eternity to reach the ocean this way, but it was part of the fun for him. Another shot of juice barely missed Zeke's boots.

"I'm not standing here all night watching you scratch your head," Frank said.

"Fine." Zeke sighed. "Can I work for it? I can do anything that needs doing." There was always work to be done. Three weeks of travel, and he had not been forced to shake the dust from his feet yet.

Full novel published by Electric Moon Publishing, 2021.

Claudia J. Severin • Martell, NE

Catch It Spinning

Summers

July 25, 1961
Lincoln, Nebraska

Daniel Adams found his father sitting out on the patio in a wicker chair, his customary spot on a hot summer night. It was nearly dark, but he saw the lit end of Bernard's cigarette glowing. He knew his father liked smoking out here because he wouldn't have to bother with an ashtray. Even though his father was a contractor and a skilled carpenter, they had an old telephone cable reel that they used for a table on the patio. Daniel climbed on top of it and sat cross-legged.

"Dad, why are girls so dumb?"

"This, my son, is an age-old question. What has your twin sister done now to get your goat?"

"It's not just Debbie. It's all girls. Today, Debbie and Vonnie were playing with their Barbie dolls. They wanted me to bring in my G.I. Joe. G.I. Joe would never hang out with Barbie. He spends his time on the battlefield shooting the enemy. Vonnie had this cute little Austin-Healey convertible for her Barbie though. I allowed Joe might drive that, in a drag race or something. When they weren't paying attention, I took the car out to the garden and had Joe racing around the flowers. When they found out, they were hopping mad. And they were the ones that wanted me to get

G.I. Joe in the first place. Mom wasn't very happy I was playing in the garden, but where else can you do drag racing? Vonnie was mad her precious car got a little dirt on it. Real cars get dirty; you just wash them. No big deal."

"I suppose they figured if they were playing with Barbie dolls and you had a boy doll, you would like to play with them." Bernard took a drag on his cigarette.

"G.I. Joe isn't a doll! He is an action figure! Ken is a doll. Debbie has a Ken doll, but she rubbed all of his flocked hair off and now she thinks he looks bald." Daniel took out his little pocketknife and started poking it into the wooden reel he was sitting on.

"Girls like different things to play with than boys. I don't think that is anything new. You have a unique problem because you have a sister who is your age. Right now, that is probably more annoying than it is fun, but when you were both little, you played together all of the time. When you get older, you should watch out for her. That's what men do, they protect the women in their families and once they marry, that includes their wives."

"Yuck. I don't ever want to get married." Daniel shook his head. "Especially to a girl."

"Your mother is a girl. Don't you like her?"

"Yeah, that's different. She takes care of me and makes pancakes and hamburgers and Kool-Aid. Oh, and lemon meringue pie. She's like a necessity."

"She takes care of me too. We take care of each other." His father patted his knee.

"So, you're saying it gets better once you get older?"

"It definitely does, yes," Bernard laughed. "You'll see."

The next day, Daniel, Debbie, and Yvonne rode their bicycles to the Eastridge neighborhood swimming pool where both families were members.

"Let's see your tag, young man," the new teenage lifeguard said as they were trying to barge through the gate when the pool opened.

Daniel took the safety pin off his trunks with his family's membership number on it, 147. "See, I am 147-3, cuz I am the third oldest in my family. That one is my little sister."

Debbie poked him with her elbow and showed the lifeguard her pin with 147-4 printed on it. "He thinks he is so cool just because he is four minutes older," she complained.

"Oh, you're twins?" The lifeguard looked from Debbie back to Daniel. "I guess you do look alike."

"Puh-leeease!" Daniel said, "Don't insult me. No one wants to look like her."

"Holding up the line, Daniel!" Yvonne showed her swimming tag to the lifeguard. "Don't mind him. What's your name?" Yvonne asked the pretty lifeguard who had long dark hair like hers.

"Ann. First week on the job. Are the kids here okay?"

"At least the girls are. The boys are impossible!" Yvonne sighed.

"Eddie!" Daniel spotted his buddy mid-pool. "Coming in!" He hurled himself in the air, flying for an instant before the cold water blasted against his sun-seared skin.

"Marco!" Eddie Perkins called.

"Polo!" Daniel emerged closing his eyes.

Debbie and Vonnie spread their beach towels on the sizzling cement and spent more time lying on them than they did swimming. Pretty soon, a couple of other girls put their towels down next to Debbie, and they were all slathering on baby oil and looking at the boys in the pool as though they wouldn't notice.

When the lifeguards whistled a ten-minute break, Daniel walked up to his sister.

"Do you have any zinc oxide in your bag?" he asked her. "Mom told me my nose is peeling too much, and I have to put the white stuff on it."

Debbie pulled a tube out of her bag and handed it to him. "Then you should have brought it yourself."

"You have a bag. Boys don't carry bags." He coated his nose with the thick white cream.

"Hello, Daniel," one of the other girls, Janine Meeks, said pleasantly.

He glared at her and walked over to join Eddie, who was sitting on the edge of the pool, dangling his feet in the water. They were only about ten feet away from the girls.

"Here's the plan," Daniel said. "Before they blow the whistle, we'll go behind the girls and get a running start and then do it right by the edge. They'll get soaked."

"And they won't be able to get us without getting their precious hair wet. It's great!" Eddie said.

A minute before the hour and the end of the safety break, the boys got up and leaned on the chain-link fence behind the four girls.

"What are you doing? Don't try to listen to our conversation." Debbie squinted at her brother.

The moment the whistle shrilled, like a champion sprinter, Daniel launched his body forward in perfect synchronicity with

Eddie's, tromping on his sister's towel, pounding the pavement hard at the lip of the pool as he leaped as high as he could, grabbing his legs, and tilting slightly backward in the execution of a splash-inducing cannonball.

The cool water slapped his back and bottom, forcing his swimming trunks to ride up, and creating what he knew scientifically was a Worthington jet, a hole in the water that creates a giant explosion as it refills.

All four girls were still screaming when Daniel's head burst to the surface and Eddie gave him a triumphant grin. Daniel and Eddie laughed so hard they got water up their noses. The closest lifeguard, a sixteen-year-old neighbor boy, laughed but blew his whistle and shook a finger at the boys.

"Hey, Danny. Who are those boys over by your sister and Yvonne?" Eddie coughed, trying to clear his lungs.

A couple of sixth-grade boys were talking to the girls. One of the boys Daniel didn't know handed Yvonne a towel and she was smiling at him.

"Let's jump off the diving board," Daniel said, whipping his head back to Eddie. "Stupid girls. Stupid screaming girls."

At four o'clock, Daniel and Debbie were due home, so they left the pool about three forty-five. Yvonne tagged along, as she was expected home at the same time.

Daniel said, "I want to go look at the creek before we leave. Eddie said he caught a tadpole there yesterday." The creek was right next to the parking lot of the swimming pool. When they reached the creek, Daniel peered in, then he put his feet in the creek and waded around. It was only about a foot deep and murky.

"Mom isn't going to like you getting your tennis shoes muddy," Debbie said.

He ignored her. "I see some. Look, there are a bunch of tadpoles right there."

Debbie wrinkled her nose. Yvonne looked where he was pointing, then laid down on her stomach on the side of the creek for a better view.

"I see them," she said. "We should catch some."

Daniel brightened. He didn't expect that. Not from a girl.

"I know. I'll go back to my house and get a Mason jar. My mom has some for when she makes jam," Daniel said.

"Let's go!" Yvonne cried.

Debbie gave her friend a dirty look. They all got on their bikes and rode home. Daniel and Yvonne changed into shorts, got a couple of jars, and went back to the creek, after explaining what they wanted to do to their mothers. They both waded into the creek and filled their jars with water and a couple of tadpoles each.

"Do you think we can watch them turn into frogs?" Yvonne asked. "I helped Clark catch tadpoles last summer and we thought we'd see frogs the next day, but they died."

"I don't know. I'll ask my dad about that." Daniel held his jar up to the sunlight and admired the little amphibians.

Just then, they heard the familiar bell of the ice cream truck.

"It's the ice cream man!" Daniel almost dropped his prized tadpoles. "I want ice cream." Then his joy turned to dismay. "Oh, I don't have any money with me."

Yvonne fished into her pocket and came up with a quarter. "I put this in my pocket the other day when we heard the ice cream truck bell. But then he ran out of popsicles so I didn't get one."

She held the coin out to Daniel. He handed his tadpole jar to her and ran over to the ice cream truck.

"What will you have, son?" the proprietor asked him.

"I'll have an ice cream bar," Daniel said. He looked back at Yvonne holding the two tadpole jars. "No, wait. How much are the twin Popsicles? You know, the ones you can break in two?"

"Same as an ice cream bar, twenty-five cents."

He sighed. He really wanted that chocolate shell on the vanilla ice cream bar. "Give me a grape twin pop."

When he got back to Yvonne, they split the Popsicle in two and sat down on the curb, licking their Popsicles and watching their tadpoles.

"You have a grape tongue," Yvonne laughed.

"So do you!" He pointed at her.

When they were done, they put the glass jars in Yvonne's bicycle basket and rode home.

Girls aren't so bad all the time, as long as they don't act stupid.

~ ~ ~ ~ ~

August 1968

The rest of the summer flew by quickly. Yvonne and Debbie worked on routines for the upcoming marching band season. Yvonne worked as a lifeguard at the swimming pool four days a week and taught preschoolers how to float. Randy came by the pool most days when she was working. People were looking at them as a couple. Gary had gone to Michigan for three weeks with his family. Another lifeguard told her he'd stopped by the swimming pool one day when she was talking to Randy, but she hadn't seen him. It might have been true because he'd stopped calling her.

Daniel was another story. When Randy started coming over to her house, she thought Daniel might be jealous. Even if he hadn't noticed Randy over at the Edisons, he was bound to find out she was seeing Randy from her conversations with Debbie.

Yvonne and Randy were sitting close together, drinking iced tea on the wrought-iron settee on the Edison's patio. Harold and Connie had gone inside after a rousing game of badminton. Randy had his arm on the back of the bench, playing with Yvonne's hair.

Things are about to get romantic. They'd been seeing each other for a few weeks, nearly every day. It was natural things should progress.

Daniel called out as he cut through the yard, "Is the game over? I thought you might need a relief player for badminton." Grover came bounding ahead of him and planted his slobbering mouth in Yvonne's lap.

"Grover!" Yvonne said, "Have some manners!" Grover sat back and wagged his tail. She swatted at the air, glancing at Daniel. "Randy, this is the loveable Grover. Shake, Grove."

The dog offered a paw, and Randy shook it, smiling.

"And Daniel. He lives next door with Grover. Daniel Adams, Randy Sparks. Randy is going to be in our class at school." The scowl she gave Daniel was frosty. *What are you doing here?*

Daniel shook Randy's hand, too, then sat in the chair across from them. Yvonne's eyes widened as she nodded and jerked her head toward Daniel's house. Daniel kept his eyes on Randy.

"I just finished listening to the Cardinals game. Gibson was on fire!" Daniel said.

"Oh geez, that was tonight? Get outta here! Are you a Cardinals fan? I watched a game earlier this summer at Busch Stadium with my dad and uncles. They're going all the way this year!"

It was like they were both speaking another language, talking about RBI, batting averages, at-bats, strikeouts, ERAs, home-runs. She knew what some of it meant, but why did they care? It was, yawn, baseball. And more baseball. Then when she thought they were winding down, they'd start analyzing another player's record for the season.

I may as well go inside and watch Peyton Place. Daniel doesn't even notice the dirty looks I am giving him.

After an hour, Daniel got up to leave. When Randy started to go with him, Yvonne stood, crossing her arms and narrowing her eyes at both of them.

Randy turned back, saying, "I'll be right back, Yvonne." The daggers in her eyes stopped him short. He looked back at Daniel.

"Yeah, she's pissed off." Daniel lowered his voice. "And I have to warn you, she's got a nasty right hook." A slow smile spread across his face as he signaled to the dog to follow him home.

"What's wrong?" Randy asked.

Yvonne flounced back to the metal bench, and Randy quickly joined her.

"I take it you aren't a baseball fan?"

She glared at him. "I thought you were here to see me. We finally had some time alone and then he barges in and wants to talk baseball. I have no interest in or knowledge about baseball. Maybe you should just go on a date with him!"

"Well, you're prettier." Her icy expression was unchanged. "Maybe I will go out with Daniel. We could be friends. Tell me, what would you like to talk about?"

~ ~ ~ ~ ~

She hoped Daniel might be too busy to bother them when he spent his earnings on a 1962 Plymouth Fury hardtop. He bought it from his uncle's used car lot in Omaha. Debbie had gotten the Bug from her uncle too. Daniel spent the next few weekends tinkering with the Fury in the driveway. On the second Saturday afternoon, Yvonne caught Randy detouring over to see what Daniel was doing instead of ringing her doorbell.

She supposed he needed to make friends with other guys since he was new in town, but she didn't appreciate it horning in on her date time. At first, she didn't think Randy and Daniel would have much in common, but it turned out Randy was a serious student, too, not to the point of being a total dweeb, but he'd been first in his class at his former school. The next thing she knew Daniel was going over to Randy's house to play a board game called Fight in the Skies.

She had to tell Randy how she felt. "I think it is nice you and Daniel have become friends, but sometimes it seems like you are spending time with him when you said you were coming over to see me," Yvonne told him one evening after they'd been late for a surprise birthday party because he'd stopped to discuss the new carburetor Daniel was installing.

"I like Daniel. Is that a problem? He told me he took you to the prom last year, so the two of you must get along," Randy said.

"What else did he tell you about me?"

"That you'd been friends since childhood, you were his sister's best pal. You dated some jerk last year who graduated. A jerk who cheated on you. And then you slugged him."

"I didn't slug him. I slapped him. For some reason, Daniel found that funny. But I don't go around attacking people, just so you know."

"The way he talked about you, I would have said he was in love with you. But he kept saying you were just friends."

Yvonne arched her eyebrows. "Huh. Yeah, that's right. We're just friends."

"Good, cuz we decided we should go on a double date."

"What? Who is Daniel going to go out with?"

"I don't know. He's going to let me know. He said we should all go to King's."

Andrea Mitchum was the girl he chose for their double date. She wasn't sure how she felt about Daniel going out with someone she considered one of her friends, although they weren't close. Andrea was a year younger and played the flute in the orchestra. Daniel was one of the few who played in both band and orchestra.

When the night came to go on the date, the plans changed. Randy told her they were going to the Starview Drive-in Movie Theater. Yvonne liked the idea.

Starlight. Moonlight. Romantic movie. All of this is custom designed for a first kiss. And maybe more than one.

She'd gone to the drive-in theater with Dick several times the previous summer and didn't even remember what movies had been playing. The drive-in featured second-run movies most people had seen or movies bad enough no one wanted to see. Yvonne thought the advantage of that was when your parents quizzed you on the content of the movie, you already knew the plot, or if it was one of the turkeys, you could invent something, and they wouldn't know the difference.

Everyone knew teenagers went to drive-in movies to neck, and she supposed the proprietors didn't mind, as long as they sold enough popcorn and Pepsi. When Randy came to pick her up that evening, she was surprised when he said Daniel was driving his car, and they were relegated to the back seat. Daniel's car was a two-door, so they had to climb around the front seat to get in, not ideal for two people with long legs. Then they had to wait in the warm car while Daniel went inside Andrea's house to get her and visit with her parents. Yvonne's pancake makeup and eye shadow streamed slowly off her face in the heat and her deodorant went on strike. They hadn't even made it to the destination yet. She didn't even want to think about how much her date was sweating.

"Do they have drive-in theaters where you lived before, Randy?" she asked, more out of boredom than anything else.

"They didn't even have a regular theater within fifty miles of where I lived," he said. "This movie is about four years old, I think, but I have never seen it."

Daniel and Andrea made it to the car, and they headed to the drive-in. Once they found a good spot to park, and Daniel added the speaker to his car window, they settled in to watch the animated shorts that preceded the movie. Almost immediately, Daniel put his arm around Andrea's shoulder, and she leaned against him.

Yvonne gaped. Her face seemed to lose feeling. They barely knew each other. Randy pretended not to notice them.

"Is that a concession stand down there?" Randy asked.

"Yeah, they have popcorn, hot dogs, candy, and pop," Yvonne forced herself to focus on Randy.

"Does anyone else want something to eat?" he asked. When no one spoke up, he went to the concession stand himself. In about ten minutes he returned with various treats.

"You should have come with me, Yvonne. They had a big variety," Randy said, pushing his way into the back seat. "I got popcorn, licorice, and a couple of Pepsis. Oh, and here was the strangest thing I found. Dill pickles. They sell whole dill pickles!" Daniel started laughing, then Andrea joined in.

Yvonne furrowed her brow and looked at Randy, who was holding up a six-inch-long dill pickle. "You're seriously going to eat that?" It not only smelled like dill and vinegar, but she also caught a whiff of garlic.

"Why wouldn't I? They're delicious. Here, have a bite." He put the pickle up to her mouth. Daniel had turned around to see her reaction and started laughing harder.

The smell made her eyes water. "I think only pregnant women eat dill pickles."

Randy laughed and took a big bite. "That's not true, my grandmother cans them all the time on the farm."

This isn't going the way I expected. I'm not sure I would want to kiss anyone after they ate that thing. Then the movie started. It turned out to be a war epic, apparently, a similar theme to the Fight in the Skies game, starring Lee Marvin and Steve McQueen. This has to be the worst movie Steve McQueen ever made. But Randy and Daniel seemed to enjoy it, whooping and hollering when the fighter planes shot down the enemy.

The second movie of the double feature was a spy thriller she'd seen a couple of years earlier, and she hadn't appreciated it the first time. Even Daniel appeared to have gotten bored, as he pulled Andrea closer and then they scooted down into the seat so only the tops of their heads were visible from the back seat.

Randy seemed oblivious to this. By this time, he'd consumed all of the food he'd bought and wormed his way back out of the car to find the restroom. Yvonne began counting how many blocks she would have to walk to get home from there.

When Randy climbed back in beside her, she decided to be more direct. "Do you know why people go to the drive-in, Randy?"

"Well, I heard that dad over there in the station wagon tell his kids to lay down on the sleeping bag, so for him, it was a way to get his kids to sleep. But I guess it is cheaper than a regular movie."

She pointed to the front seat, where Daniel and Andrea's heads had now disappeared.

Randy shook his head. "I think they're missing the movie."

And you're missing the point.

"You think this is supposed to be romantic, is that it?" He grinned. "Come here." He pulled her into his lap, positioning her so she had an unobstructed view over the front seat to see the movie screen. "Is this better?"

Yvonne sighed. Maybe a little bit. She decided to pay some attention to the show, although the audio had started to crackle in and out from the speaker. "Look out, here comes the part where someone shoots a bullet through his top hat." Then she affected a phony British accent, and added, "Egads, I'll have to have my butler send this out for repairs!"

"You've seen this movie before?" Randy asked.

"Yes, it's pitiful." She went back to impersonating the hero in the movie, "Take that, you nasty Russian spy doll!" as the hero sprayed some sort of gas out of a canister.

Randy laughed and took up her game, raising the pitch of his voice and affecting a bad Russian accent, "You Brits are all alike, all steam and no substance!" as the Russian female spy shot at the hero again.

They went back and forth like this, with Yvonne making up silly dialogue for the suave British spy and Randy making up even sillier lines for the glamorous Russian villain pursuing him. Daniel and Andrea sat back up and played along. Soon they were adopting the parts of additional characters as they appeared. Often, they missed their cues when they were laughing too hard.

When they were leaving the drive-in, Randy said, “Now I get why drive-in movies are fun. You’re all pretty good at this game.”

Yvonne had to snicker. *Is he really that naïve?*

Reprinted with permission from Pella Road Publishing.

Sammi Hoard • Alma, NE

Parallels

Starting Over

October 22, 1971

Lilly Walker closed her gran's trunk of clothing she'd been searching through with a heavy sigh. Tired, physically and emotionally, she plopped down on the attic floor. At age forty, with her marriage to Nigel Walker ending, a new beginning was being thrust upon her. Panic and self-condemnation had followed her relentlessly during her divorce. The same questions presented themselves over and over and over: How would she support herself? Where would she go? She couldn't stay at the Aurora library because it was considered *Nigel's library*. Even though she worked for the assistant director, handling the collection and patrons, Nigel was over acquisitions and cataloging. Nigel was perceived by the board and patrons as the *one in charge*.

Twelve years her senior, Nigel was forcing her to leave their marriage with less than when they'd gotten married. She'd fought it. Wanted what was hers before the nuptials. Then her beloved gran died, removing all her anger, replacing it with profound grief. She wished to see Gran again. Needed it more than almost anything else. Though, in all honesty, she missed Nigel just as much. Their quiet times together in the evenings. The stolen moments of privacy at the library. The only good thing to come from her beloved gran's death was that she'd left Lilly her house in Alma, Nebraska, an hour and a half west of Aurora.

Nigel had tried taking possession of her gran's house, but he'd backed off from it just last week. She still wondered what had caused his sudden change of heart. So, finally, it was hers now, free and clear.

"Oh, Nigel," she whispered, tears pooling. "Why did you stop loving me?" She scraped away her tears and shook off the memories. No sense in weeping for someone that was lost to her forever.

Checking her watch, she winced. It was after 5:30. Supper would not prepare itself and *The Brady Bunch* would not wait until she was ready to watch it. Best she get up from this hard attic floor and get moving. She stopped in front of the standing mirror along the west wall and studied her appearance. Her face no longer held the glow of youth, but looked perpetually tired. Fine thin lines were starting to frame her dull green eyes. Mousy brown hair that had once been shiny and thick with loads of volume now hung limply to her shoulders.

She shifted her gaze from her face and focused on her body. Had she become heavy and unattractive? Clad in an indigo-blue smock top and bell bottom jeans, she thought she looked okay. She'd only gained the Freshman Fifteen while she'd acquired her degree in Library Science. The other thirty-something pounds other women her age normally put on hadn't happened. Not that she was complaining. Yet it wasn't fair to compare her weight with women who'd had children. She'd wanted children with Nigel. It just never came to be. Sadness inched in. She shoved it away. Nigel was divorcing her. End of story.

With her move into her gran's house finished and a new job waiting Monday morning, 1971 was improving. Much better than last year, when Nigel had decided without any explanation that he wanted a divorce. After being literally pushed out of the home they'd shared for fifteen years, she'd stayed with her friend and fellow library clerk Dina Morris. The first few weeks living in Dina's basement, unemployed, she'd cried, blamed herself for whatever had caused Nigel's love for her to dry up.

Despair had taken over her entire being. Logic had crept away into the shadowy corners of that basement, creating continuous questions that repeated over and over, swirling above her. Who was she if she wasn't Nigel Walker's wife? Where did she belong if she wasn't with him? The same unanswered questions about where she would find a job and support herself were still relentlessly prodding her. Ratcheting up panic and anxiety.

Until that fateful evening when Dina came down those basement stairs with a newspaper. She had held it out to her and smiled. "Read what I've circled."

Lilly had read the advertisement aloud, "Open position at Alma, Nebraska library: Full time clerk, must be available for one or two Saturdays. Send resume to Jane Smith, director, Post Office box 232 . . ." Lowering the paper, she had stared at Dina.

Dina's dark glasses, perched on the bridge of her nose, hadn't hidden the curiosity radiating from her dark brown eyes. "It's perfect. Smaller town, sure, but it's a library clerk job. You're afraid you'll never find another library to work at. Here it is."

Lily remembered shrugging that day, unwilling to display the excitement bubbling up inside her. Would Alma even hire her? They were probably looking for someone younger, smarter . . .

As if reading her mind, Dina had murmured, "What have you got to lose? Besides the time to write a resume, getting a letter of recommendation from Simon, and the cost of a stamp?"

"Simon Hanes is only the assistant director."

Dina had rolled up the newspaper, tapped it against her palm, then held it out to her. "This job is what you've been praying for."

Lilly had taken the newspaper again, hoping while trying to suppress the anxiety of not being good enough for the job. The time between her writing a resume, getting the recommendation from Simon, mailing them, and waiting for a response, had been much different than the weeks since she had moved out of her home she'd shared with Nigel. Then her phone rang and without knowing why or how, she sensed it was Jane Smith, the Alma Library director, calling.

The interview with Jane and the Alma library board happened in a very short time frame. Practically waiting by the phone, just as nervous as she'd been during the interview, it rang two days later with the job offer.

Lilly shook off the memories and went downstairs. Staring into the refrigerator, she pondered what she could cook for dinner. Milk, bologna, one hotdog, and a covered bowl of macaroni and cheese were her only choices. The cupboards were bare also since she hadn't gone to the local grocery store yet.

"Eeny, meeny . . ." she began, then muttered, "and the winner is mac and cheese!"

Dumping the bowl's contents into a sauce pan, she grabbed the milk, poured a small amount into it, and stirred. She put the gelatinous muck on the burner and cranked it to medium. She buttered a slice of bread and slid it under the oven broiler. When the bread was toasted on both sides, she set it on a plate, added the mac and cheese. "Not exactly like eating at the Ritz, but it will suffice," she said as she carried it into the living room.

She set up her lone TV tray and placed her plate on it. Clicking on the television, she turned it to Channel 13. The 6:30 news was just finishing up when the TV screen came to life. She scooped up mac and cheese with her fork and ate it with minimal chewing. *The Brady Bunch* theme song started playing, "Here's a story . . ." Tears welled and she was fraught with anxiety. She had loved *The Brady Bunch* when she was still with Nigel. His two children from his first marriage had been a pre-teen and an early teenager at the time. They'd loved her once. Now they wouldn't talk to her. She hadn't watched the show while living in Dina's basement because Dina didn't have a television antennae. Great. Something else Nigel has taken from her without his even knowing it.

She walked to the television and turned the knob. Nothing on Channel 11 caught her fancy. Channel 5 didn't offer any hope either. She shut it off then sat down to finish her meager dinner.

~ ~ ~ ~ ~

Nigel Walker rambled from one room to another in his home. Odd how it seemed huge, and empty, now that Lilly's stuff was gone. She'd moved out months ago, but she'd left the few items that they'd been fighting over. Movers had picked them up just this week.

There were times that he missed Lilly. Also there were moments when he questioned his reasons for divorcing her. Because his children, Miles and Macey, had convinced him that Lilly wasn't a good wife. Jealousy reared its ugly head once again. He tamped it down. He couldn't think of her being with someone else without remembering when he'd first met Lilly.

He'd just accepted the director position at the Aurora library in February 1955. A petite clerk with long brown hair caught his attention on his first day. She was warm and welcoming while maintaining a professional distance. It was her green eyes that held him captive whenever they spoke. The whisper of her skirt as she walked through the library and shelved returned books had caused his focus to drift from his task at hand more than once.

Nigel forced the memories of Lilly away. He'd been so cruel during their divorce hearings, trying to take everything for himself, including her family heirlooms, and destroying her in the process. What had he done when Lilly's grandmother died? Instead of offering comfort, he'd gone for her jugular, attempted to take her grandmother's house too. The judge had called him and his attorney into his chambers, and with minimal words, had stopped the silliness of taking her gran's home out of spite. Seeing Lilly totally defeated at the final divorce hearing just last week didn't bring him pleasure as he'd hoped. He'd only felt sadness for her, disgust at himself.

~ ~ ~ ~ ~

Monday morning Lilly walked in the east door of the Alma library. Excited and nervous that she was about to start her new life, seeing the circulation desk near the book stacks brought tears. Her gran had worked here. Her presence was everywhere. Lilly's job interview had taken place at the City Administrator's office downtown and she was totally unprepared for this emotional response.

Wiping at her tears, Lilly approached the circulation desk. "Hello," she said to the older woman standing behind it. "I'm Lilly Walker. Jane Smith is expecting me this morning."

"Jane said we had a new clerk starting today." The lady pushed her dark-framed glasses up the bridge of her nose. With short permed gray-brown hair and attired in a popular *Carol Brady* mint-green pant suit, this woman was not only fashionable but very cute. She came around the desk and extended a hand. "Nice to meet you. I'm Glory Perkins."

"Please to meet you too," Lilly said.

A door north of the children's area opened and Jane Smith came into the cavernous room. With her white hair in a smooth page boy, her wire-rim glasses rested easily on her aristocratic nose. She looked chic in a cerulean-blue blouse, brown leather vest and brown calf-length culottes with brown knee-high boots.

"Hello, Lilly, good to see you again." Jane held her hand out. Lilly took it for a quick shake. "Ready for today?"

"Yes." Lilly nodded.

"You two have met already." Jane motioned to Glory. "Lilly's Sophia Jensen's granddaughter."

Glory's eyes widened. "I'm so sorry about Sophia's passing. She was such an asset here. She knew this library inside and out."

"Thank you," Lilly answered. "I hope I can come close to knowing half of what Gran did."

"Oh, you will," Jane and Glory replied simultaneously. All three women laughed.

"I'll take you down to the basement and show you where you can store your purse and such," Jane said. "Follow me."

~ ~ ~ ~ ~

The day flew by quickly as Jane showed Lilly the ins and outs of life at the Alma Public Library. The catalog drawers were a wonder: made from golden oak polished to a bright shine, they were still beautiful even though they showed minimum use from over sixty years. An original Carnegie structure built in 1911, gleaming woodwork surrounded the doors, windows, and lined some of the walls. Lilly had loved visiting her gran here as a child. When she'd helped Gran close up she was in awe at how her voice would echo from the sheer size of it. Such bittersweet memories.

Toward the end of the day, Jane and Lilly went to the adult reading area. Four round oak tables with high-back chairs were placed strategically for easy traffic flow. All showed wear from six decades of use. When she neared the table closest to where the older local newspapers were shelved, Lilly ran her hand along the edge. A slight wave of nausea edged with a waffling of her vision brought her hand to a stop. Jane was talking to her, yet she was hearing other voices. Women's voices. Glory had left an hour ago, so none of them were hers. A faint smell of daffodils drifted in the air. Her gran had used a perfume with that scent. What on earth?

"Lilly?" Jane saying her name snapped Lilly out of the sense of displacement.

"What?"

Jane stared at her, obviously confused. "Any questions before the night clerk gets here?"

"Ummm . . . not at the moment. I'm sure I'll have a hundred questions later when I'm trying to sleep," Lilly said with a nervous laugh.

Jane laughed with her. "You've done great today. Let's get your hours recorded on the time sheet."

The door on the east side opened and a woman approximately Lilly's age came in. Short and stocky, the woman wore her dishwater blonde hair in a medium-length shag. Clothed in a striped blouse of various hues of green, blue, and cream, with a blue crocheted vest over bell-bottom slacks, the woman was quite fashionable. Lilly felt dowdy in her gray blouse, slate gray jacket and slacks. She touched her hair, wishing she had the courage to try the new shag style.

"Lilly, this is Emily Fenster, the night clerk," Jane said. "Emily, this is Lilly Walker."

"How are you?" Emily stated flatly.

"I'm good. It's nice to meet you." Lilly held out her hand. Emily visibly hesitated before taking it for a quick shake.

"Well," Emily began and directed her attention to Jane. "What's in store for tonight?"

Unsure if Emily was just unfriendly or shy, Lilly hung back as the two women discussed the day's happenings. Emily abruptly walked away toward the circulation desk.

"Don't mind her," Jane murmured as she turned and headed for the basement stairs. Lilly followed her. "She thought she should get the day shift opening."

"Oh, I'm sorry," Lilly said, uncertain how to handle this information. Did Emily have hard feelings about her getting hired?

"No need to apologize." Jane picked up her purse from the table in the breakroom. "The board and I were looking for someone to groom for director in case I retire in the near future. Your experience plus your degree in Library Science are positives for you." Lilly stopped and again let her feelings of inadequacies take over. Wanted to say she wasn't qualified to be director. "Don't worry about Emily. She's a kind soul way down deep. She'll welcome you eventually."

The sense of inadequacy still waffled through Lilly, even after Jane's kind words.

"Cheer up, kid!" Jane patted Lilly's arm. "You've got this. If today's any indication of how good of a librarian you are, you're going to know more about this old library than me in two weeks."

"I don't—"

"Believe it," Jane said interrupting. She slipped on her brown waist-length jacket and tied a gold and orange silk scarf at her neck. "I'm an excellent judge of people. Want a ride home?"

"I just live down the block," Lilly answered meekly.

"I know. See you tomorrow," Jane said, then left.

Lilly walked to her gran's house on the opposite corner of the same block the library was on. Her house now, she corrected.

~ ~ ~ ~ ~

The rest of the week flew by. Saturday Lilly worked with Glory and enjoyed her company very much. At lunch time Glory went downstairs to the breakroom. A couple of minutes later she came back up, holding hers and Lilly's sack lunches and both of their thermoses and set them on a table in the adult reading area.

"I've only lived here for about three years," Glory said as she smoothed a napkin down on the table. "I got to know your grandmother fairly well before she passed." Placing her sandwich and potato chips on the napkin, she opened her thermos and poured milk into the cap. "She said that she raised you."

"Yes," Lilly answered before taking a small bite of her ham and cheese sandwich. "My father went MIA in World War II." Glory's eyebrows lifted. "He was part of the invasion of Normandy in 1944. That's the last the army knew of his location."

"Oh, how sad. What about your mother?"

Lilly filled her thermos cap with coffee and sipped. "My mother died later that year in DC. She'd gone there to get information about my father. As she crossed a busy street she was hit by a car."

"Oh, I'm so sorry that you lost both parents so close together. I had no idea!"

"That's all right. It's something Gran and I didn't talk about with other people." Lilly remembered the shame that came with her father's disappearance. "Many believed, including a few in the military, that my father deserted that day. That's why my mother was in DC, to help clear his name. I was thirteen and after Mother died, I became a handful. Gran and Grandpa Vic finished raising me. I'm so grateful that they never gave up on me."

"Oh, Lilly, your grandmother was a special lady. And we do miss her here." Glory reached across the table and squeezed Lilly's hand. "I never met your grandpa though."

"He died when I was twenty-three. I was working at the Aurora library by then." Lilly picked up her sandwich, took a bite, then another.

"I assume you were an only child?"

"Yes," Lilly replied. How could she steer this conversation away from her? "What about you? What brought you to this tiny hamlet?"

"Oh, you know. Got divorced, needed a new start."

"Yes, I understand that all too well." Lilly washed down the last bite of her sandwich with coffee.

"Is it true your husband's the director at the library you came from?"

"Soon to be ex-husband. And yes," Lilly said, knowing where this question was going. "But I didn't work for him. He was over acquisitions and cataloging. I worked for the assistant director, who handled the collection and the patrons. That would've been awkward to work for my husband."

"True enough." Glory smirked. "If I'd worked with Glen, my ex, we'd have gotten divorced way sooner."

Both women laughed.

Patronage was steady all afternoon. An hour before closing an elderly male came in and asked for help in finding an article in the local newspaper from October 1911. Lilly led him to the archived newspapers in the west corner of the adult reading area. As she took the bound book of newspapers off the shelf and placed it on the table closest to the window, nausea flitted through her tummy and her vision waffled, just like the other day. Through the haze surrounding her she could see women attired in long dresses with large fancy hats milling around the tables. Voices of varying pitch filtered through the room. Her gran's voice was one of them. This can't be! Gran had died just six months ago. Lilly grasped the edge of the table, feeling like her knees might give out. She took a couple of steps back. The room righted itself.

"I'll let you look," she said to the man. "Let me know if you need more help."

He nodded, then sat down and started going through the book of 1911 newspapers.

~ ~ ~ ~ ~

Saturday afternoon Nigel sat in front of an open box on the coffee table. Inside were some of Lilly's doo-dads that he'd never understood their importance to her. Until now. These items had been given to her by her now deceased grandmother. He plucked out a white ceramic horse with a princess in a flowing pink gown riding bareback. Turning it over, it had printed on the bottom: To my darling Lilly. Love you forever, Mama. 1944.

Why had he been so obstinate to make Lilly leave with nothing? How could he make this right? *Give her this box* was his conscience's immediate response. So be it. Take it to her and leave right after. He closed the box, grabbed his car keys and jacket, and went out to his car. Glancing at his watch, he knew that Lilly would still be at the Alma library. The hour and a half drive to Alma would put him there around 6:00. Hopefully enough time for her to eat an early dinner. He'd find something to eat on the way back home.

He steered his cherry-red 1965 Mustang onto the west-bound ramp of I-80 then clicked on the radio. He'd grown up listening to Big Band music. Now he enjoyed modern rock, such as Three Dog Night and Creedence Clearwater Revival. "Mustang Sally" by Wilson Pickett came on and he found it appropriate for his latest acquisition, this very car. It wasn't brand new, but it was in pristine condition. He tapped the steering wheel in time to each song that played during his journey.

Brilliant hues of gold, orange, and purple streaked across the sky as he parked in front of Lilly's house. A single light shown through the front window. Her yellow Chevy Impala sat in the driveway. Mixed emotions warred inside of him. He'd hurt her, would she welcome him or shut the door in his face? Only one way to find out. He stepped out of the car, retrieved the box from the trunk, and walked to her front door. Timidly he knocked, shifted the box to his other hip. The door creaked open. Lilly stood inside, cast in shadows, already in her fuzzy pink pajamas.

"Nigel? Why are you here?" Lilly ran a hand through her shoulder-length mahogany hair.

"I brought you this box," he said, then immediately regretted it.

"A box?"

"Yes. It has things your grandmother gave you."

An acrid burning stench filtered through the open door. "Oh, no. My bread!" She turned to leave, then faced Nigel again. "Come in."

Nigel entered hesitantly. He trailed behind her, trying to figure out the best place to put the box. Entering the kitchen, he set it on the counter.

"Have you eaten?" She stirred something in a pot on the stove. He shrugged with his palms up. "What you smelled was my garlic toast getting too toasty." Taking the pan from the burner, she drained the water from spaghetti noodles. "Have you eaten, Nigel? There's enough here for both of us."

"No, I haven't eaten. I just wanted to bring you this box. I'll grab something on my way out of town."

"You're going to eat gas station food? Which you dislike intensely." She stared at him with her mesmerizing green eyes. "Come on. Eat with me. We can be civil to one another, right?"

He stuffed his hands into his jeans pockets as she scraped the burned spots off the garlic toast. "You're right. I've never been a fan of an overcooked hotdog from a spinning wheel. You know me too well."

She laughed. He'd missed hearing her laughter.

"Where are your plates? I can set the table."

"Upper cupboard to the right of the sink."

He should have known. It was still that way at his house. His house without Lilly. Taking down two plates, he opened the cupboard next to it on instinct and retrieved two glasses. After filling them with milk, he put them on the kitchen table. "Silverware?"

"Drawer under the plates." She finished rinsing the spaghetti noodles, plopped them into a large bowl, and carried it, the spaghetti sauce, and the garlic toast to the table. She sat down and looked over her shoulder at Nigel.

Nigel took a chair to her left, feeling awkward. Lilly gave the blessing, then took his plate, heaped spaghetti on it, and spooned a generous amount of sauce on top. Adding a slice of garlic bread, she set it back down in front of him. She filled her plate and began to eat.

Nigel picked up his fork and hesitated. "I never asked. How's the new job going?"

"It's good," she answered after swallowing a bite of food. "It's not as busy as Aurora's library, of course."

"The staff is nice?" Nigel spun noodles around his fork and ate it.

"Yes."

"What was it like without your grandmother there?'

Lilly's eyes welled with tears as she continued eating. He took a few more bites, hoping whatever caused her sadness would subside. Tears slid down her cheeks. He laid his fork down on his plate. "Lilly?"

"Her presence is everywhere." Standing, Lilly took her plate to the sink.

Nigel followed her. She was sobbing. What should he do? Leave and go home? Try to comfort her? He wrapped an arm around her shoulders.

She untangled herself from him and went to the box. "What did you say was in this?" Scraping tears away, she opened it.

"Things from your grandmother." Nigel walked over, reached into the box and brought out the princess on the horse. He turned it over and showed her the message on the bottom. "Your mother gave this to you?"

"Indirectly, yes," she said, her voice cracking. "After Mother's death, they found this in her suitcase." Covering her face with both hands, Lilly wept openly.

Nigel pulled her close and held her. Emotion for her overwhelmed him. He lifted her chin with one finger and kissed her lightly. The salt of her tears didn't detour him from kissing her again. She offered no resistance. Each kiss went deeper, became more frantic as he sought a resolution to the emptiness he'd felt since Lilly had moved out. But they were getting divorced, niggled at the back of his brain.

Breaking away, Lilly ran to a room just off of the kitchen. Nigel joined her. He stopped, realizing it was her bedroom. He faltered. Stared at her. How was he ever going to break this soul-deep connection to her?

With tears streaking down her cheeks, she slid a trembling hand up his chest and murmured, "Nigel."

Their mouths met, tentatively, before their kisses deepened again. All logic and reasoning why he shouldn't be here ended.

~ ~ ~ ~ ~

Lilly woke up at five in the morning. The other side of the bed where Nigel had slept was empty. She missed him and had since she'd moved out of their house. His house now, she amended. Emotions warred inside of her. Last night shouldn't have happened; it would muddy up finalizing the divorce.

"How could you be so foolish?" she whispered as tears spilled down her cheeks. She could blame Nigel, that would be the easiest. Yet she was at fault too. Determined not to dwell on it any longer, she got dressed and fixed her breakfast. When she finished eating her meager egg and toast, she slipped her plate into the ancient dishwasher.

Going up to the attic, she opened one of her gran's trunks. She fingered the long dresses in it that Gran had saved from her own mother. This coming Wednesday was the sixtieth anniversary of the library opening. Jane had said that they'd be wearing apparel appropriate to 1911. Even though Lilly wasn't heavy by any means, hoping she'd fit into one of her great-gran's dresses was a stretch. She carefully took out several of them and laid them on a covered dresser. Some had miniscule waists, some were more generous in size. After careful consideration she selected a matching blue silk shirtwaist and skirt with an elastic waistband.

Lilly went back to the trunk and looked at the pairs of button-up boots that had been saved. Comparing her feet to the bottoms, Lilly realized that women of her great-gran's generation had much smaller feet. "I could wear my black boots with this. I'm surely not the only one unable to fit my size seven foot into a size two boot."

~ ~ ~ ~ ~

Nigel stayed busy all day Sunday, detailing and polishing his Mustang. He'd pushed away the memory of Lilly from the night before every time it popped up. Which was more frequent than he cared for. He couldn't go back to the way it was before. Wondering if Lilly and Simon Hanes, the Assistant Director at the Aurora library, had been involved. Something his daughter

Macey seemed to know about. Anger and jealousy rose up. Distracted him. No! Was his immediate response.

Going into the house, he flicked on the TV and turned the dial to Channel 11. He instantly regretted it as *Gunsmoke* came on. Lilly and he had watched it together for several years. How was he ever going to forget her and get on with his life?

To be continued . . .

Bill Roberts • Omaha, NE

Hose Crime

Chapter Seven: Bad Dreams

One chilly May night the spring winds kicked up, disturbing sleep for persons of interest in Far Wevendell and Bisonton.

Sean Large dreamed that the person he shared the house with was a low-down bastard lurking in the basement just waiting for him to make a mistake. The bastard was the color of dusty lilac bushes, dry, and reptilian, with raspy breath. Whenever it spoke, it lied. Sean looked in on the bastard in its cage down there, and what if the bars began to bend, yes they were slowly bending, it was certain now, and Sean jolted upright in bed. Cautiously he went down to make coffee.

Andy Fulcrum—the actual other person in the house, who slept upstairs just down the hall from Sean Large—dreamed that he was trying to arrange a set of chess pieces on a low coffee table. But they kept sprouting legs and walking away. "Stay put, stay put," he mouthed while sleeping. Occasionally there was a reversal of scale and the chess pieces towered over him like skyscrapers. Sometimes the chess pieces became small as gnats, fitting between his thumb and finger, and he had to call on his powers of sensitivity, which he luckily retained even when sleeping. Then the chess pieces became horses, then larger still. Andy writhed in bed.

Sam Chrysler dreamed that Chicago Drew was putting them on, in some way laughing at Sam and all the Neverthelessers, laughing behind their backs. He's such a city slicker, that Chicago Drew, and thinks he's so smart. Plus this: Sam felt a tap on his shoulder, whirled around to see, but the tapper had moved on. It happened a couple of times, and Sam began panting. He'd been a good sport but this wasn't funny anymore. When the exertion woke him up, he went downstairs for brandy, but that just gave him heartburn and made sleep impossible. He got up and stared at the TV.

Ruth Wrightfield dreamed the same thing Sam did—Chicago Drew was laughing at her and her friends. She didn't exactly mind when people laughed at her, but she didn't exactly like it either. There was music, costumes, and maybe a sing-along, hard to tell. When she awoke her jaw hurt.

Chicago Drew dreamed that the flowers he planted so carefully had turned into hands that reached up from the ground. Hands erupted all around him as he sat in the garden and played piano quietly, being careful not to wake the others. The garden hands reached for his keyboard, and he tried to be polite while swatting them away. He made bubbles of spit on his lips and muttered himself awake. "Doesn't anything good ever happen in Bisonton?" he whined to the night.

Loren Wrightfield dreamed that he had resumed being King of secret riches, but now the crown of his head had stuck to the ground and the earth was moving. He cycled his legs, trying to keep the crown of his head connected to soil, but what really surprised him was that he never knew the earth could move in the ways it was moving. He woke up slowly, rubbing his head doubtfully and blinking, but he was glad to be still an ex-King. Loren was a good Neverthelesser.

Judy Salerno dreamed that Chicago Drew would take her out to a nice purple dinner somewhere velvet with milky candles and then wreck everything by asking her to marry him. Then she would bump her head against prison bars (this actually had happened to her when she forgot where she'd put the mice) and start crying, just falling to pieces. Oh my. She had not got away with it, even though she thought she could, and it made her sad. "Why don't you please leave now," she said, aloud, waking herself up. She heard the wind and regretted having spent the other night with Chicago Drew, so she decided she'd better call her old friend Traci to ask how to get free of the guy.

Traci would know how to shake off a bothersome guy. She did it a lot because she was so attractive. In fact Traci's beauty made Judy uncomfortable, but by phone it would be OK. Judy had special affection for Traci; she introduced Judy to the Neverthelessers and she was ex-Queen of the weekend and of the non-rats, an unusual combination. Traci never answered phone calls, but just before lunch she called Judy back.

"Let's be clear here," Traci said. "Is he really asking you to marry him? Or did you just dream that part?"

"So far I've only dreamed it. But it was convincing, and I'd like to nip it in the bud. Shoot, I don't know. I can't really get a good read on this guy."

"You just feel guilty about banging him, sounds to me."

"Yeah, there's some of that. True enough. So you don't think he'll do anything like that? Propose, I mean?"

"Who can say? Tell me this: What does he want? Generally, I mean. Why did he come to town in the first place?"

"High school reunion. He's successful, made a lot of money, wants to let everybody know, rub their faces in it."

"That's understandable," Traci said with a shrug.

"There's also this: He said he wants to find the place in Bisonton where he made out with some chick back in high school. I don't know who. Guess he never said. Thing is, he doesn't want to find the girl—just the place. For some reason he can't find it, can't remember it right or something."

"He was wasted, probably. I mean, you know: high school."

"Also he was looking for a Sillifier meeting. Almost forgot that. Ever hear of a support group called the Sillifiers?"

"Sillifiers? Sure. I know them. They had a presence in Detroit, when I was back there hiding out. Sillifiers, hmm?"

Traci fell silent and Judy wondered if it was good or bad that she knew the Sillifiers. "I'm intrigued," Traci finally said. "Why don't you set up a dinner date for the three of us? Just tell him I'm familiar with the Sillifiers and I'll take it from there. You won't have to worry about Chicago Drew anymore."

"Thanks, Traci. That's just what I was hoping to hear."

Chapter Eight: Outsider

Some who live in Far Wevendell like to start their Monday mornings with an Expellian meeting at the local diner known as Egg Linkin. They see it as a way to flush out any overnight negativity, gain the support of like-minded Expellians and begin their workweek on a positive note. Egg Linkin has a plastic statue of our sixteenth president in the entryway, and there's a "log cabin" feel to the laminate paneling on the hostess lectern, in the booths, on the screen for the restrooms, and on the south wall of the back room where the Expellians had their meetings. On this Monday morning a dozen of them turned out to expel their nasty thoughts, wishes, and dreams.

"Truth is, I look forward to this meeting because as long as I'm here, I'm not at my goddamned job," said a pot-bellied man, about thirty-five, who wore a short-sleeved shirt with a tie. "Every minute with you is a minute away from my idiot supervisor. Brad. A name now ruined for me because it will always, always make me think of incompetent idiocy." He paused, and then brightened. "OK! That ought to do me. Oh, almost forgot: I'm Phil and I'm an Expellian."

"Thank you, Phil," the attendees said in unison as the disgruntled one sat back down. Then a big-eyed ball of a woman pushed herself out of her seat and back from the table, allowing extra room for her belly as she stood, head back and arms bowed out. She breathed with a thick nasal rattle.

"My name is Faye Striggs, and I am here to expel my unhealthy—although realistic—notion that I am an outsider here in Far Wevendell," she announced. "I mean, look at me. A woman alone, which makes me rare in a neighborhood known as a good place to raise kids. Fat and unattractive, again, rare; most of you keep yourselves trim and healthy. And I don't really like Far Wevendell, with its gates, kids, activities, and overall sense of being on top of the heap. I know a lot of you pay a premium to live among these rolling hills. Sorry, but I just gotta tell you: It's a load of crap."

She paused and looked around, almost daring somebody to contradict her. Of course, that's not done in Expellian meetings. Besides, ever since Faye moved to F-Dub two years ago to stay with her mother, people had figured out there was no percentage in taking up the gauntlet she threw down. Being unlovable was something that seemed to make Faye feel special.

"I yearn to be rid of the sense that I am an alien, a stranger, a foreign presence in the utopia that is Far Wevendell. A utopia, I might add, where an unpopular person might find himself gunned down. Murdered. If not in cold blood then in garden hose. I send a big Sorry to victim Patrick Hoffand—wherever you are!"

Faye sat back down, satisfied. Nothing she liked better than delivering a scathing critique. Couldn't happen to a nicer community. It did make her hungry though. Last thing she'd eaten was a Snickers, before the meeting started, and that was getting to be a good half hour ago. She began thinking tacos on the way home.

Sure enough, within the hour she was in the drive-thru lane of Toby's Tacos. And she was stuck. Her Chevy Cavalier stalled and wouldn't restart. As she wondered what to do, an old guy shambled up and offered to push it out of the way. It was Bisonton Police Detective Gene Merle, who'd stopped by for a breakfast burrito. She told him she was Faye Striggs and put the Cavalier in neutral while Gene pushed it off to the side. Afterward Gene stood panting, waiting to be thanked. A long wait. Faye called Triple A and went inside Toby's. Gene followed her in, to talk with her and see if she knew anything about the Hoffand murder case.

They sat in a booth, but Faye seemed distracted until their order was ready. Then she came alive—the shell-crunch of her first taco, its springy lettuce, grated cheese, and greasy, spicy meat. She softly burped and visibly relaxed. She asked Gene, "If you're a cop, how come you're not driving a cop car?"

He chuckled at her innocence. “I’m a detective, so I don’t have to wear a uniform or drive a cruiser. Also, I’m from Bisonton, not Far Wevendell.”

“Bisonton, huh? So what brings you to our fair utopia?”

“I’m investigating the Hoffand murder. I imagine you’ve heard of that. The local force doesn’t have any detectives, so here I am. But tell me: Do I hear something in your voice? Are you not a fan of Far Wevendell?”

She wiped away the residue of taco one and smiled. The detective was thinking that some fat people often seemed uncomfortable, unhappy. Not Faye. She was as settled and self-confident as a bird on a perch. Probably an owl.

“That is a diplomatic way to put it. I think Far Wevendell is snooty, ugly, and hypocritical. More, but that’s all I can think of right now. And let me tell you about the Hoffand murder. Don’t be surprised if you get zero cooperation. Nobody liked that guy, so it’s something nobody cares about.”

“Oh yes, I’ve come to realize that. But it’s like I tell my pooch, Dixie Cup: Murder is still a crime—even when the victim is unpopular.”

The detective smiled as she tucked into her second taco. “Here’s something I ask everybody: Do you know anything about the murder? I’d love to solve it. If you could help, wow, that’d be peachy.”

She dabbed sauce off her mouth. Gene smiled harder, still hopeful. Sometimes an outsider is the key to unlocking an investigation.

“This could be your lucky day, detective. First, let’s get this straight: I did not see it happen. OK? But early that morning I did hear a couple guys talking about it. Seemed pretty likely they were the ones who did it."

"Why do you say that? Who were they? Where were you to hear them?"

Faye enjoyed having something this man wanted. "I sleep with the window open, second story, and if I happen to wake up early and hear someone out there, well, I don't turn on my light. So I have had occasion to hear some morning conversations around here. Lots of them, actually." She lifted an eyebrow and sucked pop through a straw.

"Hmm, hm. You said two men, right?"

Her first taco was being converted into tasty little burps, and she let one go. "Two men. I didn't know them. They weren't from around here. They had East Coast accents. Ever watch *The Sopranos*? They talked like that."

"OK. What did they say to make you think they did it?"

"One of them said stuff like, 'There were too many people around, I couldn't move him, what are we gonna do, we're going to get caught.' The other guy says, 'OK we gotta think of something.' The first guy says, 'So think of something!' Back and forth like that. Tense. Nervous. Finally one of them says they gotta use Sillification. 'I bet Sillification can get us out of this,' he says."

"Sillification? What's that?"

"I don't know. Thought you might." She let go of a burp that opened up more room down there. "That's what they said though. Sillification."

Faye took a pull on her straw and began scooping bean dip with tortilla chips. Ah, that salty-sweet combo of soft ooze and hard crunch. She took three scoops.

"Then they ask the guy two doors down, Otherdam, to borrow his garden hose. He says OK, and they start spraying each other. I know! Crazy, huh? I snuck over to the window and looked, just to be sure, because it seemed so weird. Yeah, they were spraying water on each other. Otherdam got in on it too. Then a bunch more F-Dub men joined in. Lots of them. I've noticed that they tend to move in herds."

"Wait, really?" Gene said, getting excited. "Are you saying that's where the hosing started? Outside your window? Can you show me where you live?"

Faye let out a long, slow one. "Sure, I can show you. But you'll have to give me a ride. Look, here comes Triple A to tow my car."

As the tow truck pulled away, Faye Striggs rode with the detective over to her mother's house. Faye explained that her mother stayed on the ground floor since it was difficult for her to move around. The detective looked at ground zero for the hosing. He saw how Faye's window was set back, architecturally, so that passers-by would hardly even notice it was there. While Gene interviewed Faye about the two East Coast guys, the mother fixed coffee and offered cookies, brushing Gene's shoulder as she reached to set down the cookie plate. Hmm. Gene made sure to mention his wife and happy home, as he didn't wish to break any hearts in Far Wevendell.

Chapter Nine: Dinner Date

Chicago Drew tried to be the kind of person who arrived early, and this evening he reached Mane Hump five minutes ahead of Judy and her friend, Traci, who knew about Sillifiers. Judy had told him this was the hip new restaurant in Bisonton, and he had to admit it was pretty good for his little old hometown. Mane Hump was a popular gentrified island in a rundown part of town, offering a carefully chosen menu. He suavely told the hostess he was waiting for two lovely young friends, but he didn't know how right he was until he got a load of Traci. Even a well-traveled guy like him stared. They were shown to a table, and as they sat he announced Mane Hump pleased him so much that he would be paying the tab—no protests, now. Judy giggled and Traci smiled.

They ordered drinks and talked about Sillification. He learned that Traci wasn't actually a Sillifier but was familiar with the concept from being in Detroit. No, she didn't know of any groups in the area. In fact, she added, she herself was a Neverthelesser, as was Judy. Chicago Drew smiled at Judy to charm her before turning back to Traci.

He then explained to Traci (Judy had heard this) that he was in town to enjoy his upcoming high school reunion, yes, but what really drew him (his eyes flashed; Drew's his name) was the chance to find a certain location in or around Bisonton. At that location, once in high school, he and a girlfriend had touched each other in a very special way one very special summer night. So the real reason he came to Bisonton, odd as it may sound, was to find that special location again.

"What about the girl?" Traci asked, with a smile so sexy Judy had never seen it outside of movies. "Don't you want to find her too?"

Drew stammered something about how locations had a special importance for him, but around this point Judy lost the thread of conversation. Looking over the menu, she thought she might order the bison-and-gouda-cheese-burger on the third page, although since Drew was paying maybe that pricey lamb chop with couscous on the second page. She noticed the menu was printed on thick fancy paper. The window blinds were like purple enamel. And look at the big long block of marble or granite that served as the bar. Shiny and obviously heavy, it summed up the place. The customers seemed stylish if not friendly. About this time Drew excused himself and made for the restroom. Judy watched him leave and then thanked Traci for suggesting this restaurant.

"Yeah, I don't think you have to worry anymore about him proposing," Traci said, laughing. "What a goof. Say, would you mind taking it from here? I think I'd really rather leave."

Although Judy did mind a little, she said fine, call you later. But when Traci worked her way through the crowd she saw Drew talking to an overweight woman with big eyes. Traci hadn't meant to be seen, but once she was, she decided to stay after all and go to the ladies room. She heard the large woman say something to Drew about high school.

At the table, Traci barely had time to explain her continued presence before Drew returned and announced that Faye Striggs, an old friend of his—"girlfriend," Faye corrected—he'd just run into was going to join them for dinner. Introductions followed, another chair was pulled over. Faye asked if they'd ordered an appetizer yet, and she told the waiter to bring a double order of nachos deluxe. "You'll thank me," she told her new tablemates. "They tend to scrimp on appetizers in places like this."

Well! Faye turned out to be the very girlfriend Chicago Drew had made out with back in high school. Judy expected Drew to be delighted at finding her, but he seemed more shell-shocked. Faye sat down and put her palms on the table.

"Back in high school I hadn't put on so much weight yet," she declared. "Instead of eating food every chance I got, I was chasing boys. Back then it seemed exciting. But those days are over. I mean, yuck. Right?"

"A lot of things that seemed valuable in high school don't last into our adult years," Traci observed.

"Tastes do change," Judy piped in.

"Hey, Drew, know what I remember about that time you and me hooked up at that woodsy? I remember you were excited! Woo! More than most boys—although I'd hate to get too graphic."

Judy asked, "So Drew: Was that the 'special time' you mentioned?"

"I know *you* thought it was special," Faye said.

Drew frowned. "Wait. Was that a woodsy? Are you sure? I remember lights. It was bright as day."

"Sure it was bright," Faye said. "All the kids circled their cars in the field, headlights on, and in the center we had a keg and a bonfire."

"Were you making out in the middle of the circle of cars?" Judy asked.

"I can't remember. Maybe—was I drinking beer?"

"We weren't in the middle. The keg and the bonfire were in the middle."

"If it was bright, couldn't everybody see you making out?" Judy asked.

"It was more glare-in-your-eyes bright," Faye said.

Drew was nodding. "OK, yeah, a circle of cars with their headlights on. Yeah, that makes sense."

"I suppose you could see everything, if you walked up and looked, but I don't think anybody did. Ha! But how would I know? I had my head down!"

"OK, this isn't exactly helping my appetite," Traci said. "Can we change the subject before we order?"

"This is it, it's really it," Drew said. "Faye, could you find that place? Where we had the woodsy and all that? Could we go back to that exact same place?"

"Well, now, I'm not going to do 'all that' with you again, you know."

"Oh no. That's not what I meant."

"Because that once was enough, Mr. Drew Chambers!"

"I realize, Faye, truly: It's just that I really, really want to go back to that location. It's the place I've been trying to remember."

Faye, having got all she could out of the moment, said sure, and Drew set a time to pick her up the next day at her home in Far Wevendell. The waiter took their orders: Judy went with the bison burger, Traci got the Athenian salad, Drew ordered the lamb chop with couscous, and Faye ordered a meat loaf Wellington.

It seemed the meal would be remembered as a feast of embarrassment: Judy was embarrassed when Drew ignored her in favor of Traci; Drew was embarrassed when Faye reared up from his past; Traci was embarrassed when she planned to leave but then stayed; and Faye was embarrassed when she dropped a nachos chip on herself and didn't notice it for several minutes.

Before the waiter brought their entrées out, a siren sounded. Outdoors a spring storm had been building up, and now someone in Bisonton had reported a tornado. There being no basement in the Mane Hump, everybody in the establishment, patrons and staff, crowded into the walk-in cooler and pulled the door shut. The manager had a radio but the reception was terrible and the storm outside was noisy. Cold and crowded, they looked at one another. Most of them were annoyed or bored. A few seemed concerned or even frightened. Traci was shaking uncontrollably, her teeth chattering and her eyes welling up tears. She gulped, hiccupped, and repeatedly said things like, "How in the hell and what in the hell and holy hell." The manager shouted at her to get hold of herself and several patrons backed away. Faye Striggs tried to slap her but she ducked. Traci's panic began infecting others. Then the lights went out, and screaming was general.

Johnnye Gerhardt • Omaha, NE

Digger

Chapter One

"Still don't believe me, do you? Read this."

Foley Connor handed over a piece of paper folded small enough to fit the inside pocket of his suit jacket. He glanced down at his shoes dulled by the sand and then scanned the lake. The water rippled in calculated intervals and rhythmically lapped at the shore. The pattern remained steady, an indication it had not been disturbed by a boat, an intruder.

A shaggy willow leaned precariously over the water. Its fringed branches trailed on the surface and undulated with each pulse of waves. Trees and rushes along the shore hid the couple from anyone who might be trolling in deeper parts of the lake. A break in the foliage framed the opposite beach. It was deserted as expected at this hour of the morning.

Forest on either side of a winding gravel road concealed their cars from anyone speeding along the highway a quarter of a mile back. The cove had proven to be the perfect spot for all their rendezvous.

As the note was read, Foley stared off into the woods. Moments later, his fingers lingered on the extended hand as he accepted the note's return. The paper again refolded, he stuck it back inside his suit jacket. He plumped up the gray silk hanky protruding from a chest pocket like the petals of a wilted lily, then smoothed the silver hair at his temples. Foley wished he could be as convincing here as he was at his real estate office. He always closed the sale. Local farmers never doubted he had their best interests in mind when he talked them into selling their land to developers. Foley held out for top dollar, seven percent of which made him the richest man in the county.

The hand that had relinquished the note slid into a front pocket of worn, low-slung jeans. The motion pulled the waistband further down and exposed a smooth, flat stomach. "So you're leaving Ardys. What's that supposed to mean to me?"

"It means, my little tart, that I will pick you up at midnight tonight. Wait for me in the vacant lot next to the church. Keep close to the bushes." Foley dabbed perspiration from his forehead and neck with a monogrammed handkerchief and wished they could have met some place with air conditioning.

His companion's other hand was pocketed and the waistband dipped even lower. "What about—"

"No second thoughts." Foley glanced at the exposed navel and pictured what lay just below.

"I don't want to hurt anybody."

"You have to." Connor ran his finger along the gap between denim and flesh and then hooked it into a belt loop. He gave it a tug. "You're the one who wanted out of here. I left Ardys the house and some stock. She'll be okay." He withdrew his hand. "Since when have you cared about other people?"

A sandaled foot, toenails glossy with clear enamel, leveled a miniature dune. Foley stepped back as a cloud of dust swirled toward him and threatened anew his once polished and buffed wingtips. He studied the icy blue eyes, unblemished by age, deepen in color as they scanned the shoreline. For one of those bizarre unexplainable intrusive moments, he couldn't remember what color his wife's eyes were. Christ, he couldn't even remember what color her hair was.

Green. Her eyes were green. Dull, muted like a fifty-year-old car that had never been waxed. She always glared up at him when they had sex. And he glared back. The disgust she obviously felt excited him. But even that wore off. He looked elsewhere. A twig snapped and jerked his thoughts back to the cove. He glanced in the direction of the noise. A scraggly bush growing next to a boulder the size of a crouching bear trembled, probably a rabbit or squirrel. Foley turned back to the angelic face with its lips pursed to speak.

"You're right. I don't care." One of the hands that had been thrust in the jean pockets raised in farewell. The sandals stirred up more dust as they retreated.

Foley shouted into the trees. "You care about me."

The blue eyes glinted over a shoulder. "As long as you have money, honey."

Foley laughed. "Tonight. Midnight."

The hand waved acknowledgment. A two-carat diamond ring Foley had placed on one of the fingers just a week ago glinted in the sunlight.

"Take the ring off before going into town. You can wear it all the time after tonight. Maybe I'll buy you a bracelet to match when we get to Los Angeles."

The responding grin guaranteed Foley everything would go as planned. He squinted past the pine scrub and cottonwoods as the Ford Tempo pulled onto the gravel road. He winced inwardly as a gritty cloud kicked up by the tires floated too close to his right-off-the-show-room-floor Lexus sedan.

"Why?" a voice hissed from behind him.

Foley whipped around, incensed and terrified. "What are you doing here?" He raised his hands as a shield against the face distorted by loathing. "Wait. Let me explain."

Fists white with furious tension gripped a picnic basket and brass candelabra. Released, the basket dropped with a rasp to the sandy ground. The hand still grasping the candelabra uplifted as though to strike.

Foley sputtered, "I understand how you must feel."

"You've never understood how I felt. You understand nothing."

Foley backed away and cautiously lowered his arms. He knew exactly what buttons to push on this one. "Clarify something for me. Are you upset because I'm leaving—I know how much you care—or because you came in second?"

He smiled as the cocked arm shook and dipped slightly. A ray of sun ricocheted off the brass and blinded him. Foley turned his head. Screaming white pain as harsh and sharp as the light pierced his skull just behind his left ear. He dropped to his knees. A second blow drove him sprawling to the ground. He inhaled sand and coughed violently. Squinting across the miniature dunes radiating from the tip of his nose to his hand just inches away, he caught sight of a pair of seamless, rubber fishing boots running toward his assailant's tennis shoes planted firmly at his side. A dory's prow interrupted the shore just beyond. Frothy peaked waves slurped around it. He strained to see who the boots belonged to but his range of vision ended just above the ankles.

The sun again spotlighted the motion of the candelabra; the mirrored rays danced on the sand. He waited for the third assault but it never came, the weapon's descent obviously checked by the fisherman.

Terror shredded Foley's mind and confused his thoughts. All sound muffled as though he had slipped underwater. But his hand rested in parched grains, his manicured fingernails buried in arid drifts. Cold crept up his legs. He closed his eyes against the pebbles and dirt being flung at him by the frantic shuffling of tennis shoes and boots. He strained to check the wound behind his ear but his arms did not respond to the effort. A chill snaked up his back to his neck and slithered out along his biceps then to his fingertips. Foley opened his eyes, expecting to behold the icy aggressor. He raised his head just enough to see a reddish-brown stain spreading outward from where his cheek had rested. The sight sickened him and he let his head plop down onto the sand again.

The boots approached. The fisherman knelt close, his knee almost touching Foley's shoulder. Foley recognized the face thrust into his. Its mouth formed words he couldn't hear.

Foley Connor mentally disconnected from the scene and he worried he might not make it to the empty lot by midnight. His quaking fingers clawed the sand. When he realized he could be bleeding to death, he relaxed and concentrated on breathing. Was he breathing?

From inside himself, somewhere in the shadows at the back of his skull, he looked out at a surreal world. He closed his eyes, his brain freezing, each cell crystallizing one at a time until the orange glow radiating through his eyelids darkened and he was no longer aware of even the black.

Tasha Hackett • Stromsburg, NE

Wildflower on the Prairie

"Psst."

Hannah jerked awake at her mother's hiss and the sting of the pinch that accompanied it.

"Really, darling. Don't make a spectacle of yourself. You may be exiling yourself to the frontier, but you needn't neglect your upbringing the moment we cross the river." Mother snapped her fan and eyed the other passengers as if they were the cause of her discomfort.

"We crossed the Missouri miles ago, Mother."

"Bridle your tongue, child. If I could turn this train around, I would. It's bad enough your father agreed to this, and it's only by the grace of God himself your brother hasn't been kicked by his oxen, or pigs, or whatever he's playing with on his homestead. I won't take your lip along with the rest of my pains today. With Hiram gone, I prayed your sharp tongue would settle. Somehow you've always been the instigator, though I assumed it was only because you had a willing ally. Why God cursed me with twins I'll never know. You'll never survive the winter together. Books can't be eaten, you know. You with your distractions and him with his animals. Farming. I never dreamed of it for my children. Son of a surgeon, the world at his feet, and he chooses to live in a dusty, barren field." She took a shuddering breath. "How much longer do you suppose? This car is beginning to sway again. We can put a man into a drug-induced sleep, remove his appendix, and the man can live to tell about it, but we haven't discovered how to travel in comfort? What would it take for a few men to put their heads together and insulate this car? The dust that blows through is insufferable. It all comes down to money. They'll charge whatever they can get from poor folks like us and put it in their pockets. Never you mind how the money should have been spent to increase the comforts of its passengers."

Hannah yawned behind her own fan while listing her silent rebuttals. *Hiram isn't playing homestead; he's finally escaped and will do whatever it takes to stay out from under your thumb. I hardly think pigs kick . . . I didn't ask you to travel with me; in fact, I would have preferred you didn't come . . . Poor folks? Mother, please. We're likely the wealthiest passengers on the whole train.*

She imagined a new and improved train car. *Sleek, shiny. No, scaled. A machine with scales like a snake. Or a dragon. Yes. A graceful dragon that took flight with a mere leap into the air and once in flight, only the wind. Rushing wind? No . . . more like a gentle breeze. The dragon flight would be one that surpassed all other forms of travel. Soaring high enough to drown out Mother.* Hannah clenched her fists. She'd packed her drawing books and pencils away. They were safely tucked in her trunks. Hidden. Drawing fanciful creatures in front of Mother would never do. Not when she needed to be on her absolute best behavior today.

Men in suits down the aisle read the paper. A mother with a toddler sprawled across her lap rested her head against the window, her hat askew. The father, arm around his wife and sleeping child, slept with his head at a sharp angle. The other son sat facing his parents, lost in a copy of *The Hunchback of Notre-Dame*.

Hannah's own copy was buried with her drawing notebooks. Nestled tightly between *Frankenstein* and *Emma.*

Hannah craned her neck. If she squinted, she could just make out the headlines of the man's newspaper.

"Answer me, child." Mother flicked her fan against Hannah's knee.

"Yes, Mother." Twenty-one. She was twenty-one years old. Twenty-one and her mother still treated her like a mischievous twelve-year-old. If a self-imposed exile is what this was, so be it. But, no. She was not being exiled. Nebraska, though vast, could hardly be considered the frontier. After all, it was admitted to the Union twelve years ago. More than enough time for civilization to take root. However, neglecting her upbringing was her favorite daydream. Her upbringing, along with Mother's dispositions, hadn't done her favors in the city. She wasn't sure what good it would do her out here.

A smile tugged the corners of her mouth. One more day. In one more day, Hannah would be delivered to her brother's homestead and would revel in the distance from her mother. If letting her sleepy head bob on a train made her a spectacle, she looked forward to the motherless possibilities of the west. Perhaps she would venture into the sunshine without a head covering of any kind and let her bare feet dig into the mud. Hannah wiggled her toes in her pinching shoes and a giggle slipped out.

Mother glared at her as if she'd bitten a lemon.

Ignoring her, Hannah watched the father across the aisle. Bleary-eyed, he focused on the sleeping child on his wife's lap until his own eyes fluttered shut again.

"Don't. Stare." Mother hissed through clenched teeth.

"Yes, Mother." A spike of fear churned through her stomach. *What if Mother prevents me from staying?* Hiram would meet them at the depot and again offer for Mother to see his place, but she would refuse, as expected. She had wrongfully assumed he lived in a sod house, and they hadn't felt the need to correct her. They would stay one night in a hotel, give a tearful goodbye—joyful tears—to Mother and plop her back on the eastbound train. Hiram would bring Hannah to his homestead. And then freedom. Glorious freedom.

Hiram insisted all would be well. She clutched at her satchel, the words from his letters running through her mind again. Her brother would ensure that all went well. He would find a way to keep her here. The twins had been planning this scheme for years. Hiram to set out first and establish the homestead. As soon as it was livable, he would send for Hannah. Things hadn't gone as smoothly as they'd hoped, but Hiram was ready to board the train himself and steal her out during the night if Mother hadn't agreed to let her go. Hannah slowed her anxious breathing and focused on her posture. Now was not the time to prod Mother. Let her believe her upbringing was fully intact. She pulled out her copy of *The Poetical Works of William Wordsworth,* Volume One. A gift from Mother for her twenty-first birthday. Though what she really wanted to read was *Black Beauty* safely and secretly packed in her trunk. She had hoped if Mother saw her reading the gifted book, it would soften her disposition.

"Hannah, dear. I'm worried about you and Hiram. I still don't understand why the two of you can't settle down in the city with the rest of us. Mrs. Tyrel says they still don't have piped-in water in most of the state out here. Whyever would you give up the city for this wasteland?"

Don't whine, Mother, it's unbecoming of a lady of your stature. Hannah reached over to grab Mother's hand and squeezed it before handing her the book of poetry. "Here, Mother. Why don't you read. Take your mind off the stress of the day. There's a lovely poem on the second page, just there."

The soured look on Mother's face deepened, but she took the book, nonetheless.

The telegram wires, drooping and rising, drooping and rising, pulled at Hannah's gaze. What important messages shot back and forth? She saw the whole scene play out with a twist. No longer was she on the plains, but an ancient medieval village. A young woman, with a face about like hers, sat at the machine, quickly transcribing the Morse Code: ENEMY ADVANCING WEST. SEND IMMEDIATE REINFORCEMENT. *Men and women scrambled to gather shields and swords. Only a few of the trained warriors remained; the war had been too fierce, too long. A woman in leather trousers and tunic slung a water skin over her back and grabbed her spear. Originally trained as a rear guard, she was now one of the best scouts their battalion had left. She would run along the leeward side of the army. No, leeward was for ships, wasn't it? Could she scout leeward on land?*

Hannah blinked her eyes shut, but the lines continued to travel through her mind. Drooping and rising. Mother slapped the book cover and thumped it back on Hannah's lap.

"You're giving up piped water to keep house for your brother, who gave it up to play with pigs. Will someone please explain to me the logic behind these decisions? The excuses the two of you crafted the past year are not convincing anyone. Nobody in their right mind desires the adventure of self-sufficiency enough that they willingly dig in the dirt for their own food. If Hiram needed to prove himself self-sufficient so badly, Father would have let the guest house to him until he married and bought a place of his own." Her fan sped faster and faster in time with her rant. "Both of my children. Turning their backs on their parents in the same year. There won't be anyone suitable for the two of you to marry so far from civilization. I don't care what you've said about Ockelbo. It's the end of the rail line, therefore, it can't be anything worthwhile, it doesn't even have . . ."

"Have what, Mother?"

"Oh! Piped water, among other things." She snapped the fan shut and then immediately opened it again.

One more day. Be on your best behavior for one more day. And then . . .

Well. And then she would *live*.

Sammi Hoard • Alma, NE

Love Lines: Michael Reilly

Chapter Two

After the coffee crowd cleared out, Alex let Jill, the other server, go home. Gathering sugar containers from the tables, she set them on the bar to be emptied and washed. For the ten-hundredth time she'd found Sally staring at her.

"Please quit looking at me like that. If you have a question, ask."

"Are you going to go out with Michael?"

"What do you think?" Alex emptied two containers into a small, clean bucket and picked up two more containers.

"You should go."

"That's not what I meant and you know it."

"Go out with him," Sally repeated, sliding empty containers into the sudsy water. "He's a hunk, he's rich, and the way he was looking at you, he's very interested."

"He's rude and arrogant and . . . and . . . he tied my apron!"

"I thought you were going to slap him," Sally said with a laugh.

"I was so stunned it took a moment for it to actually register. It's a good thing he stepped back when he did." Alex tried forgetting the brief moment that his hands had been at her waist. Pushed aside the warring emotions inside of her. She was a Christian woman, she wasn't supposed to acknowledge any of these feelings. "Besides, he didn't want me to say yes."

"What makes you think that? He looked at you like you were dessert."

"I know it from the relief that crossed his face when I said no." Alex looked up. Sally was struggling not to laugh. When Sally finally let loose, Alex, unable to resist, joined in.

Grabbing a wet sponge, Alex wiped down the bar. "What's with his southern drawl? Jason doesn't talk with an accent."

"Michael was raised in Virginia." Sally set clean containers on the drain board. "Jason grew up in Kansas with his mother."

Alex didn't respond. She wanted to finish so she could go upstairs and go to bed.

"You're not even the tiniest bit interested?"

"Nope. Please drop it."

"Only you would pass up a date with a handsome millionaire." Sally smiled before growing serious. "Michael's a good man. A *really* good man. You couldn't go wrong if you went out with him."

"I don't want to go out with him. End of conversation."

Too much had happened in Alex's life. She had no reserves left to try starting a new one. Especially with the likes of Michael Reilly. She doubted he was a Christian, and that was her number one requirement for the man she finally said yes to. They must believe and attend church. It was nonnegotiable.

Not that she wanted to date anytime soon. Maybe someday, with the help of her therapist, she might be ready. During the early years of her life, she'd questioned God and Christ and hadn't trusted Christ to give her life completely to Him. After she'd gotten pregnant with Chaz and later married Will, she'd spent too many years of her adult life with a man who only paid homage to God on Sunday mornings.

It had taken the illness of her daughter, Annie, for her to seek the Lord. Annie's death three years ago had nearly killed her. It was her newfound faith and Christ comforting her that had sustained her. No way was she ever going to drift away from Him again.

So to explore finding someone, particularly someone she could share the rest of her life with, was on the back burner for now.

That was the least of her concerns. Alex hadn't told any of her employees that Michael, a.k.a., Computer Mate Incorporated, was striving to buy the coffee shop and the other businesses on the block.

"Will's been dead for a year and a half," Sally said, her hands settling on her hips. "It's time to get back with the living, time to start dating."

"No, it's not—"

"It's not like you have to honor a mourning period for Will. He was a snake. He cheated on you!"

"I'll repeat," Alex said, calmly, "end of discussion."

Dwelling on Will's infidelities, and when he'd finally left her for another woman, was not something she wanted to do tonight. Sally was right about him being a snake though. Surprised to find a tear trickling down her cheek, Alex brushed it away. The sheer loneliness of her life—when she allowed herself to feel anything—was sometimes more than she could bear.

A knock on the glass door brought Alex out of her troubled thoughts. She smiled at Jeff Malone, her brother-in-law, who was on the other side.

Sally rushed over to open it. "What can we do for you, Chief Malone?"

"Have you dumped the coffee yet?"

Jeff's navy-blue uniform was neatly pressed, and it accentuated his blonde hair and startling green eyes. His flashlight hung at one hip, his holster on the other, and the radio receiver was attached to his left shoulder. Before Will's death, Alex had never really noticed how much the two brothers resembled one another. Now it was the first thing that caught her attention.

"Not yet." Alex poured coffee into a foam cup, put a lid on it, and handed it to him. Jeff pressed money into her palm, she gave it back. "It's free for the police."

"Thanks. See you at the folks' place tomorrow night?"

Alex hadn't been over to Will's parents' house for several weeks. It was too painful. They still thought of Will as a stellar human being even after everything he'd put Alex and Jeff through.

"They miss you. You're the daughter they never had," Jeff murmured. "Think about it, okay?"

"All right, I'll consider it."

He started toward the door then turned. "You ladies be sure to lock up behind me. Goodnight."

Sally slid the lock into place after Jeff stepped out. "You could go out with him. Lord knows that man has a thing for you," she said, walking to the sink.

"Jeff's family. Dating him would be like going out with my brother. When Ginger left him for Will, it nearly destroyed him. He's still hurting, he thinks I am too."

"True enough, but it's obvious he wants to get on with his life—with you."

Alex shook her head.

"Deny it all you want. He has feelings for you now. Just as he did in high school. He only married Ginger because he couldn't have you. But he's right about one thing."

"What's that?"

"You're still hurting. It pains me to see you this way," Sally said, tears gathering in her lashes. "We've been friends forever and I love you like a sister. I only want to see you happy."

"I know you do. But I'm not ready to start dating," Alex murmured. "I probably never will be. Besides, you know my criteria—"

"They have to be a Christian," they said in unison.

Sally sobered, touched Alex's cheek gently. "When you're ready, all you have to do is say yes." Dropping her hand, she slid more containers into the sink.

Grateful that Sally changed the subject, Alex leaned back against the counter. Stared at her reflection in the mirror behind the coffee bar. Noting the fine lines at the corners of her eyes, she cringed. They seemed deeper somehow.

"Maybe I'm getting too old to date," she said more to herself than Sally.

"What?" Sally glanced up, her voice incredulous. "You're still a beautiful woman."

"I turn forty this year!"

"Forty is not old," Sally countered right back.

"Give me a break!" Alex picked up a sugar container to dry when Sally placed a hand on her arm.

"You don't see what the rest of us do, do you?" Sally's voice softened, her eyes were kind. "You're still a beautiful woman—"

"You said that already."

"Let me finish, okay? You're beautiful, you're smart, and you have a body that most women would kill for at any age. Men still look at you and like what they see."

Alex didn't buy Sally's theories. A frumpy woman stared back at her when she looked in the mirror. Lord knows that Will had called her that enough for her to believe it. "They see the lines as clearly as I do."

Sally stared at her dumbfounded. "Are you talking about these?" She gestured at the corners of Alex's eyes.

Alex nodded. How could she admit to her dearest friend, whom she loved like a sister, too, that she was still vain enough to care whether she looked young or not?

"Ah, honey, they're laugh lines." Sally wrapped an arm around Alex's shoulders. "Some people would call them *love lines*," she said, then paused, chewed on her bottom lip. "What else is bothering you tonight?"

"Everything," Alex said and sat on a bar stool.

"Hon, are you strapped for cash? Have you talked to your attorney about using any of the money Will hid?"

"That's blood money and I won't touch it. Besides, Will had no intention of me inheriting any of it."

"Screw Will Malone. That money is yours." Sally studied Alex intently for a couple of beats. "Fess up, what else is troubling you?"

"Computer Mate wants to buy the property on this block."

"Michael Reilly owns Computer Mate."

"Yes, he does."

"Why, that's a sneaky, underhanded thing to do. Why on earth would he want it?"

"So they can build another store closer to UNK. His lawyers included a five year profit plan with the bid. Like I care," Alex said, rolling her eyes.

"Like Michael Reilly needs any more money. What kind of cash are they offering?"

"Five percent over market value. But that's not the issue. This was my grandmother's home. She lived here long before the area was rezoned to commercial. If I sell, it would be like losing part of her."

"I understand. What if the other businesses take the offer? What will you do?"

"I don't know." Alex shrugged. "The sale price is good enough I could move the Victorian to a residential area. Plus I'd have enough left over to buy a lot two blocks west of here. I could build a new coffee shop. It would have modern wiring and plumbing, which would be a blessing in disguise.

"I don't want to start over, though. I want to stay here based on principle alone. Why should I or the other businesses sell just because Computer Mate wants the land? I plan on chatting with the others again to make sure we stand together. But please don't say anything to the other waitresses, not for a while anyway."

"My lips are sealed. I know how stubborn you can be. I'm not worried about our jobs in the least."

~ ~ ~ ~ ~

Jeff Malone drove past Computer Mate later that night, tempted to go inside and chat with Michael Reilly. But what was the point? Michael would be busy going through merchandise. Last week Michael had asked him a simple question: What was needed to arrest someone for theft? Jeff had explained about paper trails, possession of stolen goods, and so forth.

He'd also suggested that Michael hire professionals, both inside the store and out. A private detective could shadow their prime suspect. It would be less painful for Michael and Jason in the long run. Jeff's advice had fallen on deaf ears. Michael Reilly gave a whole new meaning to the phrase *a stubborn Southern gentleman.*

Yet, even though he'd only known Michael four years, Jeff considered him one of his closest friends. Michael knew when to back off from other people's business. He had quietly-with-no-strings-attached helped Jeff through the agony, and the scandal, that followed Will's and Ginger's deaths.

Without much thought, Jeff drove toward Alex's. Parking on the lot, he walked to the front door to ensure it was locked. A lone light shone over the small coffee bar inside. Everything was quiet, in its place. He went back to his cruiser and glanced at the upper level of the Victorian. A golden-orange haze filtered through the blinds of the apartment's kitchen window. From knowing Alex most of his life, she was probably brewing a cup of tea before going to bed.

He'd loved Alex since high school, but Fate had seen fit to match her with his brother instead. Will had been a faithless boyfriend then abandoned Alex at a time she'd needed him the most. When Will refused to marry Alex, Jeff had volunteered to do it, to give her baby the Malone name. But their father had balked at Jeff getting married at sixteen. Will was nineteen and the baby's father. It was Will who would marry Alex. Convincing Will of this had taken too long. Will didn't marry Alex until after Chaz had been born.

Carrying a baby out of wedlock had damaged Alex's sense of self-worth. Her father had banned her from the family. Will had treated her like a door mat during their entire marriage. Will's many affairs had hurt Alex more than most people realized. Jeff knew all too well how much she'd suffered.

Jeff's feelings for Alex had hindered his own marriage. He'd loved Ginger, but she had been his second choice. Was that the reason Ginger had ran off with Will, to humiliate both Alex and him? That question would remain unanswered forever.

What he wanted to know, needed to know, was if Alex returned his love. He was the one she turned to for advice and to do handyman chores around her apartment. Whenever she looked at him, was it love, or kindness, that radiated from her?

The worst of it was that he couldn't ask or say anything to her about how he felt. He still had six long months left to the mourning period for his dead wife. Two years is what his parents had demanded. Now he was hard pressed to continue obeying it.

He wanted to get on with his life, hopefully with Alex beside him. They had so many things in common, their past and present, and they went to the same church. Even though Alex's early years had been difficult, she now was a woman of God. That was the strongest bond they held, and it would cement their love when they got married. If they got married, he amended with a heavy sigh. He put the car in drive and headed west.

~ ~ ~ ~ ~

At 3:00 a.m. Michael scrubbed his hands over his face, yawned for about the five hundredth time. He swung his laptop around so he wouldn't have to look at it anymore. The numbers were merging together; he was so tired. For the first time in the last two weeks, he didn't honestly care if someone was stealing from the business. He just wanted to go home and go to bed.

Standing, he stretched his arms over his head, bent down to touch his toes, and yawned again. He walked to the window where he'd seen the face the night before. Had it been real or had he been so exhausted he'd imagined it?

Instead of going back to his office Michael headed to the showroom. Blue metallic warehouse racks stood ceiling high against stark white walls. An additional ten rows ran down the center. All were chock full of merchandise, from computer furniture to accessories and everything anyone with a computer might want or need.

How long could he and Jason continue trying to figure out which missing merchandise matched up with specific shipments? It would take time, possibly a lot of time. What a foolhardy notion this was proving to be.

He went to the front window, tucked his hands into his trouser pockets, and stared outside. It was snowing for the third night in a row. A haze of white created halos around the street lamps. The lights of the local Supercenter on the opposite side of the four-lane avenue glowed eerily back at him.

Melancholy swept over him. This is what his life had been reduced to since he'd ended his engagement to Felicia Pence a year ago. He was staying up all night, searching for a needle in a haystack, as his grandmother would have said. The breakup with Felicia had left some emotional scars and he was taking time off from dating, to heal his heart. But he couldn't deny anymore what he wanted. He longed for a woman to go home to, someone who was soft and gentle and who could ease his loneliness. And right now—tonight, this moment—only one woman came to mind.

Alex Malone. He couldn't get her out of his head. Couldn't stop thinking about the scent of her hair, the perfume on her skin. She was the only woman in the last year that had had this effect on him.

Was it time to finally start dating again? He didn't have a clue how. *You'll know when you meet the right woman*, his sister, Darcy, who was a psychiatrist, had recently advised.

Leaning his forehead against the cold glass, he closed his eyes and pushed all thoughts of Alex Malone away. Four more months and he'd be relocating to his childhood home in Manassas, Virginia. There were good points, and bad, to this move. He'd be starting a new chapter in his life, but he would be leaving Jason behind.

He'd lived here for five years and he'd liked it. Clean and attractive, Kearney was a thriving college town. Reminiscent of towns long ago forgotten except in classic movies, it was growing at record speed. People were friendly and warm, and he'd made some lasting friendships. He'd miss all of it.

With a heavy sigh, Michael headed back to his office. Sitting at his desk, he muttered another inappropriate word before moving the cursor to the next item on the computer screen.

A click-clicking sound came from behind him. He tensed and gazed over his shoulder, attempting to see where the noise was coming from.

"Michael," a soft, almost feminine voice whispered and it swirled in the air as if it was floating on a cloud of mist. "Michael," it repeated, this time sounding more masculine.

Standing, with the hairs on the back of his neck tingling in anxiety and fear, Michael took a tentative step. A shadow zipped along the back wall. The air shifted and rippled toward Michael. He withdrew his cell from its holder and tapped in Jeff's number.

"Michael," the voice murmured and the shadow moved toward him.

"Yep," Jeff said as he answered on the fourth ring. "What's up, Michael?"

"Get over here, there's an intruder in Computer Mate," Michael said, fear building inside of him.

To be continued . . .

Bill Roberts • Omaha, NE

The Moment

Any life, no matter how long and complex it may be, is made up of a single moment—the moment in which a man finds out, once and for all, who he is. ~Jorge Luis Borges

Chapter Six: After the Meeting

Sam Chrysler closed the Neverthelesser meeting in the usual way. He asked God to grant these former royals grace to deal with their loss . . . nevertheless, all saying the final word together. Finally, as chairperson, Sam called out, "The King is ex," and everyone responded in unison, "Long live the ex-King."

While Sam signed court cards for those who had to show a judge they were improving themselves, Theo Kowalligan looked around for someone to talk with. Spinning in his own disco ball of excitement, Theo still reeled from his realization that he was ex-King of the Stupidophiles. A finger tapped his shoulder.

"I just wanted to say congratulations, Mr.—Kowalligan, was it?" said the cheerful face of Andrea Vitapenny.

"Yes! Theo Kowalligan! Very nice of you to say so, Miss Vitapenny," the grounds maintenance man boomed. "Oh, this realization is really something. Why, not more than ninety minutes ago I was telling Sam Chrysler—the gentleman who led the meeting?—telling Sam how proud I was to be a Stupidophile. So full of myself—as if I were King of the Stupidophiles! Then I come to this meeting and—ka-pow!—I understood. I *am* ex-King of the Stupidophiles!"

"Oh my. You may think I belong in one of your files of stupid people, but I truly do not know what that word means. Will you enlighten me?"

Theo was pleased to take special note of Andrea.

"Why, it means just what it says, Miss Vitapenny. 'Phile' means you love something, and the thing I love is gals who aren't all hung up on showing off how smart they are to every passing fellow. You know—brainiacs? Nope, they are not for me. I like women who are more modest and genuine. Women like yourself, if I may be so bold."

"I'll take that as a compliment," Andrea said, looking down.

"And I'll ask you a question in return," Theo said. "Based on something from the meeting. How is it Neverthelessers don't realize they are royalty until it's too late—when they're not Queen or King anymore? That just seems . . . odd to me."

She cleared her throat. "Counterintuitive, I've heard it called. I don't know that it's a hard and fast rule. It just seems to usually work out that way."

"Well," he smiled at her. "I'll be."

Sam stepped into their conversation. "Theo, we need to get going to meet Mr. Breen at the sandwich shop. For lunch? And a ride back to work?"

"Oh! Right! Jeez, I am discombobulated! Miss Vitapenny, I hope I get to see you again. Will you be here at this meeting next week?"

She laughed musically with both shoulders, a gesture that Theo took to mean Yes, then turned and walked away. Which seemed to him abrupt or even rude. But so what? Theo interpreted it as her ignorance of social niceties that, to tell the truth, didn't matter to him anyway. He made a purring sound.

Sam steered him out the door and toward the sandwich shop. On the parking lot, big and wide open, Theo's heart thumped, a horn honked, and a tire squealed, all under a sky that was like ten bowling pins ready for a strike.

~ ~ ~ ~ ~

Andrea took a few steps, listening, then turned to make sure Sam and Theo really had left. She exhaled and saw the room colors paling around one lady who was putting chairs away. Andrea found herself more bug-eyed and flush-faced than ever by that confident, big-shouldered Kowalligan. She was used to acting in a pretty way for men, just to help make sales, but this guy? Oh my! He had an air and a forcefulness about him that made, well, quite the impression.

And wasn't it something that he would ask her about the very thing that gave her agitations at night when she tried to sleep: *Why is it Neverthelessers don't know they're royal until they're not anymore?* She wondered many times why she didn't understand the Midwestern work ethic 'til she was ex-Queen of it.

Andrea worked at Vissinity Furnishings, a large local store known for "Sinfully low prices." Everybody in Bisonton shopped there for furniture. It was a tradition, you couldn't beat the prices, and it was where Andrea worked fifty-four hours a week selling the hell out of living room and dining room sets. She had the knack of dressing like a Barbie doll, painting a blank smile on her face and feeding customers a steady flow of reasons they should buy a set that cost slightly more than they'd wanted to spend, but gave them way more than they expected to get. When she stepped off-stage to get the paperwork, her customers would whisper how amazing it was that this ditzy blonde salesgirl would know so much about furniture. It was preparation, of course, hours spent memorizing and rehearsing, and that was why she ruled the Midwestern work ethic. That was what had made her the store's No. 2 salesperson (Mr. Vissin would always be first). Until, of course, she met Brad and went with him on that Mexican party boat cruise. That was some cruise! It caused her to miss two weeks of productivity, which was what knocked her off her throne. But gee! After four years, didn't she deserve a vacation? It was fair and it was right, but nothing's free in this world. The price she paid for the vacation and the ring that came with it (yes, she and Brad were affianced) was just that loss of royalty. Her crown was usurped by some young salesman named Seth. Seth! Now she was no longer queen of the Midwestern work ethic. When she had her crown, it seemed like the most natural thing in the world; when she didn't, it was a crying shame. Not that she cried every night. Not every night.

The lady putting away chairs asked Andrea to leave so she could turn off the lights. Andrea gave the lady a business card and a smile, and obliged her by going back to work.

But as Andrea drove lonely Hoofway Boulevard back to the store, she still had the agitations. She thought of what she might think of to say—should she plan something out?—if the next time she went to a Neverthelessers meeting she ran into that ex-King named Kowalligan.

Chapter Seven: Annelida

Sam and Theo pushed open the door of the sandwich shop Annelida, and their locomotion slowed. Annelida enclosed them in bright, colorful walls covered in illustrations of long tubes in red, blue, and yellow snaking and crisscrossing all around the restaurant, up and left, right and down. Sam supposed the tubes were meant to echo the tubular shape of the sandwiches in their buns, or maybe the sausages the meat came from. Theo wasn't sure what it all meant, and he hoped the place wasn't outsmarting him. Keith Breen, who'd been waiting for them to arrive the last twenty minutes, walked over to help.

"Hi, guys," Keith said. "Sorry I had to leave your Neverthelessers meeting. It was just—well, I took in as much as I could. Anyway! It's lunchtime now. Bet you're hungry. Ever eaten in an Annelida sandwich shop before?"

Neither one had, so Keith helped them out. "They say the name is from the Condensed Latin for 'Segmented eating is faster,' but who's got time to learn a new language? Point is, when you're hungry and in a hurry, this place is focused on fast."

He pointed at a sign. "Follow the segments, in order, and do what you're told. Before you know it, you'll have lunch in your stomach."

"I guess this makes sense," Theo said and read the sign:

Segment 1: Stand and order your sandwich.

Segment 2: Select your sandwich parts and cookie.

Segment 3: Pay for your order.

Segment 4: Sit and eat your sandwich and cookie.

Segment 5: Stand and leave.

So they followed the segments in order. Sam remarked it helped him manage the jumble of choices. Wheat or white? Provolone or Swiss? Mustard or mayo? "It's a lot to take in," he told Theo and Keith as they all sat down. Keith grinned, because he already had the hang of the place, and it made him feel a tiny bit superior to old Sam Chrysler, a rather revered Neverthelesser. Theo looked puzzled; he thought Sam meant the sandwich was big.

A guy wearing a green shirt at the next table over caught Theo's eye and struck up a conversation. "Heckuva place, isn't it?"

"Annelida? I guess so. Pretty bright."

"Oh, you mean the colors? Yes, yes, it is. Sure is. Hey, let me ask you this. Ever eat dirt when you were a kid?"

Theo laughed and said no. So did Sam, who had overheard. It was a surprising thing for him to say.

"I think this place appeals to the child within us, especially the deep desire that children have to eat dirt," the guy in the green shirt said. "Look around. It's even painted for kids! Bright, like you said. Reminds me of when I was—you sure you never ate dirt when you were little? Boy, I couldn't get enough of it. Ticked off my mom. Anyway, a lot of kids do, take my word for it."

After a moment the green-shirt guy said, "Really, my point is, this restaurant is devoted to earthworms."

"The hell you say," Keith, overhearing, piped in.

"Look up annelida," he said. "It means earthworms. They're segmented. And they go through their whole life with their mouth open, eating the path they travel, right through the dirt. It all ties together. Go ahead, look it up."

Keith already had his phone out and was, in fact, looking it up.

"That's why gardeners like earthworms," green-shirt guy added.

While they were waiting on Keith, Sam stuck out his hand. "Glad to meet you. My name is Sam Chrysler."

He stuck out his hand back. "Wendell Gorth. Glad to meet you too, Sam." Then Sam and Wendell turned toward Theo, because it was his turn now. But Theo just stared at a TV set mounted high up in a corner of the room.

"Breaking news," it said across the top of the screen. There was a picture of a house surrounded by yellow crime tape and a jittery reporter with a microphone. Her lips were moving but made no sound. There were printed words at the bottom of the screen: "Woman shot dead in Bisonton house. Homeowner being sought. Police find message on wall." Then the TV showed a photograph of the message on the wall. It looked like it was written in red crayon: "NO ADULTERY HEAR."

"Wow. Adultery," Theo said, wide-eyed. "Think that's why she's dead?"

"Hey. Could be," Wendell said.

"Hold your horses," Sam said. "Don't jump to conclusions. Who knows what happened? It's all speculation at this point."

Keith looked up and said annelida did indeed mean earthworm, but by this time all of Annelida was buzzing about murder. Customers and employees bumped into each other to crowd before the TV, trying to take it all in. The place was abuzz as people kept whispering, "Murder."

Keith made an observation. "Weird thing is, that hand-lettered message is a mistake, but you can't tell exactly what kind. It could be a misspelling of the word 'here,' meaning 'in this place,' and maybe the murderer punished a sinner." More buzzing, and he had to raise his voice. "Or it could be a warning. Like somebody slapping you: 'I better not catch you doing adultery, you hear?' If that's what it means, what it lacks is proper punctuation."

"So one way or another, this guy didn't do the right thing," Sam said.

"Either he messed up the spelling or he messed up the punctuation," Wendell said, adding, "I mean besides messing up and murdering the woman."

"Which is even more serious," Keith said and waited for a laugh.

There was no laugh, but that didn't surprise him. Keith in his own hard blue world was surrounded by people who didn't get him, colors that were too bright, and distracting murders on TV.

Chapter Eight: Murder Updates

That afternoon the hunger for murder updates made it hard for everyone in Bisonton to focus on their daily business. How could such a crime happen in their sweet community? Who was the victim? Who the killer? And why? She'd been shot dead but nobody knew where (head? torso? kitchen? bedroom?) or whether by pistol, rifle, or shotgun. Was she a budding young woman, a plump matron, or a dried-out crone? And could someone explain that wall message? The whole day was as trembling as skin about to be touched.

Keith listened for news on his radio while driving back to work with Sam, who also tried to catch any new details, and Theo, who draped an arm over the car seat and shared murder opinions and speculations. A gunshot indoors must be deafening.

What part of a shot body would produce the most blood? Placing the victim in a bathtub, now that would simplify cleanup. Does a puddle of blood coagulate to make a scab? They returned to Gonaway Foods, each of them trying to stop thinking about murder and concentrate on his work. With little success.

Keith woke up his desktop computer and sighed. During lunch he'd gotten several emails from Miss Vodnil, each one fretful. They concerned the shiny beef jerky he had developed and presented at the morning meeting, the shiny jerky that Gonaway Foods now planned to launch as soon as possible.

One email said, "I fervently hope our new product idea won't be leaked or stolen. But what is there to prevent competitors from putting a Gonaway Foods shine on their jerky? I shudder to think of such a fate befalling our new shiny jerky." Hmm. Keith had to decide how he felt about her use of *our*. Long ago he had resolved to be *in* the company but not *of* the company, so logically he shouldn't worry who got credit. But if there were any credit, it damn well should be his. Especially if the stuff actually made money. Another email from the chief marketing officer said, "Never should we impute any dampness or moisture to our new jerky. Simply call attention to the shine and let drop the seed of implication. It roots. Sales flower. Profits reap." Poor Miss Vodnil had cranked her excitement level so far up she may have passed her own abilities. But Keith couldn't tear his eyes from the TV screen. What if he missed an update?

Sam stood in his office, hands on hips and frowning, before getting back to work. He had to get the packaging department ready for this assignment while the department head was still out of town. Nothing must be overlooked! He would need measurements of the finished product in its consumer-sales state. Then he could design a shipping package. Then shipper displays and the packaging for those displays. He also mustn't overlook the weight of cardboard needed for every stage of shipping. He should make notations about possible snags along the way. Sam was a process man. He hoped that when the department head returned next Monday, distressed to have missed that watershed meeting, Sam's preparation would soften the distress and equip his boss with everything required. When Sam finished his first stage of work, he leaned over, stretched his arms and legs, rotated his head to loosen the neck, and enjoyed a long moment on tippy toes.

Theo went to the grounds maintenance garage and found the door closed. He knew what that meant: The guys didn't want any bosses to catch sight of them watching murder updates on TV. That would work: Theo didn't want any of the guys to catch sight of him mowing. Theo hated the guys. Whenever he walked through the garage their heads popped up, saw it was only him, and made soft Donald Duck noises. Making fun of him. When Theo pushed his mower past them he asked if there had been any murder updates. No reply, so he proceeded into his green afternoon. While mowing, he noticed a good-looking guy walking by and flirted. It might have gone somewhere, but when Theo leaned in the guy said, "Damn! You smell like you just ate Annelida," and walked on. Theo checked his phone for murder updates and saw a press conference had been set for 3:15. Back to mowing.

Everett Horne was home about two thirty when police detective Gene Merle and a uniformed cop knocked on his door, asking to speak with him. Everett had been home all day with the flu in a house that still stunk from the flooded basement of last weekend, and his diarrhea didn't help matters. The kitchen had an exhaust fan, so he led them there. The uniformed cop stood around looking stern while the detective did all the talking, and he started by naming the woman who was murdered. He told him she had emails from Everett on her computer and asked why. Everett said probably because he'd been dating her. Then he looked at them and echoed the word "Murdered." He cried and his face became wet and red. He belched, passed gas, sneezed. His body, wearing a robe and overhanging a chair, shook with sobbing. Detective Merle observed but did not try to comfort Everett. The uniformed cop just looked stern. After Everett cried a while, Detective Merle said they were leaving but asked Everett not to leave town before their investigation was done. He sniffled, "OK. I won't."

A little after three p.m. Detective Merle and the uniformed cop came to the high school where Brad Calhoun taught math. They asked the principal for an empty classroom where they could talk with the teacher. Brad joined them with an annoyed expression. They shut the door, told Brad the victim's name, and told him they'd found passionate emails from him on her computer. Brad's confidence disappeared like a blackboard full of chalk equations erased in a swoop. Yes, Brad told the detective and the officer, yes he had occasionally or sometimes dated that girl. But the night before he had been to a movie with his buddy Ray Honeycutt—they could check on that with him—and he hoped the authorities would keep their conversation confidential. It embarrassed him, he admitted, because he didn't want his fiancée to be told about the girlfriend. He knew he shouldn't have fooled around. He planned to break it off. Couldn't they, he asked, avoid telling her? Soon they'll find the killer and that'll be that—right?

The detective paused a long moment, just to make Brad squirm. "Yeah. When we make our arrest, that'll be that." He warned the teacher not to leave town, then checked his watch. It was about time for the murder press conference at headquarters.

At four in the afternoon Keith got a call from the receptionist that he had visitors, not identified, in the atrium. One last check of the computer showed a police spokeswoman in a room with a photo of his girlfriend, Sheila Eggar, on the stand. What the what? But he had to go to the atrium and meet the mystery visitors. What should he see but a ramrod straight uniformed cop and a rumpled police detective there in the Gonaway Foods lobby. The detective asked him if there was a room they could talk in. There he confirmed it. The woman who was killed had been Sheila Eggar. His girlfriend. His Sheila.

Feelings like paintballs machine-gunned through Keith. Panic: Do the police make announcements about the boyfriend a murder victim had been sleeping with? Curiosity: Was it protocol for a married man to explain he preferred this not to come out? Would cops do that? Sadness: He had held Sheila close just a few days ago. Relief: He had needed to get rid of her, after all, before Tawni found out. Rage: Somebody had lied to him, he was more certain than ever, and it might have been the murderer. Outrage: Somebody actually killed Sheila! Murdered her! That's so senseless! Bewilderment: Who would shoot his girlfriend in a house with the word *adultery* written on the wall? Shiver: Would Tawni? He knew she had a gun. Could she have gotten that mad? Was he going to have to cover for her? Deeper shiver: Would he be next on her list?

Keith looked up and noticed the detective studying him. Uh oh, Keith thought. He stood up and shouted: “No way! Don’t try to give me murder guilt for some lousy adultery!”

Memoir

Tricia Tennesen • Divide, CO

Finding My Flow

If you had asked my twenty-one-year-old self what I would be doing in my sixties, I would not have said fly fishing or fly tying. I was more interested in fashion than the outdoors, bugs, or fish—gross. Unfortunately, my fashion style now is grey, baggy, rugged, and expensive. Have you seen those bulky waders along with the galumphing boots and the gear that hangs off your body as a fly fisher? Not a pretty sight.

It was volunteers who piloted me to this passion for fly fishing and fly tying. Unexpectedly, cancer also played a role. Just the diagnosis of cancer can be transformative. It slaps mortality in your face like an auto accident.

With my breast cancer diagnosis came the opportunity to participate in a fly fishing cancer retreat. At this retreat, we learned that our prognosis comes with baggage we may not be aware of—PTSD. We were taught to cast, tie flies, catch and release, read the water, and most importantly, to find our flow when uncertainty reaches for us. We learned how to remain calm when we get that feeling in our gut that cancer has returned, or we have to step foot into the chemo area of any hospital. The smell alone can return survivors to terror.

These volunteers give their precious time. A gift offered with patience, kindness, and dignity. These angels could be on the river fishing for their own catches. Instead, they guided us on technique, optimism, and the fullness of life with cancer. Fly fishing is beyond a sport; it overflows into an art. When done correctly, it is as beautiful as ballet, with the river providing music.

These volunteers recognize that nature heals, that being with other survivors is magical. They understand the healing power of music, offering fifteen cancer survivors live music at the Sit and Whittle cabin. They showed us that dance serves up happiness, so we danced until exhausted with joy. We also learned how to deal with PTSD, if and when it shows its ugly head. We returned home fully armed with the defenses needed to fight the unknown.

I discovered on day one that being on the water isn't about the fish. It's about focusing on something other than your health. It's forgetting about the treatments you may face and the doctor's appointments on your calendar. We set those aside and poured ourselves into learning new skills while sharing fears.

In a few days, I will again be in the oncologist's office facing my mortality. I have growths in odd places and had my second CT scan last week. The doctor will tell me if these nodules have grown. If they have, we may have a problem.

Because of these angels, I will not be alone. I will enter the doctor's office equipped with knowledge empowered by our natural world and the peace offered as I craft flies. I know what to do. I walk to the small lake near my Colorado home, where I focus on practicing a roll cast and the knots required to attach tippet to the leader and fly to the tippet. I take in the glorious day and forget about tomorrow.

In winter, I tie flies. Being new to this craft, my flies lack beauty and symmetry. I am in the process of making and naming flies for each of those beautiful volunteers who gave me this gift of distraction. I've decided my newest fly will be called Mary's

Margarita after one of those angels. I select yellow chenille, a gold bead, and white-tailed deer fur. I slip a hook in the vice. The cat curls up on the corner of my desk among the thread, beads, feathers, chenille, and tools. Later I will find pieces of my craft that have mysteriously shown up in other rooms.

This joy begins with the selection of textures, colors, and names. Soon I have a few messy examples of what an insect should look like. Just like the fish in the water, the result of my tying isn't important. It is the process, it is the creativity, it is snuggling down in my tiny office with buckets of snow outside. I become so immersed in the process that I lose track of time and forget about illness.

I refuse to give my cherished time to worry. Whatever happens, I will accept my reality and all that is possible within that reality. I'll find a quiet space on the South Platte river, pull my hat on, and stand among the hearty pines. On the water, I see a riverbed of possibilities. When this is no longer enough, I will take a deep breath and find my flow.

Janet McMillan Rives • Oro Valley, AZ

Keep Searching

After her husband and her mother died the same year,
the year of my first birthday and her fifty-third,

I never thought about my grandmother's double loss in 1945 until I read the headstones on a visit to Evergreen Cemetery, the resting place of my sister, my parents, grandmother, grandfather, great grandmother, and great aunt. My grandmother and five siblings had come with their widowed mother from Kentucky to Tucson in 1902. She married my grandfather in 1913, so she was still quite young when he died shortly after her mother's death. He had always been a "railroad man" with the Southern Pacific, starting as a surveyor and finishing as an engineer on the run from Tucson east to El Paso and west to Yuma. During the period when he worked as a fireman on a steam engine, filling the firebox with fuel, there was an explosion and my grandfather swallowed "live steam." This event, the family conjectured, was the source of stomach cancer which brought his life to an end at age fifty-six. His obituary suggests age fifty-eight, but I heard that he had lied about his age when he was a kid so that he could start working in his mid teens.

my grandmother began using her railroad pass
to cross the country and visit us at our home in New England,
the second floor apartment in a farm house
owned by the university and surrounded by barns.

We had moved into the apartment in 1944 when the entire faculty, it seemed, lived in university-owned housing. Some of my friends lived in Rainbow Alley, tenement style apartments painted bright colors to disguise the shabby construction. Others lived in Quonset huts which had been erected during the war. Boy, did we luck out by living next to the horse barn, in front of the cow and pig barns, down the hill from the chickens. It was like living on a farm with none of the chores. How we had the good luck to live in the farm house on Horsebarn Hill was a matter of someone else's bad luck. In the summer of 1944, the Hartford circus fire took 167 lives including the agricultural college dean and his wife who lived in the farm house. They had attended the circus with their grandson, the dean's secretary, and her daughter. All five perished in the fire. The university sectioned the house into two apartments, one upstairs and one downstairs. By the fall of 1944 when I was six months old, we began our nine year stay upstairs.

Grandmother's blindness never limited our adventures.
If she came in winter, we'd belly flop on the sled
and careen down the hill, me yelling from my perch on top:
steer, Grandma, steer, as we sailed toward the maple.
If she came in summer, we'd put a dime in a Chiclet box,
a yellow one, and hide it in a stone wall
on the hill up beyond the horse barn.

That's the thing. I barely knew she was blind. How would I? She did everything with me short of reading a book—played ball, played cards, played dolls, taught me to iron. She wasn't afraid to board a train alone in Tucson, Arizona, and disembark days later in Hartford, Connecticut. She sought out adventure, was happy to travel and make discoveries; she told stories and, most important of all, she developed and maintained connections with people. I look back today and realize the ways in which I have followed her example. I have traveled to Europe many times and once to China; I've moved for my education, for job changes and in retirement. Through all of that, I've stayed close to family and old friends while creating connections with people in new places. And I've tried to practice one more lesson from my grandmother: Never give up.

On her next summer visit we'd search for the dime.
We never did find the right wall or the right stone,
but we kept on hiding dimes and we kept on searching for them.
More than anything else, that's what she taught me to do.

The embedded poem, "Keep Searching," was originally published in Lyrical Iowa*, Des Moines, IA: Iowa Poetry Association, 2010, p 18.*

Cathy Beck • Omaha, NE

A Step into Death

It was supposed to be a simple trip to the hardware store. Mom and I needed gardening supplies, planting soil, fertilizer, and new trowels. And we wanted to see the new hardware store.

Growing up, the Dundee Hardware Store, at the corner of 50th and Underwood, had obviously been there since before dinosaurs. The wood floor, aged and warped, sagged and groaned with each generation of handymen, electricians, carpenters, gardeners.

Every time my dad took me into the store, I smelled the sawdust of the old floorboards. Dad went to pick up a new tool or screws to fix the wagon, but mostly to hang out. He purchased his first hammer there, the hammer I asked for when he died.

We were devastated when news arrived of the store's closing. At the last minute, the very last second of time, however, it was rescued. A buyer had been found. The new owner moved it kitty-corner across the street to a vacant building, once the site of a grocery store that had met the same fate. Hinky Dinky (yes, that was the food store's name) closed a few years before and the building hosted a couple of start-ups, soon to be end-ups, dumped on the heap of not-well-funded ventures.

Mom and I entered the new hardware store, during what they called their soft-opening week, and things were still a little rough around the edges. The first thing we noticed was the tile floor. There would be no memory of wood and sawdust to trigger our nostalgia. But at least the store stayed open.

As this was their soft-opening week, things were still a little rough around the edges. The grand opening was scheduled for the following week.

I'd been in the grocery store a hundred times growing up. Living a short three blocks away, as a seven-year-old, I'd walk to Hinky Dinky with my younger sister to buy candy with my allowance. The old grocery store was unrecognizable.

Mom and I meandered. "I don't see any lightbulbs, do you?"

"Yeah, Mom, I saw them a couple of rows over."

"I think I see gardening stuff in the next row. Let's head over there."

We walked around the corner and started perusing the long row of flower and vegetable seeds, gardening tools of all kinds, planting soil, grass seed, hoses—everything we needed to start digging our hands into the rich spring soil.

I turned the corner to go down the next aisle. In that flash of time when everything comes together, the universe, your entire life, all your memories and loves and family, I realized I was falling to my death.

A deep stair case to the basement that must have been hidden behind walls when it was a grocery store appeared out of nowhere. An open pit, with no walls, no guard rails, no warning. I dropped off the ledge.

As I fell, I saw the cement floor at least fifteen stairs down. I was going to die. Really, I knew was going to die. I thought of my family and how this would devastate them. Mom, my siblings, my kids!

I wasn't afraid. Just concerned for my loved ones.

I felt my body turn parallel to the steps. My two feet stayed together, solidly hitting on a step about six down. In that flicker of a second, I knew to throw myself backwards onto the steps behind me. My fall stopped. I landed on my butt.

Had it been luck, or the arms of my guardian angel?

I was alive.

I heard Mom somewhere above me. "Cathy, where are you?"

"Mom. Mom . . . I'm down here."

She was horrified. I was just trying to breathe. And thank God. And find the strength to stand up.

I checked for broken bones, which I knew I didn't have. I checked to see if I was breathing, which I knew I was. And I looked down at the concrete, grateful to be sitting on wood.

Yes, we told the guy working the cash register who seemed to shrug it off, the way many of us do when we are too ashamed to feel the guilt. *No big deal. She didn't die.*

The store manager wasn't in, but I left my name and phone number asking him to call. I received no follow-up phone call, no apology, no free purchases for life coupons.

I opted not to sue. I think because at that time in my life I hadn't done the internal work to find my voice. I'd find the courage to do that work years later.

Instead, I settled with being grateful to be alive.

Flash Fiction

Tricia Tennesen • Divide, CO

Slippery Slope

I climb the embankment, stumble, fall onto my hands, then collapse onto my elbows. I look around to see if anyone noticed—a stupid concern. I'm alone on the South Platte River. It's one of those days one dreams about when stuck inside mid-winter.

I pick myself up and take a look at my granite-scraped hands, check my painful elbows, then my waders. Thank God—minor scrapes and no holes.

A personal disruption created this crazy passion. First, the cancer diagnosis, followed by the necessary treatment, then to a women's cancer retreat. This group of beautiful women helped me discover the healing power of fly fishing.

About halfway up, I lean my rod against a tree, pull up a fat boulder, and take a seat. After a morning on the river, this ritual offers meditative time. I marvel at the sky and the river's blue reflecting off one another. The pinon pines standing tall and erect like soldiers in *The Nutcracker* ballet, protecting the aspens from the powerful winter winds that storm up this valley. The rippling water, the magpies, and the mountain chickadees join the delicate breeze, creating a flawless performance.

I unhook the top of my waders, pull my hat over my eyes, and listen. Glory surrounds me, for I am not rushed. I am contemplative, allowing the voices of nature to heal. I float beyond the day-to-day and lean into mother earth.

These moments are rare and powerful. They offer reflection and contentment. Today must be as it was born to be. The morning sun on the river, my line dancing in the water, the fabled trout, the reel clicking as it engages, and the water streaming over my boots. Despite my frustration with my own poor casting, I find incredible serenity in this space.

I push my thoughts deeper. A pebble rolls down the bank and bounces over my body. I tip my head back, able to see only the boulders above. I twist and look towards the top of the trail. There perched above me, a silhouette of a man standing. His hands on his hips as if preparing to ask me for my fishing license.

I gather my belongings, pondering if I should use the whistle that sits on the ready around my neck. I wave. He doesn't. A snap judgment deems the whistle foolish.

I hear boots descending. I turn and see he is less than five feet away, slim, middle-aged, worn out. Like an old pickup, used and abused, with little maintenance. He speaks, "Hello, young lady."

Secretly hoping to transform what I take as a threatening look off his face, I tell him, "I'm not young."

He chuckles loudly, gruffly, as if he's had one too many smokes.

I locate my natural deflection—kindness, saying, "If you're here to fish, I can point you to some great spots. I left that sandbar about an hour ago," pointing upriver. "It was worth the hike. Lots of rainbows near that pool."

"Nah, I don't fish."

I begin to stand, hoping to return to the safety of my car. He reaches for my shoulder. My legs start incessantly quaking like the aspens around us.

"Hang on just a second," he says. "Don't run off on my account."

"I'm pretty sure my husband's beginning to worry. I'd better get home," I say.

"Sit down. Tell me what it was that made you marry your man. I'm just curious 'cause I don't seem to understand women."

I spit out my response, too fast without thought, without sitting down as he patted the rock beside him. "He's great with children," I say.

"Well, shit, that's all? I can pretend to like kids."

I turn away, taking my first step readying the whistle. I bring it to my lips, prepared to blow.

He turns again, looking up as though he's expecting someone to join him. "What's your name, young lady?"

I lie, "Michelle," using the name of two of the strongest women I know.

"Well, I'm David. Nice to meet you. I need your help. I'm suffering from female rejection. Was contemplating jumping off this cliff when I saw you. You might just be my savior, put here just for me. You got to tell me what I'm doing wrong with women. I'm just me, and sometimes I smell of tar and sweat. Sometimes I have dirty nails, but I'm a nice guy."

My mind races. If he reaches for my leg, we'll both go down the bank. I realize, if I can get three feet beyond this guy, I'll be beyond his reach. I inch up the bank, but his eyes focus on my boots. Terror has me choking back coffee-flavored bile.

He looks up. His eyes are pleading.

Searching for anything to say, I come up with, "Maybe you scared them." I fake a nervous, light-hearted chuckle. "Why not allow some of that charm to come through. Women like charm, but just a little. Don't overdo, or they'll think you're a phony."

He stands and reaches for my hand. This is it. I sense it the way one feels a storm. I peer into the river below—my end at his fingertips. My rod and reel offer no defense.

I allow his hand to take mine and close my eyes. I wait for the expected pain from bouncing down the boulders into the river below.

What I receive instead is a polite handshake. "Thanks for talking. It was nice meeting you, Michelle."

Rita Paskowitz • Omaha, NE

When You Find Me

Trigger Warning: Suicide

When you find me, my wrists will be opened by the red-handled knife I last used to thinly slice a riddled wedge of Jarlsberg. And a sallow Bosc pear. The water in my bathtub will be cold. Swirls of blood like the inside of a cat's-eye marble floating indifferently around my still body. Lips frozen in a prayer to a God that refused me. My eyes will be open in panic, yes. But also in peace. Knowing they will never again search for someone or something to save me from myself.

I can only ask you to forgive me for any pain I may have caused. Any disappointment or anger. Remembering how much I was alone. Both inside and out. And no recriminations, please. There was nothing you could have done to stop me. In my life, the timing of its ending was the only thing I ever controlled. There was so much more that was missing. And left undone.

Sometimes death is the only thing to contain all the emptiness without spilling.

Jon Kalantjakos • Omaha, NE

A Beautiful Place

Siobhat Nasdan, the Oscar-winning actress most famous for portraying Julie in the Fox Studios remake of Jean George's *Julie of the Wolves* eight years ago, has returned to the country of her birth.

Nasdan is a black Native American who left the United States, renouncing her citizenship, after the recent spate of incidents involving white cops murdering innocent and unarmed people of color. She left for southern Libya, where she stayed with an old relative. Now, however, she was hiking up the Catskills on a trail that would take her past the Thomas Cole sight in the village on a gorgeous day in late August as the violets, lilies, and bugloss burst with color, making full use of her hundred-and-twenty-dollar Kodak PIXPRO.

For the moment she was taking a breather at a bend in the path where she could hear water, and sure enough, the paparazzi caught up to her later and shoved a microphone in her face.

"Have you changed your mind about America?"

She shook her head.

"You still hate it?"

She looked up at the balsam fir overhead, then the white pine and the red maple next to it across the path.

"No," she said. "Just the people."

Brandy L. Prettyman • Papillion, NE

Our Vacation

The last thing from the twentieth I remember is the ringing of the phone as I pulled Eric's sweatshirt over my head, feeling the fleece feather across my face and engulf my diminutive body in its downy softness as it drifted down my body. The blue marching band hoodie fell across my shoulders, wrapping me in the warmth of the dryer I had just pulled it from just moments before. It was a gag gift, a memento of the hellish first (and only) year our oldest, Caden, played in his high school marching band. Though Eric wasn't musically inclined and *never* wore hoodies, he laughed when he opened the box tied with the glittery bow. *"Guess I'll have to spray my cologne on this after we wash it so you can steal it from me!"* His laugh was infectious as we giggled together over our drinks on the back deck that hot, sultry night.

I do remember it was cold in the apartment on the twentieth; I loved to wear his oversized clothes, so I let the thermostat plunge to the low sixties and pulled out whatever was clean and still had the smell of his cologne on it. Eric loved to keep the apartment hot enough to boil water, but I was much more comfortable when our home could be used as an ice box.

Eric and the boys had left Hawaii just a few hours before. It was supposed to have been a family vacation, but I came down with a case of walking pneumonia. He didn't want to leave me behind.

"What if we just delay until next year?"

"We've been hyping this up for the past five months with the boys. Why should the boys be punished because I'm sick? Besides, Caden may not be here to go on vacation with us next year if he decides to join the military."

"We spent so much money on the ticket, though . . ."

"That's what travel insurance is for, right?"

"Who's going to take care of you? You should be resting and recovering!"

"Sweetie. Stop. I'll have your mom come over. It's only a three-hour drive for her; she can stay in Liam's room. Go and have an amazing vacation with our boys."

It ultimately took me two days to convince him I would be alright if he took the boys to Hawaii without me. Truth be told, it was only after Eric spoke with his mother himself that he finally relented. He and the boys finished packing their luggage and we had my mother's almost famous chicken pot pie for dinner the night before they left.

I remember giving each one of the boys a kiss the morning of the twelfth; only Dakota didn't shy away or try to duck his head from my goodbye kisses. I walked over to the driver's side window and pressed my lips to Eric's.

"Don't forget to call me every morning when you get up; I want to hear all about what you and the boys are doing every day!"

"I promise to call if you promise to actually rest. You have a whole week without the boys and I driving you batty."

I smiled as he spoke. "I promise to rest, as much as Mom will let me!" I said with a sly grin.

"Love you."

"More."

I stepped back and watched as our Acadia, packed with everything one husband and three boys would need for a week of fun in the sun, backed out of our drive.

The next week flew by and within just a couple days I was feeling much better. When my follow-up appointment confirmed my recovery, I sighed. Maybe I should have gone after all. I told my mother-in-law she could go home, but she insisted on staying; she promised her boy, after all.

Eric and I spoke the night before just before they got on the plane to come home.

"Only a few more hours. The boys and I will be home tomorrow by lunch."

"Can't wait to see you. Are the boys around?"

"They are off grabbing some food. I refused to pay to let them in the sky lounge on the way home."

I laughed. *"They don't even care—probably happier at the food court in the airport."*

"You aren't wrong."

"Well, give them a hug and a kiss for me. I'll see you all tomorrow!"

I got up on the twentieth missing Eric and the boys, excited for them to be home in just a few hours. I had started a batch of chili to welcome them all home. My mother-in-law would tell me later while I was in our room pulling Eric's oversized blue hooded sweatshirt on, there was a breaking news report. Talia Sokloff, my childhood friend turned local news reporter, would be the one to announce the explosion of Delta flight 18235 over the Pacific Ocean, just an hour outside Seattle. As she was listening to the report by Talia, the phone rang. My mother-in-law would tell me that I called out saying I would grab it. I don't remember falling to the floor or screaming out, nor do I remember my mother-in-law running to my side or taking the phone out of my clenched hand, gripping it in a vice as I lie on the ground sobbing incoherent noises like an animal with its paw in a trap.

It's been one month since I woke with no memories past slipping on Eric's soft hoodie, waiting for him and our boys to come home. Now that I face a lifetime without them, I am not sure how I will survive the quiet that has enveloped me since I came to.

Julie Haase • Omaha, NE

A Fair Day

"Daddy, I wanna ride on the carriage."

Mindy's father held her six-year-old hand in a death grip as she pulled and yanked and tried to steer him toward the horse and carriage rides in the northeast corner of the park. Her auburn curls bounced like a Slinky against her shoulders, and her eyebrows furrowed above the red glow overtaking her freckled chipmunk cheeks.

Roller coaster screams wafted from the midway in another corner of the park. The breeze that carried them did little to cut through the damp misery of the hottest August day in three years. Mindy's father, Joe, craned his neck to look above and beyond the hordes of bodies that bustled from one booth to the next. He checked the signs above each food stand. He knew only one stand promised "real Southern grits on a stick," and that became his destination, his one ambition, a pilgrimage to save his soul.

Soon they passed a booth selling roasted peanuts and almonds, and Mindy pulled and pointed and begged. Then came the kiosk of handmade jewelry that sparkled in Mindy's eyes. Her little hands reached desperately toward a low-hanging necklace, but Joe tugged her away before her cotton candy fingers could make contact.

Joe said little as he guided Mindy through the throng. The occasional "Stop it" or "Not now" or "Maybe later" passed over his lips but drifted unheard into the sweltering ether. He checked his watch. *Almost three o'clock,* he thought. He checked again.

Be at grits-on-a-stick at three o'clock. And again. *Eye on the prize, Joe. Eye on the prize.*

Under normal circumstances Joe would do just about anything to make his daughter happy (or at least to appease her), but today Mindy's energy and curiosity would *just not stop*. They had started the day playing in a park near home, then had made the forty-five-minute drive to the fair during which Mindy had pointed out every sight that had flown past her window, from cows lazing in green pastures to dilapidated Leaning Tower of Pisa-style barns to bright-colored billboards with pictures of yummy-looking food and happy families. Joe loved his daughter very much, but even the most doting parents have their please-for-the-love-of-God-just-go-to-sleep moments.

Besides, they'd already spent three hours in the big fair building—the one with the broken air conditioning—looking at the 4-H exhibits and the vendor booths. Mindy's demanding behavior left as much to be desired inside as it now proved to be outside. And on top of that, stepping outside didn't offer much relief from the stuffy heat, although at least outside the air *moved.*

But Mindy didn't notice the heat, despite its threatening to pull the bounce from her curls. Mindy just wanted to crawl on the hot tubs, to ride on a camel, and to have the man in the straw hat draw her cartoon. She wanted to look at the pigs, until she smelled them, and then she wanted to look at the sheep. The aroma of buttered popcorn tickled her nose, and her eyes bulged like expanding balloons with each monstrous ice cream cone that melted and dripped down lucky *other* kids' arms. Mindy strained and jerked but could not dislodge her hand from her father's frustratingly strong grip.

Her pleas became more urgent and shrill as each temptation flew by.

"Daddy, I want a ring."

"Daddy, I want a pinwheel."

"Daddy, I wanna play bingo."

"Daddy, *let go*!"

But Daddy did not let go. Daddy had spotted his destination, his salvation. "Finally," he muttered and wiped his drenched brow on his also drenched t-shirt sleeve. He weaved his way to the back of the food stand where a woman stood dipping frozen mounds of grits on sticks into batter and gingerly placing each one into bubbling hot oil.

"It's three-oh-one. Take her," he said to his wife, and he scooped up Mindy and held her out in front of him.

Mindy's crinkled face relaxed into the broad smile of someone contemplating renewed possibilities.

"Mommy, I want a funnel cake."

Rita Paskowitz • Omaha, NE

Forgiveness

Just last week, I sold my soul to the Devil.

In my defense, it was week two-trillion of COVID-19. The temperature was stuck at a bleak and breezy fifteen degrees. I hadn't seen another person for over a week—unless they were televised or streamed. I'd been eating an excessive amount of cheese. My bowels were on strike. And I hadn't fallen asleep before three a.m. in God only knows how long.

In Satan only knows how long.

Sorry, Lord of Darkness. I meant no disrespect. I assume you're like Santa and know when I've been bad or good. Or had a tiny blip, for badness sake.

Anyway, my life was duller than Mike Pence. And, since no one was around to hear me—or so I thought—I began to rant and rave about my predicament.

"What's the point?" I shouted to my living room ceiling. "I'm stuck in this apartment like a fishbone in my own throat with no one to perform a psychological Heimlich. I'd give anything to have some excitement in my life."

The room suddenly got cold. As if someone had forgotten to close the front door during a blizzard.

"Oh, great!" I roared. "What fresh level of Hell am I stuck in now?"

"I like to call it 'The Winner's Circle,'" said James Earl Jones.

I swung around, expecting to see the man who immortalized the phrase "Luke, I am your father." Instead, I found a smiling seven-year-old girl in a bright pink ice skater's outfit. Executing a flawless camel spin on my hardwood floor.

For the first time in recorded history, I was speechless. I quickly grabbed a marker and a blank piece of paper, wrote "10.0" and held it up like an Olympic judge on the payroll.

She bowed gracefully, then stared deeply into my eyes. "So, you want some excitement, huh, Pumpkin?"

I nodded dumbly, trying to look away. But I was no match for her magnetic gaze.

"Rat got your tongue?" She let out a baritone giggle that made me wish I could take a hot shower.

"Um, did we have an appointment scheduled?" I asked, feigning nonchalance.

I failed miserably.

"Look, Pumpkin," she growled. "You called me."

"I couldn't have," I timidly responded. "My phone isn't charged."

"Excuse me," she snarled prettily. "I should have used the word 'summoned.'"

"I don't think I did that either," I demurred. Knowing it was a mistake, but unable to swallow my words without choking.

She skated around my apartment, pausing only to sample my plants. Before I could stop her, she took a big bite out of my mother-in-law's tongue. And smiled in ecstasy.

"Spit it out," I freaked. "My cat died from eating that!"

"Do I look like I purr?"

It was a rhetorical question. But I answered anyway. “You appear to be able to do anything that you want.”

She tilted her prepubescent head and pursed her child’s lips. Then, in a perfect imitation, she repeated my earlier words, “I would give anything to have some excitement in my life.”

“Did you or did you not say that?” She looked amused.

“Uh, yes, I guess I did.” I fussed with the zipper on my sweatshirt. Frantically making it go up and down like a roller coaster on drugs.

“Gosh.” She glared at me. “Do I make you nervous?” Then she emitted a low Darth Vadar-ish sound of glee.

“Well, I am a bit taken aback,” I admitted, my face burning. “Have we met before? I can’t seem to place who you are.”

“Hi, my name is Satan, and I’m the God of Evil.” Her face cracked into a malevolent grin as she skated up to me. Keeping me trapped with her unforgiving stare. I noticed her eyes were the green of spring grass. And her pupils the red of the setting summer sun. She smelled of sulfur. And s’mores.

“Do you remember when you were a child, and you had that recurring dream you were riding your bicycle over a cliff?”

“Every once in a while, I still have it,” I recalled. “Why do you ask?”

“Who do you think was at the bottom, calling for you and waiting to collect your bones?”

If I’d been more flat-chested, my jaw would have dropped directly to the floor.

Jesus.

Again, I heard my voice in her mouth. “I would give anything to have some excitement in my life.”

"You got it," said the Great White Hope, in girlish attire. "Now what exactly are you willing to give up?"

"Whoa!" I cried. "I was just talking to hear the sound of my own voice…"

"Isn't it funny that I heard it too?"

"No, it's scary. And I take it back. Let's just pretend I never said it, and I promise not to complain ever again."

"Sorry, Pumpkin." She shrugged her little shoulders. "I'm here to make you an offer you can't refuse. All you have to do is sign on the dotted line, and you'll have more excitement than you ever dreamed was possible."

Suddenly, a contract written on what appeared to be parchment paper appeared on my coffee table. My guest put a fountain pen into my trembling right hand. And guided my signature as if it were her own.

Before I knew it, my apartment vanished. I found myself on a gurney. Being rushed to a unit specially set up for COVID patients.

"God of Goodness," I sobbed. "Please, forgive me."

He or She or It didn't.

The last words I remember hearing were "Sorry, Pumpkin. There are no ventilators left."

About the Authors

Susan Baron

Susan Baron lives in Omaha, Nebraska. She has been published in volumes II, III, and IV of the Nebraska Writers Guild anthology, the NWG *Verses from the Plains: A Poetry Collection*, and *Flashes from the Plains: A Flash Fiction Collection*. She is currently working on a historical novel about the settling of Nebraska.

Cathy Beck

Cathy is passionate about writing. She's attended UNO Creative Nonfiction classes, as well as Iowa University Summer Writing Festival workshops. She loves writing short stories, essays, and the occasional poem. Two daughters call her mom and two precious granddaughters call her nana. Doesn't get any better than that.

Rob Czaplewski

I am a history enthusiast by nature, a marketer by profession, and a painter by desire. Most importantly, I'm a father of a twenty-one-year-old daughter who loves her horse as much as her parents. In 2021, I was published in the NWG flash fiction collection. I'm in healthcare business development and live in Grand Island.

Shoshana Sumrall Frerking

Shoshana Sumrall Frerking is the author of the dark urban fantasy series *Weatherbone*. She is also a technical writer living in rural

Nebraska with her husband and four cats. For more of her stories, art, and nightmares, visit www.shoshanasumrallfrerking.com.

Colleen Gallion

Colleen Gallion is an associate editor for a local magazine who loves to bake cookies in her spare time when she's not writing. She enjoys music from the '80s and taking naps. She lives in Grand Island, Nebraska, with her husband and son and the rest of her four-legged animals.

Conor Gearin

Conor Gearin is a writer from St. Louis living in Rhode Island. He studied grassland bird conservation at the University of Nebraska–Omaha. He is a digital producer for BirdNote Radio and a contributing editor for *The New Territory* magazine. He writes a newsletter called *Possum Notes*.

Johnnye Gerhardt

Ms. Gerhardt has been an acquisition-and-contract editor for a small press; an editor for *Fine Lines Literary Magazine* and the Nebraska Writers Guild. Johnnye currently serves on the Nebraska Governor's Education-Outreach Speakers Bureau and has served on the Nebraska Film Association and the Nebraska Writers Guild Board of Directors.

Julie Haase

Julie Haase is a freelance copyeditor and the Online Business and Publishing Manager for The Writer's Ally, an editing and publishing services company. Julie is the author of *The CopySitter's*

Tips and Tricks for Great (Narrative) Writing and is the Publications Chair for the NWG. Find Julie at www.copysitter.com.

Tasha Hackett

Tasha Hackett writes with hope and humor to entertain and encourage women. Her debut novel *Bluebird on the Prairie* was published in 2021. Most of her time is spent with four chatty children and an incredibly supportive husband. They give her the kind of love people write books about.

Amy Haddad

Amy Haddad is a poet, nurse, and educator who taught in the health sciences at Creighton University where she is now Professor Emerita. Her poems appear in *AJN*, *Janus Head*, *Journal of Medical Humanities*, *Touch*, *Bellevue Literary Review*, *Pulse*, *Persimmon Tree*, *Annals of Internal Medicine*, *DASH*, and *Oberon Poetry Magazine*.

Sammi Hoard

Sammi and her husband, Rod, live near Harlan Reservoir. They have three children, two grandchildren. After retiring from a medical device facility five years ago, she now works in a library. She enjoys spending time with her family, reading, painting, sewing, and writing historical and contemporary romance and romantic suspense.

Ellie Luebbe Janda

Ellie Luebbe Janda is a stay-at-home mom, short on time to write, and even shorter on sleep. When she isn't making sandwiches for lunch boxes or treating stains in laundry, she enjoys time with her family and going on adventures.

Jon Kalantjakos

Jon's spent the last ten years since receiving his Associate's teaching himself to write through practice, research, and a continuously improving ear for how his malarkey sounds. He's self-published two books and has a story in *Crack the Spine*. He was born in Greece but currently lives in Omaha.

Leopold J. Kovar

Leopold Kovar, a retired federal worker and current substitute teacher, lives in Brainard. He has written short plays, fiction, poetry, and memory pieces. He lives in a converted one-room school house on his family farm. For twenty-four years, he took care of disabled family members.

David Kubicek

David Kubicek has published a novel, *In Human Form*, and a short story collection, *The Moaning Rocks and Other Stories*. He wrote the *Cliff's Notes* for Willa Cather's *My Ántonia* and is a writer and photographer for the *Midlands Business Journal*. He hangs out at https://davidkubicekwriter.com.

James Luebbe

James Luebbe lives near Beaver Crossing, works full time in Lincoln, and is endlessly amused by his grandchildren. You will often find him driving his rebuilt '79 Camaro if the noise doesn't find you first. He has published poetry in a few literary magazines years ago and in recent NWG publications.

Tammy Marshall

Tammy Marshall is a lifelong Nebraska resident, a retired language teacher, and mother of two grown children. She's a novelist, a newspaper feature writer and columnist, and a blogger. She loves to swim and to make watercolor paintings and bookmarks. She's fluent in Spanish and conversant in Italian. Website: tammymarshallauthor.wordpress.com.

Ricardo Moran

Ricardo Moran has been published in several journals including the *Willa Cather Review*. In 2020, he received the Peter K. Hixson Memorial Award for Poetry. He sits on the board of San Diego Writers Ink and considers himself to be an honorary Cornhusker. Find him at www.ricardomoranwriter.com.

Charlene Neely

Charlene Neely's books are *The Lights of Lincoln* and *The Corn Fairy's Wigs & Other Poems*. She co-edited the *Guide to More Nebraska Authors* with Gerry Cox. A member of Nebraska Writers Guild and Lincoln Chapparal Poets, her poetry has appeared in *Naugatuck River Review*, *Persimmon Tree*, *Plainsongs*, and other journals.

Julie S. Paschold

Tansy Julie Soaring Eagle Paschold is an anxious alcoholic bipolar gender fluid queer poet and artist from Norfolk, Nebraska, with synesthesia who likes growing things. They have been published in several literary magazines. Julie sells their sketches at the Ravenwood Art Gallery. Please read https://medium.com/@jpaschold or https://jpaschold.blogspot.com/.

Rita Paskowitz

Rita Paskowitz's business card lists her as a storyteller, presentation coach, facilitator, and educator. She also writes odd and interesting things, making people think and laugh and ask questions—though not always in that order.

Mark M. Peyton

Mark M. Peyton is a former teacher and biologist turned storyteller and writer. He has two published books and a third soon available for purchase. He writes for the *Gothenburg Leader* and the *REA Nebraska*. He lives in Gothenburg with his wife, Cindy, a dog, three cats, and a snake.

Brandy L. Prettyman

Brandy L. Prettyman is a writer, mother, army veteran, and coffee snob. She has spent the last decade (maybe it's longer, but let's not make this awkward) writing poetry. She lives in Papillion, Nebraska, and can be found at her desk frantically writing her thoughts down in verse before they disappear.

Kathy Jewell Raabe

Kathy Raabe is an author who loves fiction and children's books. She is working on both now and has formed Jewell Publishing LLC. She lives in Gretna, Nebraska, with her husband and two dogs. Besides reading, Kathy enjoys quilting, sewing, crocheting, and her five grandchildren.

Janet McMillan Rives

Janet McMillan Rives grew up in Connecticut and Arizona, her current residence. She retired as professor of economics (Northern Iowa). She's published in *The Avocet*, *Lyrical Iowa*, *Raw Art Review*, *Ekphrastic Review*, *Sandcutters*, *Blue Guitar*, and *Fine Lines*. She authored *Into This Sea of Green: Poems from the Prairie* (2020).

Bill Roberts

Bill Roberts is a retired Omahan whose wife is an Episcopal priest. He writes fiction about folks who join groups that offer identity and support. The groups include Actators, Expellians, Sillifiers, Stupidophiles, and Neverthelessers—former kings and queens who meet regularly to help one another carry on . . . nevertheless.

Joslyn Rojewski

Joslyn is an amateur baker, proud supporter of the Oxford comma, and lover of irony. A professional copywriter by day, Joslyn uses her evenings to write other things that are more fun than digital ads.

Steve Rose

Steve Rose has been published in *And So It Goes*, *Midwest Quarterly*, *Journal of Medical Literature*, *Voices from the Plains*, *Dime Bag of Poetry*, *Joan Ramsey Anthology*, *Backchannels*, and *Lyrical Iowa*. He authored two books: *Hard Papas* and *Nebraska and Other States*. He writes, serves public office, fills pulpits, fishes, and bicycles.

Claudia J. Severin

Claudia Johnson Severin grew up in Lincoln, Nebraska, in the Eastridge neighborhood. She went back to her high school twirler days for the *Twirler Quartet* series. Like her main characters, she found hours of practice together developed friendships which led to many adventures outside of school.

William L. Smutko

William Smutko is a retired wine grape grower who served in the United States Army for six-and-a-half years, two consecutive years in Vietnam. He has a Bachelor's Degree in English and an MBA. He has had eight of his short stories and one memoir published.

Kim Sosin

Kim McNealy Sosin is a Professor Emerita of Economics at the University of Nebraska–Omaha. Her interests include writing and photography/art photography. Her poems and photographs have appeared in *Failed Haiku*, *Daily Haiga*, *Voices from the Plains*, *Wanderlust Journal*, *Ekphrastic Review*, *Beyond Words Literary Magazine*, and *Sandcutters*.

Tricia Tennesen

Tricia Tennesen spent years selling sugary soft drinks to unsuspecting shoppers. A walk through a prairie preserve told her it was time to move on. She returned to school, relocated, and began anew. Now she reads, writes, walks, fly fishes, and marvels at God's glory.

Valerie Lee Vierk

Valerie Lee Vierk lives near Ravenna, Nebraska. She has published many of her poems, essays, and short stories and six books. Besides writing, she enjoys nature and capturing the beauties of it with her camera. She is also an animal lover, with particular emphasis on cats, both large and small.

Katherine Wielechowski

Katherine Wielechowski is a Nebraska native and self-published author. She writes in many different genres including romance, urban fantasy, and supernatural/paranormal, in addition to her blog, *The Blank Page*. She is excited about her latest book, *Quarantine Monster Shorts*, a collection of stories set during the 2020 pandemic, published October 2021.

About the Nebraska Writers Guild

The Nebraska Writers Guild is one of the oldest writing organizations in the country. Founded in 1925, the Guild's charter members included Bess Streeter Aldrich, Dorothy Canfield Fisher, Louise Pound, and A. E. Sheldon. In its first two years, two members of the Guild were included in the *Saturday Review of Literature*'s list of the ten writers most representative of American life. The original purpose statement from 1925, which we still maintain today, reads: "The purpose of the Guild shall be the promotion of good fellowship among Nebraska writers; to encourage the recognition of professional writing and writers in the production of fine literature; and, to foster the development of the talent of those who desire to write and who show definite possibilities of authorship."

Our Mission

Nebraska Writers Guild is a nonprofit 501(c)3 organization dedicated to empowerment and individual growth through involvement with a community of writers and related professionals; promoting authors and the craft of writing through events and publications; and advancement through professional development.

Our Vision

Nebraska Writers Guild will: advocate for literary causes; nurture creative community; expand organizational outreach;

foster personal growth through education; and increase exposure for members.

Our Core Values

Nebraska Writers Guild holds a set of values that provide the foundation for its leadership in honoring its original purpose and achieving its current mission and future vision. These include: community, through acceptance, advocacy, appreciation, compassion and cooperation; creativity; learning; motivation; and professionalism.

Our success is measured in the number of people we can help with the quality of programs and services we provide. These programs are fueled by our dedicated staff, caring volunteers, and generous donors.

For more information about the Nebraska Writers Guild, go to www.nebraskawriters.org. You do not have to be from Nebraska to join the NWG. If you're a writer and you want a community for support, check us out!

Acknowledgments

Thank you so much to everyone who helped bring *Stories from the Heartland* to fruition. It would not have gotten done without the help I received from my wonderful volunteers: Brandy Prettyman, Anna Weir, Mary Bernier, and Shennon Helms.

Thank you to the authors who submitted their works and to the Guild membership as a whole for again trusting me with this greatly important undertaking. I continue to be grateful for your trust in me.

Thank you to the NWG Board, specifically Charles Lieske and Victorine Lieske, for their support.

~Julie Haase

Project Coordinator: Julie Haase
Submissions Manager: Brandy Prettyman
Communications Manager: Anna Weir
Volunteer Coordinator: Mary Bernier
Marketing Manager: Shennon Helms
Poetry Evaluators: Sharon Carr, Charlene Pierce, Kim Sosin
Fiction Evaluators: Margie Lukas, Gina Barlean, Katherine Wielechowski
Nonfiction Evaluators: Conor Gearin, Jody Keisner, Mark Peyton
Cover Photo: Kim Sosin
Design and Formatting: Julie Haase
Proofreading: Anna Weir, Johnnye Gerhardt

Index by Author

Index by Title

Made in the USA
Coppell, TX
05 December 2021

67253576R00256